Ref!

EDINBURGH UNIVERSITY PUBLICATIONS

SCIENCE AND MATHEMATICS TEXTS 1

AN INTRODUCTION
TO THE PHYSICS OF
MASS LENGTH AND TIME

NORMAN FEATHER FRS

EDINBURGH
At the University Press

© EDINBURGH UNIVERSITY PRESS 1962
One George Square
Edinburgh 9

U.S. Agent
ALDINE PUBLISHING CO.
64 East Van Buren Street, Chicago

Printed in Great Britain
by T and A. CONSTABLE LTD., Hopetoun Street,
Printers to the University of Edinburgh

PREFACE

If one seeks for an alternative to the time-honoured designation *Mechanics and Properties of Matter*, other, at least, than the now more popular *General Physics* (which is sadly uninformative), one is hard pressed to discover—or invent—any form of words at the same time brief, comely and precise.

In offering the title of this book as a possible form, obviously I have had to forswear brevity: if I have thereby achieved any novelty, it is not for novelty's sake alone. For my aim is precisely to introduce the beginning specialist in physics to those parts of his subject which in any well-designed course he should study first, and to effect that introduction by examining first of all the bases of measurement of the fundamental physical quantities, mass, length and time. Derived quantities are then introduced, as the concepts which specify them take on significance in the course of a survey of the world of phenomena. In the end the result is not very different in scope from any elementary *Mechanics and Properties of Matter*, but the emphasis is different—and of that the present title is intended as an advertisement, and a warning.

The book has been written for the beginning specialist in physics —whether his specialisation begins, as is general in Scotland, during his first year at the University, or whether it begins, as it more frequently does in England, in the scholarship form at School. Indeed it is addressed, and has in part been addressed these dozen years in unscripted lectures, to a wider audience. The Ordinary Class of Natural Philosophy in a Scottish University includes many students who do not intend to proceed even to a second year of physics, let alone to pursue the subject, as some will do, for three further years of undergraduate study. These humanists, and others elsewhere in ever increasing numbers, are at this time, and with good reason, looking for an answer to the question, 'What is physics all about?' This book does not, I know, provide an adequate answer to such a question, but I am suffi-ciently old-fashioned to believe that a carefully-told story, starting at the beginning, is likely to be more satisfying to any serious questioner, whatever his speciality, than the most colourful fairy-tale of television and nuclear energy could possibly be. Even though much of the story must remain untold, I believe he will still find satisfaction in it.

I shall probably be criticised by the intending physics specialist in that I have disdained to use the calculus throughout the book. May I ask him to reflect whether to have used it would have made my basic task any easier—the task of attempting to uncover the ultimate structure of our subject. And, having said so much, may I encourage him, when he has read them, to translate my long-winded sentences into his favourite shorthand. He will certainly get on more quickly that way in future. His teacher, should he have adopted this book for his class, may have another criticism. He may say—and truly—that I have not provided 'examples' as tail-pieces to the several chapters. He is not to conclude, from this omission, that I think little of the working of examples, once the principles have been understood. But may I suggest, with due respect, that he will know better than I do the type of example best suited to the particular needs of his pupils. And I wager he will find plenty of such examples in examination papers, and elsewhere.

I had the temerity—and the intuitive wisdom—to submit this book in galley-proof to Dr. R. Schlapp for his comment. He not only read the proofs closely for trivial errors, but provided me with a wealth of gently censorious criticism on matters of substance, which, had I acted on all of it, would, I am convinced, have forestalled certain rebukes which I may still incur. If any such come to the reader's mind, he will know that it is I who should be their object.

NORMAN FEATHER.

4 January 1959.

CONTENTS

CHAPTER 1
INTRODUCTION

Physics is one of the sciences. For more than two hundred years the word Science, as used in this connection, has had a definite meaning. Science is organised common sense; it deals with the orderliness which we find in the world, with the regularities of nature. Indeed it proceeds from the assumption that the phenomena which impinge on our senses are essentially regular, subject to the rule of law, and it has as its aim the discovery of that body of law. 'To see what is general in what is particular and what is permanent in what is transitory is the aim of scientific thought,' a twentieth-century philosopher has said (A. N. Whitehead, 1911).

Physics is distinguished from the other sciences chiefly because it involves measurement more systematically than they do; to this extent it is the basic science. It deals with the varied interactions of dead matter: it may be defined as the body of knowledge derived by making measurements on things. Obviously this is not a precise definition. Nowadays the divisions between the sciences are less clear-cut than they were earlier assumed to be: our definition, then, will suffice for present purposes.

Measurements are made through our senses, aided by instruments. 'Common sense', from which we start, developed largely from unsystematic observations made through man's unaided senses of perception. Traditionally it is assumed that there are five such senses—sight, hearing, touch, taste and smell. Traditionally, too, the science of physics is divided into subjects—the bulk properties of matter, heat, light, sound, and electricity and magnetism. Our organs of sight and hearing are highly differentiated structures. That we are not blind arises from the fact that certain pigments laid down in the retina have certain specific sensitivities; that we are not deaf from the fact that the basilar membrane of the cochlea has different sensitivities, equally specific. That these two organs, so different in structure and sensitivities, should be found in land-based living creatures generally, surely argues for the exits-

A

ence, in the external world, of 'radiations' as distinct physically as the organs are different structurally, and for the validity of the traditional division which recognises the separate subjects light and sound within the science of physics. To associate the subjects heat and the bulk properties of matter with our much-less-differentiated sense of touch is perhaps more fanciful, though anthropomorphic notions of force and energy, in which this mode of sense perception is certainly involved, have been refined into scientific concepts which are basic for the subjects in question. It is easier to dismiss taste and smell as of no concern to the physicist. The differences in the external world to which these senses respond fall largely within the province of chemistry.

In this attempt at correlation, the subject electricity and magnetism is left without a counterpart among the human senses of perception. It is indeed true that differences in the states of electrification or the states of magnetisation of gross matter cannot generally be appreciated by our senses alone. We learn of them through the use of instruments specifically designed to translate these differences into different 'pointer readings', which in common with the pointer readings of all scientific instruments are ultimately recorded through our sense of sight. In the external world we do not normally encounter electrified bodies, and the general magnetism of the earth has had little impact on the evolution of the human species. The lack of an electric or a magnetic sense organ in man is, therefore, understandable.

But science develops towards unification: the physics of gross matter, with its disparate subjects, has become one in the physics of atoms, which in the first analysis is the physics of electric charges. Visible light is a feeble component only of the broad spectrum of electromagnetic radiations—and the biologist will tell us that, though we have no electric or magnetic sense, yet our every sense functions through the transmission of electric impulses along nerves to the brain. We have claimed that physics is the basic science; in physics, it would appear, electricity is the fundamental subject. It would indeed appear so, if scientists were not already heavily involved in the physics of the atom nucleus. There is a new subject there, but that is for future understanding.

Throughout the remainder of this book we shall be concerned almost exclusively with the physics of gross matter—with the properties of inert matter in bulk, and with certain aspects of the subject heat. If electricity is fundamental, we shall not be probing to fundamentals; if the concept of atoms is the all-unifying concept, we shall not be seeking such unification—more often than not we shall be disregarding the fact of atomicity altogether. But our considerations will be fundamental from another point of view. We shall be tracing the emergence of macroscopic physics out of the welter of common-sense experience. The pattern of that emergence is essential; it epitomises the whole nature of the methodology of science. In anticipation, and in summary, then, let us set down some of the rules of the game:

1. Accepting the regularity of happenings in the inanimate external world, the physicist is prepared to find that every event in that world has some relation with—is partially determined by, or partially determines—every other event.

2. His aim being to attempt to unravel the complexities of these relations by observation and experiment, the physicist will so design his experiments that each allows him to examine a simple situation in which one type of relation is predominant. He will never succeed absolutely in this, but in each case he will adopt the fiction that he is working with an isolated system, and he will only later review the inferences which he draws from its investigation to see whether some of them may require modification—because his fiction is a poor approximation to fact.

3. He will attempt to make precise his common-sense categories of thought. So he will be able to establish certain scientific concepts. He will also introduce other concepts which do not derive directly from common sense. But he will not introduce any such concept unless from its adoption there issues the possibility of measurement of some recognisable attribute of matter, or of some distinct element common to a large class of physical situations. He will not introduce a new concept unless his consideration of observations already made forces it on his attention—or unless, in a moment of insight, he recognises that such a concept brings order into observations which under previous scrutiny appeared devoid of order.

4. The introduction of new concepts will involve definitions—qualitative definitions, and quantitative definitions relating to the measurements which the concepts imply. The physicist will find it essential to be clear in his own mind, in respect of each new concept, whether or not the quantitative 'definition' enshrines one of

the 'laws of nature' which collectively mark his ultimate goal. He will instinctively refuse to accept as an expression of fundamental law any statement which does not subsume in simple form the observed results of a large number of diverse experiments, or one which is known to admit of exceptions in situations to which it should apply. The definition of any good concept should satisfy both these requirements, but the expression of a law of nature should also provide a basis for the prediction of the results of future experiments in a wider field, and it should be such that it is true to say of it 'it might conceivably have been otherwise'. If this cannot truly be said of the quantitative definition arising from the introduction of a new concept in physics, then the 'definition' is mere definition. On the other hand, if the claim 'it might have been otherwise' can be sustained in respect of any general statement which is both novel and true, then new knowledge regarding the world has been won: the universe has this particular character—not that possible one.

These are broad generalities: specifically, in this book, we shall have opportunity of noting their relevance in a somewhat narrow field only. Our main concern will be with matter in motion, with the planets in their orbits round the sun and the molecules of a gas in random motion in a vessel in the laboratory. Our preoccupation with matter in motion explains the *Mass, Length and Time* of the title. But the logical sequence of these concepts is length, time, mass. The dictates of euphony and usage may influence the choice of a title, but they must not determine the order of presentation. Adopting the logical order, we shall deal first with motion in the abstract, then with matter in motion. Later there will be other concepts, not concerned directly with motion, but in the derived units which issue from their acceptance reflecting nothing more than our choice of the units of mass, length and time, which we shall wish to introduce and consider. It is not too extravagant to claim that they, too, are covered by the title of this book.

CHAPTER 2

GEOMETRY AND THE MEASUREMENT
OF LENGTH

2.1. SPACE AND TIME

From birth to death we live our lives in being and becoming. It is ancient wisdom concerning the life of man, 'so soon passeth it away'. The becoming, the passing, are in time. We pass our lives on the surface of the earth—in the great river valleys, maybe—in the far distances there are the everlasting hills, above the ever-changing clouds, and the stars at night in their fixed constellations. These intimations arise from the immediate deliverances of our senses; our intuitive appreciation is of the flux of time—and of a vast arena of space determined by the stable earth and the stars. In seeking to build up the science of physics on these foundations, we consider separately the two notions which they involve, the notion of time and the notion of space. In this chapter we attempt to formalise the second, alone, man's intuitive notion of space.

2.2. PRACTICAL GEOMETRY

Many thousand years ago in the great river valleys of Egypt and Mesopotamia the kings' surveyors mapped their masters' fields, the royal architects planned the temples and tombs and palaces. Practical geometry had already developed into a serviceable body of rules: in relation to the comings and goings of daily life the structure of local space was understood. There was a secure tradition and great uniformity of practice. Evidence from the buildings which remain, or have been excavated, shows clearly that over a score of centuries the master builders of Egypt were employing a unit of length—the cubit—which did not vary by much more than 1 part in 200 from the mean. This bespeaks great attention to the preservation of a linear standard. We know from the records that the royal standard of volume—the apet—was for a long time preserved in material form in the dromus of Anubis at Memphis. Somewhat later, as regulating all measurements on the rise and fall of the waters of the Nile, a standard cubit was kept in the capital in priestly custody in the Sepulchre of the Sacred Bulls, and on the road from Memphis to Faium there was marked by official decree the schoenus, an itinerary standard of 12,000 cubits. Nearly a thousand miles away, in Mesopotamia, during much the same period, essentially the same standard of length, the cubit, was maintained, with almost equal exactitude.

2.3. ABSTRACT GEOMETRY

Such were the achievements of a practical civilisation three thousand years before the beginning of the Christian era. As that civilisation was passing into slow decline there was developing around the shores of the Aegean sea another civilisation of a very different character. Individual Greeks visited Egypt over many hundred years as travellers, or in pursuit of trade; in 332 BC under Alexander the Great they arrived as conquerors. Among the early travellers was Thales of Miletus (*c.* 624-547 BC), and a little later Pythagoras (*c.* 572-497 BC). In these two the genius for abstract thought which was to be typical of their fellow-countrymen for another five hundred years was already fully developed. To the Egyptians (it has been said) the geometrical point was realised only as a mark or position, the straight line only as a stretched string or the tracing of a pole, a surface merely as an area: to Thales it seems these entities took on the much more exciting nature of elements in an artifact of the mind, a formal logic-bound system, a new abstract language in which the perfection of actual space should be exhibited unsullied by the inconsistencies which derive from imperfect measurement. We speak of that formal system, that new language, as abstract geometry.

From Thales, through Pythagoras and the great Greek mathematicians, Eudoxus (*c.* 408-355 BC) perhaps the greatest of them all, the subject received successive additions and refinements until it was systematised by Euclid, the founder of the mathematical school of Alexandria—that new city which the Macedonian conqueror had caused to be built on the delta of the Nile. The dates of Euclid's birth and death are not known, the extent of his original contributions to geometry cannot be clearly assessed—they may not in fact have been great—but the thirteen books of his *Elements* remained the standard treatise on the subject for the best part of two thousand years. Euclidean space was accepted as satisfying in every particular the intuitive notion and the accumulated experience of man at large in the world; it was accepted in consequence as providing the spatial framework of mathematical physics.

2.4. DEFINITIONS AND AXIOMS

The theorems of Euclidean geometry, by which the detailed properties of figures in space are derived, are based on definitions, axioms and postulates. The definitions draw attention as precisely as possible to the typical entities out of which the figures may be regarded as built up—points, lines, surfaces, geometrical solids, angles. The axioms record what is commonly agreed regarding these entities.

Any set of axioms should consist of individual statements which are mutually consistent, each one being independent of all the others: the axioms of Euclidean geometry have the further character that what they accept as assumption in respect of Euclidean space is commonly believed to be true of the space of experience. Thus, whilst we should distinguish at the outset between the solid bodies ('rigid' bodies) of physics and the geometrical solids of Euclid, there is, nevertheless, the underlying belief that the mere properties of extension of physical bodies are the properties attributed to, or formally derivable for, the solids of abstract Euclidean geometry. This belief has been no embarrassment to the physicist, at least until very recent times, and we shall adopt it unquestioningly throughout the remainder of this book.

The postulates of Euclid are not uniquely distinguishable from the axioms. They are of the same nature, in that they are assertions which are unprovable within the logical system to which they belong. They differ from the axioms only in that they are the less obvious of the assumptions which must be made in order to remove all the ambiguities inherent in the situation. If it were not for the requirement that Euclidean space should be the exact formal counterpart of the space of experience, there might be a basis of distinction; when this requirement obtains, however, definitions and agreed assumptions regarding the entities defined should be sufficient basis for the abstract geometry. We therefore make no further distinction here between axioms and postulates.

2.5. STRAIGHT LINES AND PLANE SURFACES

Euclid adopted the synthetic method, building up by definition from the point, the ultimate abstraction—position in space, devoid of extension—through the line and the surface to the geometrical solid, a finite portion of space, completely cut off from the rest of space—by a continuous surface, or by surfaces intersecting in lines—having the fullness of possible extension, in length and breadth and thickness. (In our statement here we have allowed the analytic approach to appear, recognising the bounding surfaces of the solid, and their linear intersections.)

The particular notions of the straight line and the plane surface are more difficult to formulate in the abstract than they are in the practical geometry of experience, just because they are particularisations of the general notions 'line' and 'surface'. To the Egyptian surveyors the stretched string was an obvious real adjunct to their art—and a plane surface was to be found wherever a large expanse of still water was unruffled by the wind. The paving-stones for the temple courts were worked plane, and laid in position so that the courtyards themselves should have the same character. The intuitive approach to the notions 'planar' and 'straight' was direct. Let us here, in the general Euclidean tradition, attempt the abstract approach: 'a straight line is uniquely determined by any two points in it'; 'a plane surface is such that the straight line through any two points in the surface lies wholly in the surface', or, alternatively, 'a plane surface is uniquely determined by any three points in it, provided that the three points do not lie in the same straight line'.

2.6. MEASUREMENT OF LENGTH IN ABSTRACT GEOMETRY

In relation to physical measurement the most important axiom of Euclidean geometry is one which was implicitly assumed by Euclid, but not explicitly stated: 'figures may be freely moved in space without change of shape or size'. This is the counterpart of our intuitive belief in the permanence of the rigid bodies of the physical world. We move our measuring rods from place to place and we assume that they do not change in any way in the process. In particular we may move any segment of a straight line along that line, say from left to right, setting it down successively in such circumstances that the left-hand extremity of the segment coincides with the position previously occupied by its right-hand extremity. In such a way we are able to produce, in the abstract, a rectilinear scale, equally divided, providing multiples of any arbitrary length as unit length; we are able, in fact, to construct a segment of a

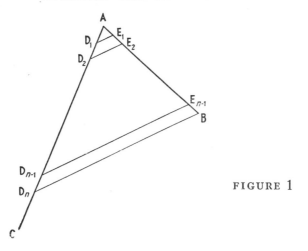

FIGURE 1

straight line the length of which is any integral multiple of a chosen unit. We may then move this rectilinear scale as we will, and, by bringing it into coincidence, along its length, with any other straight line, we may estimate the length of a segment of that line, with an uncertainty less than one scale unit, by the simple process of counting.

To estimate length more closely than this we obviously require a method of subdividing the segment chosen as unit in our previous consideration into a whole number of sub-multiples. Such a method is available on the basis of Euclid's theorem that a line drawn parallel to one side of a triangle cuts the other two sides proportionally. For let AB (fig. 1) be our unit length, one division of our scale, and let AC be any other straight line drawn through A. If it is required to subdivide AB into n equal segments, take any length AD_1 and set it off n times along AC in the manner above described in relation to the construction of an equally divided scale, so that $AD_n = nAD_1$. Join D_nB, and draw, through D_1, D_2, ... D_{n-1}, lines parallel to this line. If these lines cut AB in E_1, E_2, ... E_{n-1}, the last-mentioned points subdivide AB as required. The requisite construction is that of drawing a line through a given point parallel to a given line, essentially that of constructing an angle equal to a given angle—say $\angle AD_1E_1$ equal to $\angle AD_nB$.

So far with Euclid, but abstract geometry is not subject to the limitations of magnitude which determine the practicability or otherwise of actual manipulations of bodies in the physical world.

Thus we can extend, in thought, the process of subdivision of our linear scale to whatever degree of fineness we can imagine, and so provide ourselves with the means of estimating the length of a straight-line segment (or the distance between two points) to within any specified residual uncertainty. Let us consider the operations involved if such an estimate is to be expressed in the decimal notation of Stevinus (1548-1620) and Henry Briggs (1556-1630). The rectilinear scale, uniformly divided to give multiples of the unit, is brought into coincidence with the straight-line segment of unknown length. One of the points by which the scale is divided is made to coincide with one end of the segment, and it is found, by counting, that the other end of the segment lies in the $(A+1)$th unit interval along the scale, A being the appropriate integer. The $(A+1)$th unit interval is then divided into 10 equal sub-intervals by the method just described. When this is done, the end of the segment is found to lie in the $(a+1)$th sub-interval, let us say, a being another integer. The $(a+1)$th sub-interval is therefore divided into 10 equal smaller intervals and the position of the end of the segment in these is determined, as in the $(b+1)$th smaller interval, say, with b integral. The process of successive subdivision, location and counting is continued until the residual uncertainty is less than the originally specified small quantity. The length of the unknown interval is in fact $A \cdot abc$ . . . units of length, to as many places of decimals as required.

If the segment of unknown length had been the diagonal of a square of which the side had been taken as unit length, we know from Pythagoras's theorem that the process of 'measurement' would have yielded the result: length of diagonal $= 1 \cdot 41421356$ . . . sides. And it is clear that in imagination, that is with full validity in the abstract, the geometrical procedure in this case is no more limited than is the arithmetical procedure of extracting the square root of 2. And so in general: in the abstract the problem of determining the distance between two points has been solved, once the unit of length has been chosen, at least as long as we are satisfied with an end-result which is inexact in the sense that the ratio of incommensurables (as an arbitrarily chosen unit length and any other length must generally be) cannot be exactly expressed in the decimal notation by digits in a finite array. We have now to consider the problem in practical geometry and the limitations therein encountered.

First, however, there is one further consideration of relevance. We have so far regarded the rectilinear scale of our abstract geometry as subdivided by points. We could equally well regard the divisions as marked by parallel straight lines, or by parallel planes, through these points, the dividing lines, or planes, as the case may be, being at right angles to the length of the scale. The perpendicular distance between two parallel lines, or two parallel planes, is, equally with the shortest distance between two points, a single-valued quantity.

2.7. MEASUREMENT OF LENGTH IN PRACTICE: UNITS AND STANDARDS

The first problem in practical length measurement is the choice of a unit, and its preservation in a material standard. Reference has already been made to the unit of ancient Egypt—the cubit—and to the official preservation of a material standard in charge of the priests. According to our modern British measure the cubit varied over the years from about 20·5 to about 20·7 inches. Units derived from the cubit, usually by decimal subdivision, had widespread currency throughout long periods of time. Six-tenths of a cubit, about 12·4 inches, became known as a foot, and was much used as a unit in classical Greece and elsewhere. There are some indications of its use in Britain in the Middle Ages. More generally, however, at that time the English used a foot of about 13·2 inches, derived probably from near-continental sources rather than from the old Mediterranean civilisation, and a mile of 6000 feet, or 2000 yards. This system with its largely decimal subdivision (1 mile = 10 furlongs = 100 chains = 1000 fathoms), was not, however, the legal system, at least after AD 950. Already, before then, the 12-inch foot (36-inch yard) had been introduced, and a regular system of comparison of copies with the standard (which was kept at Winchester) had been instituted. About AD 965 a law of Edgar ordained that the standard for the whole kingdom should be 'such as is observed at London and at Winchester'. Under the Norman conquerors this duplication was considered to be no longer necessary: thereafter the Winchester standards were deposited in the crypt of Edward the Confessor at Westminster. But the longer yard, of about 39·6 inches, retained considerable popularity, until its use was finally prohibited by statute of Henry VI in 1439.

2.8. THE STANDARD YARD: HISTORY

The earlier British standards have been lost in the course of time, but the standard yards of Henry VII, Henry VIII and Elizabeth I are still extant, the last-mentioned having been the legal British standard until 1824. The standard of Henry VII measures 35·963 inches in modern measure. All three of these Tudor standards are 'end' standards, unit distance in each case being the perpendicular distance between the parallel end-faces of the bar. All three carried markings of subdivision. About the middle of the eighteenth century the construction of a new standard was entrusted to John Bird (1709-1776), the most famous astronomical instrument-maker of the day. This standard was completed in 1760. The Weights and Measures Act of 1824 constituted it the legal British standard yard and made provision for its replacement in case of accidental damage or destruction. The Bird standard consisted of a brass bar, somewhat more than a yard long, with gold studs inserted near the ends. Unit distance was defined as the distance between the centres of two dots, one punched in each of the two gold studs, when the temperature of the bar was 62° F. We may refer to a standard of this type as a 'dot' standard.

The provisions of the Act of 1824 became relevant earlier than was foreseen. In 1834 the Houses of Parliament were burned down, and the Bird standard was seriously damaged. For twenty-two years the country was without a legal standard of length. A commission was appointed to supervise the restoration of the standard and advised against the procedure specified in the Act. There, adapting a suggestion first made by the French astonomer Jean Picard (1620-1682), it had been stated that restoration should be in terms of previous knowledge of the length of the pendulum which, swinging in a vacuum in the latitude of London, should have a periodic time of two mean solar seconds, exactly (see p. 48). Very properly the commission was allowed to disregard this altogether impracticable instruction and to proceed as accurately as possible to reconstruct the lost standard in terms of its certified copies. This was done in 1844-5. Five bronze bars were machined as nearly as possible alike, of 1 inch square cross-section and 38 inches long. Two cylindrical holes $\frac{1}{2}$ inch deep and $\frac{1}{2}$ inch in diameter were bored out of one face of each bar, with their axes perpendicular to the length of the bar and each 1 inch from the nearer end. Gold studs were let into the holes, each stud being engraved with three equally spaced parallel grooves which were arranged to be perpendicular to the length of the bar when the stud was inserted in its cylindrical hole, One of the five bars was chosen as the 'imperial' standard and the other four were designated 'parliamentary' copies. Use of the new standard was legalised by the Weights and Measures Act, 1856, and a precise definition of the unit, the Imperial Standard Yard, was given by the Act of 1878, of the same title. According to this Act, unit length is the distance between the axes of the central grooves on the two gold plugs, when the temperature of the bronze bar is 62° F and it is supported horizontally on eight interconnected rollers so arranged (at intervals of 4·78 in.) as to bear equally the weight of the bar. We shall shortly have to consider the implications of these conditions, and of the mode of construction of the standard itself; meanwhile we should note that the definition is that of a 'line' standard—and record the disposition of the parliamentary copies. One of the copies was immured in a wall of the lower waiting-room of the House of Commons, thus passing out of currency for purposes of comparison with the others, one was deposited with the Royal Mint, one with the Royal Observatory and one with the Royal Society. In 1879 a fifth parliamentary copy was constructed as closely as possible according to the original prescription. This fifth copy, along with the imperial standard, is in the custody of the Board of Trade.

2.9. THE STANDARD YARD: PRESCRIPTION FOR USE
Regarding the conditions specified in the definition of the unit length, we note first of all the specification of temperature. As already mentioned, the temperature had previously been specified in the Act of 1824. This is the simplest condition to understand. The observation that bodies expand when they are heated is of some antiquity: as early as the beginning of the seventeenth century thermometers making use of this effect were coming into use. The general order of magnitude of the effect (in length), for the common metals and their alloys, is 1 part in 10^5 per degree Fahrenheit.

The specification of the mode of support of the standard is also connected with temperature effects, though indirectly. Clearly, if the temperature of the standard at the start of a comparison is not the specified temperature, it must be brought to that temperature.

This is more easily achieved if the standard is not in contact with a large body, not, for example, in direct contact with a table or bench. Again the support must be such that during the process of temperature adjustment there is no possibility of frictional effects between support and standard which might interfere with the small expansion or contraction appropriate to the requisite heating or cooling. The specification of support on rollers ensures both a small total area of contact and a minimum of frictional interference. But the specification of eight rollers represents a compromise in respect of another effect. It is a fact of experience that a heavy bar, supported only at or near the ends, sags slightly in the middle. The use of eight rollers, rather than two, reduces this effect, which must in general alter the horizontal distance between any two points on the bar, if only to a small extent.

Let us consider the problem of sagging by taking the hypo-thetical case of a straight line AB of length l which becomes bent into an arc of a circle of radius R (fig. 2). AB is now a chord of the circle, and if this chord subtends an angle 2θ at the centre, we have

$$\text{arc ACB} = l = 2R\theta$$
$$\text{ADB} = 2R \sin \theta.$$

Also, since $\angle \text{CAD} = \dfrac{\theta}{2}$,

$$\text{DC} = \text{AD} \tan \frac{\theta}{2} = R \sin \theta \tan \frac{\theta}{2} = 2R \sin^2 \frac{\theta}{2}.$$

Writing $\text{ADB} = l - x$, $\text{DC} = y$, and assuming that θ is very small, from these general results we obtain, to a sufficient approximation,

$$x = R\frac{\theta^3}{3}, \quad y = R\frac{\theta^2}{2}.$$

Thus

$$x = \frac{R^2\theta^4}{3R\theta} = \frac{8}{3}\frac{y^2}{l} \tag{1}$$

In equation (1), x is the apparent shortening of the linear 'standard' of length l, in the hypothetical case of circular sagging, when the maximum sag (at the mid-point) is y.

Now consider the original straight line AB to have been termi-nated by equal and parallel straight lines A'AA'', B'BB'' at right

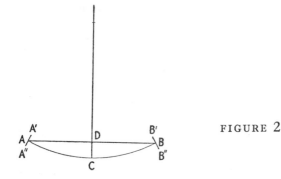

FIGURE 2

angles to its length. When AB was bent into an arc of a circle as above described, suppose that the bending took place in the plane A′A″B″B′ and that A′A″, B′B″ remained at right angles to the line during this process. Then the final situation would be as illustrated in fig. 2, with A″A′, B″B′ intersecting, when produced, in the centre of curvature of the circular arc ACB. If $A″A = AA′ = B″B = BB′ = z$, and if we write $ADB - A′B′ = x′$, $A″B″ - ADB = x″$, we now have

$$x′ = x″ = 2z \sin \theta,$$

or when θ is very small,

$$x′ = x″ = \frac{8yz}{l} \tag{2}$$

From (1) and (2)

$$\frac{x′}{x} = \frac{x″}{x} = \frac{3z}{y} \tag{3}$$

Equation (2) gives the additional shortening $x′$, of A′B′ relative to the already shortened standard length AB (and the corresponding lengthening of A″B″) under the conditions specified. Equation (3) relates these changes to the shortening of AB.

The relevance of our hypothetical case to the sagging of the actual standard, a solid rod of square cross-section, should now be obvious. We have in effect been considering, though with simplified geometry, the situation in which the rod is supported on two parallel rollers, one at each end. The lines A′A″, B′B″ of fig. 2 represent the plane end-faces of the rod. If these remain perpendicular to the length of the rod when it sags, and it is natural to assume that they do, the length of the rod measured along its lower curved face will be greater than the length measured along its upper curved face. ACB in fig. 2 represents a filament of length of the rod which has the same length when curved as it had when it was straight. Again, it is natural to suppose that there will be such a filament or filaments: it is unlikely that, in the process of sagging, the rod as a whole will lengthen (or contract), since the ends are free. Fig. 2, with our assumption $A''A = AA' = B''B = BB'$, suggests that a 'neutral' filament (a filament which does not change its length when the rod sags) lies midway between the upper and lower faces of the rod. Detailed consideration (see p. 319) shows that this is the case when the cross-section is rectangular: the originally horizontal mid-plane is in fact a neutral plane. It shows, further, that for a bronze bar of the dimensions of the actual standard, freely supported at the ends, the maximum sag (y of equations (1), (2) and (3)) is about 17 thousandths of an inch.

Consider now what would be the result if the defining marks of a line standard were inscribed on the upper face of a bar of square cross-section. Substituting $y = 17 \times 10^{-3}$ in., $z = 0.5$ in., $l = 36$ in., in equation (2), we have $x' = 1.9 \times 10^{-3}$ in., whereas, according to equation (1) (or equation (3)) $x = 2.1 \times 10^{-5}$ in. We conclude that, if such a standard were supported at the ends only, the defined length would contract by some 2 thousandths of an inch on account of sagging. We do not give a more precise figure for the contraction ($x + x'$) because of the geometrical approximation that we have made in our calculation. But our calculation also shows that if the defining marks could be made in the neutral plane of the bar the contraction in similar circumstances would be only 20 millionths of an inch, or thereabouts. This is the reason why the gold studs are let into the standard yard to a depth of $\frac{1}{2}$ inch in the 1 inch square bar. It is intended that the defining marks should in fact be in the neutral plane. With $y = 17 \times 10^{-3}$ in., $x = 2.1 \times 10^{-5}$ in., equation (3) shows that this adjustment must be very carefully made if full benefit is to be derived from the arrangement: an error of 1 thousandth of an inch in the position of the surface of the studs leads to a change of approximately 4 millionths of an inch in the defined length of the standard.

Obviously, in considering the standard supported at the ends only, we have chosen the worst case, but support on eight rollers, according to the Act of 1878, merely reduces the magnitude of the effect which we have described without altering its nature. Our

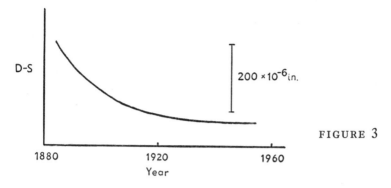

D-S

200×10^{-6}in.

FIGURE 3

1880   1920   1960

Year

considerations remain essentially valid in principle, though the
details are different. In due course we shall consider a much more
elegant solution of the problem of sagging embodied in the definition of the metric standard, the metre; first, however, we must
examine the information collected over the years in comparisons of
the imperial standard yard (S) with the four parliamentary copies
(A, B, C, D) available for observation. We recall that S, A, B and C
were made in 1844-5, D not until 1879. These five standards are
intercompared usually at ten-yearly intervals.

The general results of the intercomparisons can be very briefly
stated. In relation to the primary standard S, no systematic change
of length of any of the first three copies, A, B, C, has been detected,
at least over the last 80 years. D, however, has appeared to decrease
in length in relation to the others. As indicated schematically in
fig. 3, this decrease appears now to have ceased: over the first forty
years of observation it amounted to about 228 millionths of an inch.
It is well known by engineers that when metals are rolled, or ex-
truded as wire, or are otherwise severely treated, mechanically or
thermally, after-effects frequently occur over considerable periods
of time. The effect represented in fig. 3 is presumably of this character. Clearly, when the precision of measurement is pushed to the
utmost, after-effects may be detected which take tens of years to
die away. The practical conclusion can hardly be other than that
the imperial standard yard and its copies A, B and C also shortened
by some 200 millionths of an inch after the standard was made
legal in 1856. On that account alone the price of commodities sold
by the yard must, on the average, have increased by some 6 ten-
thousandths of one per cent during the last century!

B

2.10. THE STANDARD METRE

The metric standard of length, the metre, was introduced in 1801 by law (1799) of the French National Assembly.

The metre replaced the toise (about 76·74 in.), which had been in general scientific use for at least two centuries, and, in fact, the new unit was not very different from $\frac{1}{2}$ toise (1 metre = 39·370147 in.). Originally conceived as one ten-millionth part of the distance from the equator to the pole through Paris (strangely enough it approximated fairly closely to the old Gallic yard of about 39·6 in., use of which, in England, was suppressed by the statute of 1439), the metre was originally represented by an end-standard of platinum, of rectangular cross-section (2·5 cm. × 3·5 mm.). The fiction of the relation of the standard to the earth-quadrant soon fell into disregard, and it was officially repudiated when a new standard was introduced in 1889 as one result of the International Metric Convention of 1875. This standard, the International Prototype Metre, is a bar of platinum-iridium alloy the cross section (2 cm. × 2 cm.) of which is shown in fig. 4. This particular form was designed by H. E. Tresca (1814-1885), an engineer and metallurgist, to give maximum rigidity for a given total quantity of precious metal used, and also to ensure that the plane surface exposed in the upper channel of the bar should be part of the neutral surface when the bar sagged on its supports. The bar is slightly more than 1 metre in length (about 101·6 cm.), and the defining marks are engraved on the exposed neutral plane, one near each end of the bar, at right angles to its length and symmetric- ally disposed. The metre is defined as the dis- tance between these marks (the international prototype is thus a line-standard) when the temperature of the bar is that of melting ice, and the bar is symmetrically supported on two rollers at right angles to its length and 571 millimetres (0·571 m.) apart in a horizontal plane.

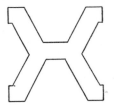

FIGURE 4

In the light of our discussion of the definition of the British unit of length, this definition of the metre appears strikingly bold— almost irresponsible in relation to the specification of the mode of support. It is, however, essentially sound, at least as sound, and as elegant in theoretical basis, as the design of cross-section of the

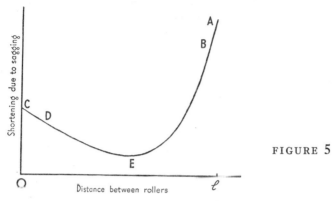

FIGURE 5

standard metre itself. The principle involved is simple: it is necessary to define an arbitrary length which can be accurately reproduced; it is not necessary—it is, in fact, valueless—to attempt to
ensure that that length should be the same as the distance between
the defining marks on the material standard when the standard is altogether unflexed at the specified temperature (such a situation has
no relevance to practice, for reasons already discussed, see p. 14).

Let us consider this matter of reproducibility. Imagine a uniform
bar with defining marks in the neutral plane supported freely on
transverse rollers at its two ends. Suppose now that the rollers are
moved inwards symmetrically by a small amount. The sagging in
the centre will decrease a little and the sagging of the portions of
the bar overhanging the rollers will, to begin with, be negligible.
In consequence the horizontal distance between the defining marks
will increase. Imagine, alternatively, the bar originally supported
(rather precariously) on two transverse rollers in contact with one
another, side by side, under the centre of the bar, and suppose
these rollers to be moved outwards symmetrically by a small
amount. The sagging of the ends of the bar will decrease and the
sagging of the portion of the bar between the rollers will initially
be negligible. Again the result will be a slight increase in the horizontal distance between the marks. Fig. 5 shows schematically the
results of a complete calculation for the rollers in any symmetrical
position, the portions AB, CD of the curve being those to which
our qualitative considerations apply. At E, corresponding to a
roller-separation fl, say, the tangent to the curve is parallel to the
axis of separation. We conclude that, provided the separation of
the rollers does not differ much from fl (not more than a few milli-

metres, perhaps, in 571 mm. in the case of the metre), the defined length is effectively constant. This result provides the assurance of reproducibility which we were looking for: it is of no consequence that the defined length is in fact a maximum in these circumstances, it would have been equally satisfactory if the defined length had then been a minimum; in each case it would have been reproducible without difficulty. The specification of support of the prototype metre on two rollers at a separation of 0·571 metre is therefore a great improvement on the corresponding specification of eight rollers for the support of the standard yard. This fact is now so obvious that the provisions of the Act of 1878 are regularly disregarded, and comparisons of the standard yard with its copies are made using two rollers as support, their axes being separated by 0·577 of the full length of the standard.

Because of the general adoption of the decimal metric system of weights and measures in scientific research, and its widespread acceptance as the legal system, or one of the legalised systems, for trade and industry (in spite of much earlier advocacy, the metric system was not finally made legal in Britain until 1897), many copies of the standard metre have been made and distributed as reference copies throughout the world. From time to time these are returned to Paris for intercomparison. Britain received a copy of the international prototype metre in 1897 of the same form as the original (mètre-à-traits), and in the following year a platinum-iridium end-standard (mètre-à-bouts).

2.11. STANDARDS OF LENGTH: GENERAL CONSIDERATIONS

We have defined the science of physics as yielding a body of knowledge through the processes of measurement (p. 1). If the matter were as simple as that, it might be thought to imply that from the very beginning, when the amount of accumulated knowledge was negligible, the procedures of measurement at least were well-defined—and that would further imply that satisfactory specifications of standards must have been possible from the beginning, without reference to accumulated knowledge. The history that we have given is sufficient to show that the precise definition of standards of length did not in fact precede the accumulation of knowledge, and the considerations of the last two sections should have made it clear that it could not have done so. A very large amount of detailed knowledge concerning the physical properties of bodies is necessary before it is possible to give a satisfactory specification of a material standard of length. Much of this knowledge depends upon observations which involve measurements of length based on an earlier and less satisfactory standard. In general, science advances through stages of successive refinement: this example of that general process is the more striking only because it carries the suspicion of a logical tautology. It may be so, but if so it is not surprising, physics is not a closed logical system at all: it is an adventure in exploration in which continual improvisation is the order of the day.

2.12. MEASUREMENT OF LENGTH IN PRACTICE: ACTUAL PROCEDURE

The modern standards, the yard and the metre, are not subdivided as were many of the legally established standards of earlier times. They are designed not for practical measurement but to define a unit of length. Practical measurement requires subdivided scales. To this end the procedure described in § 2.6 can be translated into practice, but only to a limited extent. There is a limit to the fineness with which visible marks may be engraved on material scales; there is also a lower limit to the size of subdivision which can be tolerated if the scale is to be read with confidence by the unaided eye. In general, the second consideration involves the more serious limitation. The situation may be improved somewhat by the use of low-power microscopes when scales are finely divided, but this does not contribute much more than a factor of ten to the overall precision. For unaided observation there is little to be gained by subdivision beyond the 1 mm. stage. With a lightly engraved 1 mm. scale the practised observer can generally estimate residual lengths with an uncertainty of less than 0·1 mm. either way, without optical aid; to do better with the unaided eye he requires the help of a vernier or a micrometer screw. The first of these devices, which we shall now discuss, was introduced by Pierre Vernier (*c.* 1580-1637), its principle having been described somewhat earlier by the distinguished mathematician Christopher Clavius (1537-1612); the second will be discussed after we have considered the general problem of the measurement of angle. (The fact that the practical soldier Vernier introduced his device as an improvement to the quadrant need not delay us: the principle is the same whether a linear or an angular scale is involved.)

The principle of the vernier is simply this, that if we have two uniformly divided scales, A and B, in contact, if equal lengths of A and B contain n and $(n+1)$ divisions respectively, and if in any arbitrary setting the pth graduation of A coincides with the qth graduation of B, the graduations being numbered in the same sense on A and B, then a relative movement of the scales of $\dfrac{1}{n+1}$th of a scale division of A $\left(\dfrac{1}{n}\text{th of a scale division of B}\right)$ will bring the $(p+1)$th graduation of A into coincidence with the $(q+1)$th graduation of B, and may thus be detected. In practice one of the scales is the main scale, the other the auxiliary, or vernier, scale. Again, since the measurement of decimal fractions of a division of the main scale is the normal requirement, we may choose $n=9$ and make A the main scale in the above description (the arrangement now generally favoured), or $n=10$ and make B the main scale (the original arrangement of Vernier).

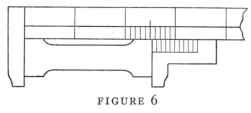

FIGURE 6

Fig. 6 shows the essential features of vernier callipers graduated in millimetres and used to measure the length (2·54 cm.) of a 1-in. distance piece (end-standard). The distance (in tenths of a millimetre) of the inner face of the movable jaw of the callipers beyond the 25th-millimetre graduation of the main scale is given by the position of the coincidence between graduations of the two scales as read on the vernier scale (at the 4th graduation in this case). Vernier callipers of high precision may have millimetre graduations and a vernier scale 49 mm. long. Such an instrument permits of the measurement of length to $\frac{1}{50}$ mm., that is to better than $\frac{1}{1000}$ in.

2.13. MEASUREMENT OF ANGLE

In two-dimensional (plane) geometry the angle between two straight lines is determined by the amount of turning of one of them, about the point of intersection with the other, necessary to bring the first line into coincidence with the second. Alternatively, an arbitrary point being chosen on the first line, the curvilinear distance moved by this point during the rotation necessary to bring this line into coincidence with the other is proportional to the angle between the two lines. Again, if two points A and B be taken on a single straight line, the amount of turning of the line about A necessary to bring the point B back into coincidence with itself (on the first rotation) is defined as equal to 4 right angles. A simple construction, based on a theorem regarding the congruence of triangles, allows the bisector of an angle to be drawn, and the construction for drawing a line at right angles to another line is a special case of this. Adopting the right angle as unit of angular measurement for the present, we have, therefore, a method of constructing a standard—and it will be noted that the unit of angular measurement here adopted in no way involves the unit of measurement of length.

The alternative description of the magnitude of an angle given above is the basis of the more generally adopted numerical definition of the unit of angular measurement. If an angle of θ radians at the centre of a circle of radius r includes an arc of length s we have by definition of the radian, $\theta = s/r$. By this definition the independence of the unit of angular measurement of the unit of length measurement is stated even more explicitly than before, and it is also clear that 4 right angles equal 2π radians.

Although for the convenience of the mathematician (or the mathematical physicist) the radian is a more fundamental unit than the right angle—although it is, indeed, the obvious fundamental unit—it suffers from the practical disadvantage that there is no simple geometrical construction for drawing a line making an angle of 1 radian, or any whole number of radians, with another line. The right angle, therefore, remains the practical unit. For subdivision, the only construction available is that of bisection, though the possibility of independent derivation of an angle of 2/3 right angle, which the construction of an equilateral triangle affords, implies that by continual bisection of these two angles (the right angle and its 2/3rds part) we may obtain an angular scale of which the finest graduation is $\dfrac{1}{2^n}$ or $\dfrac{1}{3} \cdot \dfrac{1}{2^n}$ right angle, as we choose, n being any integer. Taking $n = 5$, and adopting the second alternative, we have the basis of a straightforward construction for the subdivision of a right angle into 96 'degrees'.

We have given above the only basis of angular subdivision into equal parts which abstract geometry provides, but the logic of mathematical reasoning has not always been reflected even in scientific practice, and the subdivision of the right angle into 90 rather than 96 degrees has come down to us as a legacy from the distant past. Undoubtedly the origins of this system are to be found in the astronomical observations of the Chinese and the numerical calculations of the Chaldeans. The Chinese, at a very early date, decreed that the circle should be divided into $365\frac{1}{4}$ degrees of arc to correspond with the fact (see § 3.3) that the apparent motion of the sun against the background of the stars occupies $365\frac{1}{4}$ nights and days, and a system of sexagesimal fractions, which almost certainly derived from the Chaldeans, had become standard in Greek arithmetic soon after the time of Euclid. (A sexagesimal fraction is one expressed in the form $\dfrac{x}{60} + \dfrac{y}{3600} + \ldots$, each of the whole numbers $x, y, \ldots$ being less than 60. This system was in general use until the decimal notation was introduced early in the seventeenth century, see § 2.6.) When the whole subject was extended and codified by Ptolemy of Alexandria (c. AD 130), the division of the complete circle into 360 degrees of arc, and of its radius linearly into 60 'parts', must have appeared the most satisfactory arrangement for convenience of calculation. By this arrangement, it will be noted, the number of linear parts in the complete periphery of the inscribed hexagon was also 360. Moreover, minutes and seconds of arc were the obvious subdivisions of the degree, being its sexagesimal fractions.

From what has just been said it will be evident that the practical problem of subdividing a material scale for use in the accurate measurement of angles has been unnecessarily complicated, from the very beginning of the modern era, by the acceptance of the abstract trigonometry of Ptolemy, admirable in every respect except in its choice of unit. And, that this criticism is far removed from the academic is shown by the way in which George Graham (1673-1751) approached the task of dividing a quadrant of 8 ft. radius for the Royal Observatory at Greenwich in 1725. This project was one of the first of its kind, and Graham proceeded to describe two concentric arcs, with a separation of about 1 inch, on the circular scale, and to divide the outer arc by the method of continued bisection into 96 equal segments, then to use these to check the graduation of the inner arc in degrees ($90° = 1$ right angle) effected by a much more laborious procedure. Refinements introduced by John Bird (see § 2.8) and others did not obscure the fundamental difficulty, and it was not until 1809 that it was made tolerable by the development by Edward Troughton (1753-1835) of an ingenious method by which the errors in any circular scale can be deduced directly from observation. Only from Troughton's day onwards has the precise size of the degree of arc ($\frac{1}{90}$ or $\frac{1}{96}$ of the quadrant) been of little importance to the instrument maker. For the finest work it would be prudent to correct any scale, even one produced by continued angular bisection, by Troughton's method: it is therefore of relatively little moment whether an original scale which is to be corrected has been produced by the method of continued bisection or by some other less direct procedure. We may sum up by saying that circular master scales of high accuracy can now be produced, but that their production is essentially by the method of trial and error. It may here be noted that graduations of 1 mm. interval on a scale of radius 1 metre correspond roughly to intervals of 5' of arc, and that the use of a 60-division vernier with such a scale makes possible an accuracy of angular measurement in which the residual uncertainty is no more than 5".

2.14. THE SCREW IN RELATION TO MEASUREMENT

A screw is a piece of physical apparatus to which the concepts of length and angle have equal relevance. Its prototype in abstract geometry is the helix, a curve drawn on the surface of a circular cylinder such that at each point the angle between the curve and the generating line of the cylinder through that point is the same. (A generating line is a line in the surface of a cylinder parallel to the cylindrical axis.) It follows from this definition that, if a point traverses a circular helix, the distance through which it moves forward in the direction of the helical axis is proportional to the angle through which it rotates about that axis.

In the material screw the curve of abstract geometry has its counterpart in the 'thread' of the screw. If an actual screw were sectioned by a plane containing its cylindrical axis, the serrated edges of the plane section would reveal the ridge-and-groove profile of the thread continuously repeated along the length of the screw. The practical problem of screw cutting is to ensure constancy of 'pitch' (ridge-to-ridge distance measured parallel to the axis) through-

out the length of the screw—and to ensure that there is indeed a
genuinely straight cylindrical axis in the finished product. The
solution of this twofold problem, when the greatest precision is
required, is evidently as much a matter of art as of science. The
statement in a standard work on the subject, 'All screws made today
are copies of pre-existing or master screws', gives nothing away,
and this is obviously not the place to embark on a detailed description of processes of manufacture. Suffice to say that the final stage
in the process, if the greatest accuracy is desired, is careful grinding, using a long segmented nut which is gradually tightened on to
the thread, and the finest abrasive. Such grinding must be done
slowly; it may take days or weeks to complete. Eventually the
residual errors are reduced, and a screw is obtained which can be
incorporated, as basic component, in a measuring instrument,
possibly a travelling microscope or comparator, or used in a
'dividing engine' by which linear scales are subdivided.

In ordinary laboratory practice the most common form of measuring device based on the use of an accurate screw is the micrometer
screw-gauge. With this instrument it is possible to measure outside
dimensions of solid bodies as the distance between two plane-
parallel surfaces, just as such distances are measured with vernier
callipers (§ 2.12). As in that case, one of the surfaces is fixed, and
the other, being cut at right angles to the axis of the micrometer
screw, advances or recedes as the screw is turned in its fixed nut.
A scale is engraved on the outside cylindrical surface of the nut
along a line parallel to the axis. This line serves as an index mark
against which graduations on the bevelled edge of an outer
cylindrical collar may be read. The outer collar rotates rigidly with
the screw. Commonly the pitch of the screw is 0·5 mm. and there
are 50 graduations on the outer collar. In this case distances may
be measured directly to $\frac{1}{100}$ mm. (if the pitch of the screw may be
trusted), or somewhat more closely if fractions of a graduation of
the outer scale may be estimated with confidence. The micrometer
screw-gauge is generally used for measuring fairly small distances,
from a fraction of a millimetre to a very few centimetres; over this
range it is relatively more accurate than the vernier callipers. In
the travelling microscope, if the screw is sufficiently good, it is
practicable to use a cylindrical scale of much greater radius. Such
a scale may be subdivided into 500 divisions, then, with a pitch of
0·5 mm. as before, distances may be measured directly to $\frac{1}{1000}$ mm.

2.15. ARBITRARY OR NATURAL STANDARDS

It has already been stated (§ 2.12) that a material standard of length serves merely to define a unit of length measurement. Whatever the history of its adoption for that purpose, once the particular standard has been designated as the ultimate reference body, the unit thereby defined is an arbitrary unit: the pretence that the platinum metre of 1799 was exactly one ten-millionth part of the earth-quadrant through Paris was soon seen to be both mischievous and untenable (§ 2.10). The arbitrary standard is unique; actual measurement is effected by the use of copies and calibrated scales. For this procedure to be generally successful, it must not be excessively difficult to produce satisfactory copies of the standard. A good standard is one which, with care, can be faithfully reproduced.

In contradiction to the idea of an arbitrary standard we may entertain the notion of a 'natural' standard. A natural standard would be one which is not man-made, one which occurs in nature lavishly reproduced in a multitude of exact copies in the cosmic processes which 'created' the world. This, it will be said, is an ideal definition; there is no class of natural objects which matches up to its requirements: it is only in a qualitative, not in an exact quantitative, sense that two peas in a pod are 'alike'. But the physicist has good reason for believing that if physical analysis is taken far enough all material bodies are found to be constituted of material atoms. The chemist has classified these into about one hundred different types (recognising the distinct chemical elements, and postulating that for a given elementary substance all the atoms are alike), and the physicist has not obscured the essential simplicity of this classification, though he has elaborated it somewhat, increasing the number of different stable species to about three hundred (the isotopes of an element are distinct species according to his analysis). The physicist, then, believes, that nature has provided us with some three hundred different species of 'standard' atom: all the atoms of a particular isotope of a particular element are exact replicas, and this is true in general. If a method of using them for the definition of our units of measurement can be found, the problem of accurate copying of arbitrary standards will in principle no longer arise, nature will have provided completely interchangeable natural standards in over-abundance.

So far as the unit of length is concerned, the actual linear dimensions of atoms (about 10^{-8} cm.) are much too small to be useful, and in any case the size of an atom can only be inferred, and then with no very great precision, as the result of indirect observations. But the physicist does not admit defeat in the first round. Let us consider an ideal experiment. In this connection an 'ideal' experiment may be defined as one carried out as a mental exercise only; it is not suggested that any one person would follow the precise procedure suggested. In this book we shall make frequent appeal to ideal experiments of this type.

With a dividing engine let us rule a large number of equally spaced parallel straight lines (diamond scratches) on the plane surface of a glass plate. Imagine, for example, that the common spacing of the lines is $\frac{1}{500}$ mm. (see § 2.14). We have thus produced a scale graduated according to the unit of our conventional (arbitrary) system—and we have produced what in optics is referred to as a plane grating. Such a grating has the property, in common with a prism, of producing a spectrum of coloured light when white light is passed through it, that is of analysing the incident light into its coloured components. Now let us set up the grating as the analysing element in an optical spectroscope. A spectroscope-with-grating is an instrument so arranged that the light to be analysed enters by a narrow slit, is formed into a parallel beam by a lens, passes normally through the grating, and is finally viewed through an 'astronomical' telescope which can be rotated about an axis in the plane of the grating and parallel to the lines ruled on it. Finally, let us place a piece of common salt in a bunsen flame and allow the light from the flame to enter the spectroscope. We note that the flame emits a bright yellow light, and we find, on rotating the telescope from the 'straight-through' position (quite a lot of the light from the flame comes straight through the grating without deviation) that yellow images of the entrance slit are found at a series of angular settings, θ_1, θ_2, θ_3, say, on one side of the 'zero', and at a similar series of angles on the other side. We find as an empirical result, within the accuracy of our measurements, that $\sin \theta_1 : \sin \theta_2 : \sin \theta_3 :: 1 : 2 : 3$. We conclude that, if we can explain the value of any one angle, we can probably explain them all by a simple extension of the argument.

Now the magnitude of an angle is determined by the ratio of two lengths, also the properties of the grating itself are evidently determined essentially by one length, only, namely the common spacing of the lines. For generality let us represent this spacing by d. The other length necessary to determine the measured angle (θ_1, say) must be a characteristic of the light. (Moreover, this length must correlate with colour, since when white light is analysed by the grating the spectrum of colours is spread out in angle.) We call this length the wavelength of the light. Denoting wavelength by λ, and having regard to the empirical result relating θ_1, θ_2, θ_3, let us define λ by

$$\lambda = d \sin \theta_1 \qquad (4)$$

so that $\qquad 2\lambda = d \sin \theta_2, \quad 3\lambda = d \sin \theta_3.$

To all appearances we have here discovered a uniformly divided scale, with λ as unit, implicit in the properties of the 'monochromatic' light from the bunsen flame. A little further research will show that yellow spectrum lines are obtained at these precise angles, θ_1, θ_2, θ_3, whenever any chemical compound of sodium is introduced into the bunsen flame, so long as the same grating is used. We conclude, then, that the length λ characterises some property of the individual atoms of sodium, which manifests itself, in the circumstances specified, uninfluenced by the presence of atoms of other elements. Moreover, this length turns out to be very much greater (about 6×10^{-5} cm.) than the diameter of the sodium atom itself, and thus possible to compare, in a simple experiment, with our arbitrarily chosen unit the metre.

The position appears to be that we have chosen an arbitrary unit, defining a standard with great attention to detail, we have developed a method of putting this unit to practical use, making accurate screws with considerable expenditure of ingenious effort, building dividing engines, graduating scales and ruling gratings, when we might have adopted an infallible recipe for the reproduction of a natural standard in some such terms as 'introduce a little sodium compound—it need not be chemically pure—into a bunsen flame'.

Of course, the actual situation is not as simple as this. In the first place the optical spectroscope is not an instrument of the very highest precision, being limited in this respect by the accuracy of the subdivision of its angular scale. Assuming that we can read this scale to $20''$ of arc (see § 2.13), the accuracy with which we can compare a wavelength of about 6×10^{-5} cm., by this method, with a grating spacing of about 2×10^{-4} cm. is only of the order of

3 parts in 10,000. For purposes of measurement, our proposed natural unit λ is therefore correspondingly indefinite. It is as if the length of the standard metre was uncertain to 0·3 mm. But this difficulty is not fundamental: discussion of the grating spectroscope provided our most direct approach to the idea of a wavelength standard, and very much more accurate methods are in fact available, for the comparison of optical wavelengths with the lengths of material bodies, which we cannot here consider further.

But a second difficulty in the way of the practical adoption of a wavelength standard arises once we look for the highest precision. In discussing principles, we have taken the light from a 'sodium flame' as an example, and we have implied that the spectrograph shows just one yellow spectrum line at a perfectly well-defined angle θ_1 (repeated 'in second- and third-order' at θ_2 and θ_3). But we do not need to have a very powerful spectrograph to find that, in fact, this 'line' consists of two quite distinct lines separated by rather more than 1' of arc (assuming a grating spacing of $\frac{1}{500}$ mm., as previously), and the question immediately arises whether each of these is really well-defined in wavelength, or not. This doubt having been raised, the ultimate problem is, indeed, the problem of choosing, from the multitudes of spectrum lines to be found in the optical spectra of the various elements (taken from flames, gasdischarge glows, or sparks between solid electrodes), the one which most nearly satisfies the condition of being perfectly defined in respect of wavelength. Between 1893 and 1940 nine comparisons of the metre with the wavelength (in air under precisely specified conditions) of a certain red line in the spectrum of cadmium were made. The accuracy claimed for these comparisons may be indicated by quoting the final mean value, 1 metre = 1553164·13 wavelengths. Now, in 1957, there are good reasons for believing that spectrum lines more satisfactory than the red cadmium line can be chosen. But in spite of much consideration by international committees over many years, a final choice has yet to be made.

2.16. UNITS OF AREA AND VOLUME

When we accept the results of abstract geometry as formulae, stating, for example, that the plane area of a circle of radius r is πr^2, or that the volume of a right cone of height h, standing on such a circle as base, is $\frac{1}{3}\pi r^2 h$, we are making implicit assumptions concerning the units involved—in this case the units of area and volume respectively. Indeed, any formula in mensuration or physics implies such assumptions. Any such formula merely asserts the equality of numbers calculated according to the alternative procedures specified conventionally by the symbols to the right and to the left of the sign of equality. This statement of equivalence has significance in respect of measurements made, only if the numbers are the 'measures', in terms of appropriately chosen units, of the 'magnitudes' of the physical quantities concerned. The formula is, in any case, incomplete without a statement regarding the units; further, the formula contributes to a true statement only if the units adopted for the measures which the symbols represent are mutually consistent. If the radius is measured in centimetres, the formula $A = \pi r^2$ gives the area of the circle correctly in square-centimetre units, it does not give it correctly in square inches. The traditional point of view is, then, that each of the formulae of mensuration of area or volume determines unambiguously (or presupposes) a 'derived' unit, of area or of volume as the case may be, once the unit of length measurement has been specified. To be precise, the derived unit of area is the plane area of a square the sides of which are of unit length, and the derived unit of volume is the space enclosed within a cube each face of which is a unit square.

Obviously, once these definitions have been accepted, the formulae of mensuration are valid for measurements made on the basis of any choice of the unit of length, since the derived units of area and volume follow automatically from that choice. Let us consider, for example, the formula for the volume of a right circular cone

$$V = \tfrac{1}{3}\pi r^2 h \qquad (5)$$

Let us assume that a unit of length has been chosen in terms of which the measures of the radius of the base and the height of a particular cone are m_1 and m_2, respectively. Then m_3 the measure of the volume of the cone in terms of the corresponding derived unit of volume is given by

$$m_3 = \tfrac{1}{3}\pi m_1{}^2 m_2.$$

Suppose, now, that another unit of length is chosen, f times as large as the first, and let μ_1, μ_2 be the measures of the radius of the base and the height of the same cone in terms of the new unit. Clearly,

$$\mu_1 = m_1/f, \quad \mu_2 = m_2/f \qquad (6)$$

Then μ_3, the measure of the volume, in terms of the new derived unit of volume, will be given by

$$\mu_3 = \tfrac{1}{3}\pi\mu_1{}^2\mu_2$$

if, and only if, $$\mu_3 = m_3/f^3 \qquad (7)$$

Comparing equations (6) and (7), the latter will be recognised as an expression of the fact that the unit of length having been increased in size by a factor f, the derived unit of volume is thereby increased in size by a factor f^3. A result identical with (7) would have been obtained if we had started with the formula for any volume other than that of a cone. Thus, for example, if we had considered, instead of equation (5), the formula

$$V = a^3 + 4\pi b^3,$$

giving the volume of a cube of edge a having a hemispherical boss of radius b in the centre of each of its faces $(2b < a)$, and had followed through the same argument as before, we should have obtained a result formally identical with (7).

Equation (7), as interpreted in the sentence which follows it, is frequently expressed in words in a different way: we say that the unit of volume has the 'exponent of dimension' $+3$ in length. The phrase is due to J. B. J. Fourier (1822), French mathematician and politician, who for a time was *de facto* governor of a large part of Egypt under Napoleon; more conveniently nowadays we say simply that the unit of volume has the 'dimension' $+3$ in length. On a similar basis the unit of area obviously has the dimension $+2$ in length. Conventionally, these statements are expressed in symbols as follows:

$$[V] = L^3, \ [A] = L^2.$$

As we introduce other derived units in later chapters of this book, we shall write down similar dimensional equations showing the relation of these units to the basic units of length, time and mass which are independently chosen. In the context of any such dimensional equation, $[x]$ means 'the dimensions of the unit in terms of which x is the measure of the magnitude of a particular physical quantity', the sign of equality may be translated as 'are', and on the right-hand side of the equation the symbol L^3 means '$+3$ in length', and other symbols correspondingly. It will be observed that the numbers which are the 'dimensions' occur as exponents in these equations.

For the present, the statement of the dimensions of a derived unit may be taken merely as a convenient 'shorthand description' of the way in which the size of the derived unit depends upon the size of the basic unit or units from which it is derived; later (see p. 88) we shall explore the wider applications of this idea of dimensions. If there were no other applications, the notion might with some justification be regarded as of trivial importance. But it is not trivial, and like so many original notions which were later clarified by others, it is to be found in use, though not explicitly formulated, in the writings of Isaac Newton (1642-1727).

We have based our discussion of the units of area and volume, thus far, on the acceptance of the formulae of mensuration. On that basis there is no alternative but to adopt units derived unambiguously from the fundamental unit of length, assumed to have been chosen previously. For all purposes of mathematical physics, such a situation is natural and inevitable, and in experimental physics, also, it is most convenient, but there are many units of volume measurement in common use, and one unit, the litre, in general scientific use, which have not been derived in this way. To balance our account of the development of units of length (§§ 2.2, 2.7, 2.8), it is worth while to pay some attention here to the history of the development of independent units of volume.

Before doing so, we should note that, as far as units of area are concerned, there is no problem. The most straightforward way to determine the area of a plot of land is to survey it, and reasonably accurate rules for this purpose were derived during the first phase of the development of practical geometry. There was no temptation to adopt any unit other than that naturally derived from the unit of length on the basis of the primitive formulae of mensuration which the early surveyors employed. But in the commerce of the market-place the need for the measurement of volume arose primarily in relation to liquids, to oil and wine and perfume, and to granular solids, chiefly corn. Bulk solids, particularly the precious metals, were sold by weight; architects had not yet evolved the practice of estimating building costs in terms of cubic capacity. So standards of volume were set up, in the form of vessels to be used as wine measures or measures of corn. The potter's wheel is not well suited to the making of cubical vessels, and in any case other shapes are more beautiful. All the circumstances of the time militated against the easy adoption of a unit of volume directly derived

c

from the surveyor's unit of length, even if the need for such adoption had been recognised. More probably it was not recognised for many centuries; the development of trustworthy formulae for the mensuration of volume came later. When eventually the cylindrical shape was used, as in the finely marked standard cotyle of Gythium in Southern Greece, the actual unit represented (about 58 cub. in.) was a simple fraction ($\frac{1}{20}$) of the apet of Egypt (§ 2.2.), the unit which had been defined by the wine-jars of the kings, for a thousand years of pre-Hellenic civilisation.

In Britain the old wine gallon was defined by a roughly cylindrical standard measure (of about 231 cub. in. capacity), probably from Norman times, until its use was abolished by the Act of 1824 (see § 2.8). From that date a new cylindrical measure, of height equal to its diameter, the Imperial Standard Gallon, was legalised. The volume of this measure was about $277\frac{1}{4}$ cub. in. at a temperature of 62° F. But the Act of 1824, which we have already seen to have been unfortunately drafted in linking the standard of length (for the purpose of copying) with the standard of time, in this case also linked the practical standard of volume with the standard of mass. The imperial standard gallon was declared to contain (at 62° F), when closed by a plane glass disk, 10 lb. of water. The folly of the double definition (in terms of the cylindrical standard measure, and the mass of pure water) was recognised in the Weights and Measures Act, 1878. In this Act the gallon was defined as the volume of 10 imperial standard pounds (see § 8.8) of distilled water as weighed in air against brass weights with the water and the air at the same temperature, 62° F, and the atmospheric pressure 30 in. of mercury. Even this definition is not entirely satisfactory, however, 'brass' and 'air' each denoting a mixed substance of variable constitution. But the gallon is not used as a scientific unit, so we can leave the matter without further elaboration. Adopting present practice in interpretation of the Act of 1878, the gallon may be taken to contain 277·420 cub. in.

On the other hand the litre, as already stated, is widely used as a scientific unit of volume, and its present definition is very similar to that of the gallon. The position is complicated only by the fact that the original intention was that the litre should be 1000 cub. cm. exactly. In the grandiose scheme set out in the French law of 1799 (see § 2.10), the unit of length was fixed as one ten-millionth of the earth quadrant, and the unit of mass (see § 8.8) was to be fixed jointly by the dimensions of the earth and the properties of pure water; it was defined as the mass of 1 cubic decimetre of pure water at its temperature of maximum density (4° C). For the purposes of liquid measure the name 'litre' was given to the volume unit 1 cubic decimetre, thus by definition 1 litre of pure water at 4° C had a mass of 1 kilogramme. In 1889 the kilogramme was re-defined in terms of a platinum-iridium standard, the intention being, of course, to maintain the size of the unit unchanged. But, inevitably, this was not done exactly: the mass of 1000 cm.³ of pure water at 4° C is not exactly 1 kg. in terms of the international prototype, but about 3 parts in 10⁵ less than this. The litre could no longer be both 1 cubic decimetre and also the volume of 1 kilogramme of pure water at its temperature of maximum density. In 1901 the position was clarified by re-definition of the litre in terms of 1 kilogramme of pure water (at 4° C and standard atmospheric pressure). It is now generally agreed that 1 litre = 1000·028 cm.³.

The possible confusion, arising from the recognition, within the same system, of two volume units so nearly identical as the litre and the cubic decimetre, has been accepted for the convenience of having an accurately defined unit in terms of which volumes of vessels can be determined by weighing the amounts of liquid necessary to fill them. For weighing is a procedure susceptible of the highest accuracy. But it should be insisted that a procedure which under all circumstance assigns as measure to the magnitude of the volume of a given vessel the number which is obtained experimentally as the measure of the magnitude of the mass of water which fills it—which appears to give to the unit of volume the dimensions +1 in mass, rather than +3 in length—is a procedure which obscures a most significant distinction. 'Mass' and 'volume' are concepts which in relation to the real world are qualitatively distinct, and indeed entirely independent one of the other (see § 8.3). No formula representing a law of physics, into which enter the measures of mass, length and volume, would remain valid after a change in the size of the basic units, if the unit of volume were arbitrarily linked to the unit of mass in the way suggested. The litre may be a convenience—particularly to the chemists—but 'dimensionally' it is a monstrosity. The general definition, 'unit volume is the volume of unit mass of water (under specified conditions)', violates in essence, if not apparently in word, the first law of measurement: 'a magnitude shall be measured in terms of a unit magnitude of the same kind'. There are other substances, besides water.

2.17. SOLID ANGLE

In § 2.13 we defined the fundamental unit of angular measurement in two-dimensional geometry in terms of the equation $\theta = s/r$. Here, for sake of completeness, we make reference to the measurement of 'solid angle', essentially a three-dimensional concept. The simplest realisation of a solid angle is at the meeting-point of three planes, as at each corner of a tetrahedron. The measure of the solid angle is the measure of the 'openness' of the corner formed by such an intersection. If we imagine a sphere of radius r centred at the corner in question, and if an area A of the surface of the sphere is bounded by the sides of the spherical triangle in which the three intersecting planes cut the sphere, we may define the fundamental unit of measurement of solid angle, the steradian, in terms of the equation $\omega = A/r^2$. Further, we may extend the notion quite simply, stating that if there be any closed curve, enclosing an area A on the surface of a sphere of radius r, then the measure (in steradians) of the solid angle which this area subtends at the centre of the sphere is likewise A/r^2.

CHAPTER 3

THE MEASUREMENT OF TIME

3.1. HUMAN TIME AND PHYSICAL TIME

In the last chapter we began the attempt to discover the foundations of the science of physics in man's intuitive notions of space and time. We considered there the development of the notion of space and the systems of measurement to which it has given rise; here we consider the development of the notion of time.

The reality to which the notion of time relates is so all-pervasive that it is impossible to describe any human activity without reference to it in some way or another. Thus we have described the origin, and to some extent the structure, of abstract geometry—a particular product of human activity—and inevitably temporal images have been involved in our description. Such images cannot easily be avoided, for example in the definition of angle—the amount of turning necessary to bring one line into coincidence with another (§ 2.13), and we have noted the importance for the theory of measurement of the axiom 'figures may be moved freely in space without change of shape or size' (§ 2.6). Furthermore, when we speak of drawing the straight line through two points, we naturally think of a process having duration in time. On the other hand, intuitively we regard space and time as qualitatively distinct concepts: we take it as axiomatic that, whatever our difficulty in disentangling them, the notion of time is in no way essential to the development of abstract geometry as the logic of space in its own right. In this chapter we are left with the problem of considering the notion of time in its own right, also.

In some respects the notion of time is a more indwelling human notion than the notion of spatial extent. Cut off from all awareness of the external world, a man may still be aware of events within his own body. His breathing or his heart-beat provides him with a standard of time-reference, even with a crude unit of time-measurement. But a man may withdraw himself further from awareness of his immediate condition (indeed in normal health he has to be specially attentive to pay heed to his heart-beat), and, in recollection, experience a flow of time having no obvious relation to events currently happening in the world around him and observed by his neighbours, or any relation to his own respiration or vital processes generally. Again, even when he is aware of his surroundings, a man may be conscious that he employs two different criteria in estimating duration. One may be based, for example, on intensity of boredom—such a basis provides no numerical measure—the other may lead to a quantitative estimate, in terms of his own heart-beat or the ticking of a grandfather clock. Depending on the occasion, one or other criterion assumes the greater importance for the individual. In physics, on the other hand, importance for the individual is an irrelevant consideration; we look for a purely impersonal definition of time.

'The physicist', it has been said (Barton, *Analytical Mechanics*, 1911), 'regards time as that familiar though inscrutable one-dimensional something which separates changes in bodies and individual sensations and extends without known limits from the past to the future.' This statement, of course, is not a definition; it merely points the problem. If it approaches a definition, it is only that it implies that time is continuous. Thereby it disregards hundreds of years of recurring debate among philosophers: Thomas Aquinas (*c*. 1225-1274), William of Occam (*c*. 1290-1349), Nicholas of Cusa (1401-1464), René Descartes (1596-1650), John Locke (1632-1704), Immanuel Kant (1742-1804), Henri Bergson (1859-1941). But by the same token it adopts the only approach which makes possible the easy mathematical development of the subject. Only through this approach, which does not distinguish mathematically between one-dimensional space and one-dimensional time, may the procedures of elementary algebra be brought to bear on the problems of motion.

Aristotle (384-322 BC) spoke of time as 'the number of motion'. Today, after more than two thousand years, physicists do not profess to come much closer to a rigorous definition. Newton believed he could distinguish, in principle at least, 'absolute time' from the particular measures based on specific examples of motion—as indeed he believed it to be significant to discuss 'absolute rest', and in that way to define physical space independently of the bodies contained in it. But the contrary view of his rival and contemporary Gottfried Wilhelm Leibnitz (1646-1716), is more consonant with the modern attitude: 'Space is the abstract of all relations of co-existence; Time is the abstract of all relations of sequence.'

3.2. STANDARDS AND UNITS

It is regarded as axiomatic in respect of linear scales—material standards of length—that they may be moved from place to place without change, in particular that such a standard may be moved forward, step by step in a direction parallel to its length, thereby generating a longer, equally divided scale. In contradistinction, an interval of time may be used as a standard interval once only. In order that time measurement shall be possible, then, the basic requirement is a repetitive process in which a uniform pattern of recurring features may be recognised. Thereafter it is a matter of assumption that the recurrence interval is constant.

In respect of length measurement the 'axiom of transferability' remains logically unprovable; in respect of time measurement the assumption of constant recurrence interval, being an assumption which refers to particular processes individually, rather than to a whole class of processes generally, appears one degree more suspect to the logician. Its practical validity can be established only through the absence of consequential inconsistencies. Thus we may suppose that a particular repetitive process has been chosen as providing a basis of time measurement, and that the phenomena of the material world, having been studied against this standard, are found to exhibit far-reaching regularities susceptible of description in simple quantitative laws. In that case the original choice of time standard assumes some significance. But this significance is precarious until it is found that, starting from some other entirely independent choice of repetitive process as standard, the same quantitative laws emerge. Eventually, we may suppose that the same laws are found to follow from each of a number of independent choices of repetitive process as standard: then we have reasonable confidence that the laws are of general validity—and that our choices of standard have been made with sure intuition. Newtonian dynamics, it has been implied in the last section (p. 38), was developed in the belief that its formulae dealt in 'absolute' time: it is sufficient, however, for its justification to claim that it was in fact developed in the belief that its formulae would be found to be equally true in respect of time measured according to any one of an indefinitely large number of independent natural or arbitrary standards. That is the actual situation today—at least for the purposes of the present discussion. With appropriate adjustments for recognised contingencies, the rotation of the earth, the oscillation of a free pendulum or of a flat spiral spring, the vibration of a molecule or of a crystal of quartz, any one of these provides a satisfactory basis of time measurement once the assumption of constancy of recurrence interval is granted.

3.3. SUNDIALS, TRANSIT-CIRCLES AND CLOCKS

The ancient civilisations of Egypt and Mesopotamia and China, and the somewhat later civilisation of Greece, were the achievements of peoples all of whom lived within a broad belt of the earth's surface between 25° N and 40° N latitude. We may imagine the ideal experiments now to be described to be carried out anywhere in that wide region: the results would be broadly the same. There are other regions of the earth, in the tropics and towards the poles, where the same descriptions would not hold. It so happens that these regions do not figure in the history of the rise of science out of pre-science. We may therefore neglect these other possible results.

Imagine, first of all, a pole set up vertically on flat open ground, and the direction and length of the shadow of the pole to be observed as the sun moves across the sky day after day. In the nature of things, the shadow is long—indefinitely long—at sunrise, and again at sunset. Between sunrise and sunset the shadow progressively shortens, then lengthens again. The direction of the shortest shadow is always the same, but the directions of the sunrise and sunset shadows slowly change from day to day. Call the constant direction of the shortest shadow 'north', and the directions at right angles to this, along the ground, generally towards the sun-rising, 'east', and towards the sun-setting, 'west'. Then the direction of the sunrise shadow slowly veers, from an extreme direction a little to the north of west, to an extreme direction a little to the other side ('south') of west—and back again. And the direction of the sunset shadow varies similarly, being at its extreme north of east on the same day as the sunrise shadow is at its extreme north of west, and completing a full cycle, in step with the sunrise shadow, in a constant period of about 365 days. Moreover, the actual length of the shortest shadow varies cyclically with the same period; it is least on the day on which the sunrise and sunset shadows have their extreme southerly directions, and greatest on the day on which they have their extreme northerly directions. Let us call the former day the day of 'summer solstice', the latter day the day of 'winter solstice'.

Imagine now a surveyor's tape stretched taut, from the pole which has served for this experiment, in the direction north. Let the tape be taken up and set down again repeatedly, marking out step by step a line along the ground extending northwards from the experimental pole, as far as is reasonably possible. Let a vertical pole be set up at the far end of this line, and let the original experiment be repeated. We have said that the result will be as we have already described, but it must be added that the direction 'north' which the new experiment defines will be found, at the new site, to lie in the continuation of the line drawn thither northwards from the old site. The direction north, then, has more than purely local significance. Let us call the vertical plane containing the direction north at any site the 'meridian plane' at that site.

Now let us consider observations made by night upon the stars. These do not in general cast shadows: they are not so bright that they cannot be observed in comfort with the naked eye. They, too, appear to move in the sky, in the period between dusk and dawn, and if we look towards the east as darkness follows sunset, and select a star rising where the sun rose on the previous morning, we find, by the following sunrise, that this star also has just completed its journey across the sky to the western horizon, following the same course as the sun. Except for a very few 'wanderers', the stars keep their relative positions constant night after night, all but constant generation after human generation. But, if we repeat our observation, looking for a star which rises in the east as the sun sets in the west, we find that we cannot use the same star night after night. Slowly our chosen star gains on the sun: after many days—twenty or thirty, perhaps—we find that it is already high above the eastern horizon when darkness falls. The situation changes continuously; after 365 days, or thereabouts, the original configuration returns, the cycle of change is complete.

Here we have confined attention to those stars which rise in the east, where the sun rises: that they follow the same course as the sun indicates that the direction north, defined in terms of the sun's shadow, is significant for them, too. We see this significance deepen if we consider the rest of the heavens, also. Suppose that we look to the north, and imagine our meridian plane extending out into space, dividing the sky into two by an arc stretching upwards from the north point on the horizon to the zenith. Suppose that we watch the stars on either side of this meridian arc as the night passes. We find that stars near the horizon cross the arc from west to east, while stars near the zenith cross from east to west. We find, too, that for those stars near the horizon their lowest point in the sky is in the meridian arc, and for those stars near the zenith their highest point in the sky is in the arc. It is as if these stars were moving in arcs of circles, upwards out of the east, and downwards into the west, around some invisible 'pole', itself situated in the arc of the meridian. Supposing our observations to be made in the valley of the lower Nile, we should conclude that the distance of this pole from the zenith is about twice as great as its distance from the northern horizon. Around this pole the stars—all the stars in the sky—appear to move together, describing roughly one-half of a complete circle during the hours of darkness. So it is not just the direction north which is significant, or the meridian plane, it is above all the 'polar axis', the line drawn from the point of observation in the direction of this astronomical pole in the northern sky. Around this axis the heavens in general appear to rotate, and the sun is different in this respect from the stars, chiefly in that the sun appears to move a little slower than they, losing one complete circuit of the heavens in 365 days, or thereabouts. And the sun in its course varies in respect of its highest point in the sky from day to day with the same period of a 'year', while the stars do not.

The basic facts of observational astronomy, as revealed by these ideal experiments, were well known to Chaldean astronomers more than four thousand years ago. Here it is our purpose to enquire what ground they provide for a system of time-measurement satisfactory to the modern physicist. We can assume that the ancients would have accepted without question, if they had considered the matter formally at all, that the interval of time between successive 'southings' of the sun is constant; their problem was rather to subdivide the day into equal 'hours' for the ordinary purposes of life. To this end they developed the sundial. The modern physicist, however, is the possessor of mechanical clocks, perfected during more than six and a half centuries, and of astronomical instruments the optical power and precision of which has been steadily improved over three hundred years of intensive endeavour. Since the time of Galileo (1564-1642) and Huygens (1629-1695), the oscillation of a pendulum has provided the repetitive process of supposedly constant recurrence interval for almost every mechanical clock of high accuracy which the physicist has employed. Similarly, since its development by Tycho Brahe (1546-1601) and Roemer (1644-1710), the transit-circle has proved his most serviceable instrument for the co-ordination of astronomical and pendulum time. We shall find that it furthers our enquiry to consider these three instruments, sundial, transit-circle and pendulum clock in greater detail.

Although there were certainly earlier forms—and many that were later, we shall consider here only the hemispherical sundial which there is good reason to ascribe to Berossus, astronomer-priest of Babylon of the third century BC. In its original design this dial remained in use throughout much of the ancient world for more than a thousand years. Employing a focused image rather than a shadow, it reappeared as J. F. Campbell's sunshine recorder in 1857, and was later modified by Sir G. G. Stokes (1819-1903) to be adopted as the standard Meteorological Office instrument before the end of the century. Its long history stems from the simplicity, and from the fundamental character, of its basic principle. Into a hemispherical bowl, with its rim in a horizontal plane, the sun casts a shadow of a small bead supported at the centre of the hemisphere. In this way, in principle, the dome of the sky is projected into the bowl of the dial. The shadow of the bead in fact reproduces, inverted in the bowl, the apparent motion of the sun in the heavens. The description which we have already given of the latter motion therefore applies to its replica, and we may imagine a fine wire stretched from the bead and representing the projection southwards and downwards into the bowl of the polar axis appropriate to the site of the dial (assumed to be in the northern hemisphere, as before). Then, on any day, the shadow of the bead will move in the hollow bowl along part of a small circle around the wire. Twice each year, at the 'equinoxes', the path of the shadow will lie in a diametral (equatorial) plane: at the summer and winter solstices it will be at its greatest distance from this plane—farther within the bowl at the summer solstice and nearer the rim of the bowl at the other.

Now imagine the equinoctial semicircle in the bowl of the dial to be divided into twelve equal segments, and, through the points dividing these segments, parts of great circles to be drawn, extending from rim to rim of the bowl again, and intersecting in the southern pole (the point where the projection of the polar axis meets the inner surface of the bowl). With respect to this axis these great circles represent twenty-four equally spaced positions of rotation within the hemisphere. If the shadow of the bead moves, in its daily small circle, from a point on one of these great circles to a point on the next, the sun must have moved in the sky through an angle of 15° (= 360°/24). If, then, we add to our assumption of the constancy of the recurrence interval in respect of the daily motion of the sun, the assumption of equality of the intervals involved in equal angular portions of a full day's motion (which is an assumption of another kind), and if we agree to divide the day into twenty-four hours, the great circles inscribed in the dial are the hour lines for any and every day of the year. This construction of hour lines was first advocated by the Arabian mathematician Abu'l Hassan about AD 1230, but it was not generally adopted for civil use for another hundred years. From ancient times until the fourteenth century it was customary to divide that part of each small circle that lay within the bowl, individually, into twelve equal segments: throughout the centuries in which the civilisations of Greece and Rome flourished, the period from sunrise to sunset was divided into the twelve hours of day, and the following period from sunset to sunrise into the twelve hours of night.

However convenient this system of 'temporary' hours may have been for the organisation of daily life, for the purposes of science it is not a self-consistent system. The ancient astronomers themselves recognised this fact. We see it most clearly if we imagine our ideal experiment (p. 41) very slightly elaborated. On any night—preferably near an equinox—let us choose, just after sunset, a star rising where the sun rises at the summer solstice and a second star rising where the sun rises at the winter solstice. Before the night is over we find that the second star has set, somewhat to the south of west, while the first star is still visible, farther to the north, high above the western horizon. Remembering our conclusion that these stars move across the sky in like manner as the sun moves at the solstices, it is obvious, without recourse to measurement, that the total duration of daylight is greater, and therefore the length of each temporary hour of daylight is greater, at the summer solstice than it is at the winter solstice. In fact, in terms of the 'equinoctial' hours of Abu'l Hassan, the duration of daylight (D) at the solstices is given very closely by quite simple formulae:

$$D_s = \frac{24}{\pi} \cos^{-1}(-\tan \epsilon \tan \lambda),$$

$$D_w = \frac{24}{\pi} \cos^{-1}(\tan \epsilon \tan \lambda).$$

In these formulae λ is the latitude of the place of observation, ϵ is the angular separation of the equinoctial circle and the small circle of a solstice as measured along one of the hour lines of the sundial, and the subscripts s and w relate to the summer and winter solstices, respectively. Now the angular separation ϵ is constant for all places of observation, and is equal to 23° 27' (see p. 52); thus for latitude 30° N (Cairo) $D_s = 13$ hr. 56 min., $D_w = 10$ hr. 4 min., for latitude 56° N (Edinburgh) $D_s = 17$ hr. 20 min., $D_w = 6$ hr. 40 min. With these results in mind, the only question which remains is why it was not until the thirteenth century that anyone advocated the graduation of sundials according equal hours, and why this suggestion, once made, had to wait another hundred years for general adoption.

The angular diameter of the sun as seen from the earth is about 30' of arc; the hourly motion of the sun, as already stated, is 15° of arc. It follows, therefore, that very special precautions are necessary if a sundial is to be constructed on which the time of day may be read, or by which lapse of time may be determined, more accurately than with a 2 minutes' uncertainty. The use of transit circles and pendulum clocks enables an accuracy of a higher order altogether to be achieved. Under favourable conditions the residual uncertainty may be as little as a small fraction of a second.

The instrument to which astronomers regularly refer as the transit-circle is essentially a telescope of rigid construction mounted so as to be capable of rotation about a horizontal axis at right angles to its length, this axis lying accurately east and west at the place of observation. The optical axis of the telescope is thereby constrained to move in the plane of the meridian. Through the eyepiece of the telescope the observer may see a fine cross-wire dividing the field of view equally, the cross-wire itself lying in the meridian plane. If, then, the telescope is pointing south of the zenith (in the northern hemisphere), the instant at which a star image is obscured by the cross-wire is the instant of transit of the star across the meridian, the instant at which it has its maximum altitude in the sky, due south of the point of observation.

Suppose now a pendulum clock, maintained under accurately controlled conditions of temperature and pressure (for only when these conditions are unchanged can the rate of the clock be expected to be constant), to be set up near a transit-circle. Regulation of the clock rate is effected by varying the effective length of the pendulum (see § 9.8). Imagine the rate to be set arbitrarily. Throughout the year let a number of suitable stars be chosen and let their transit-times be observed night by night, for each star for as many nights in sequence as is practicable. In such an experiment it is found that the interval of arbitrary clock-time between successive transits of any star is constant throughout the sequence, and for all stars is the same. The two assumptions, of constancy of the repetition interval for the star motions, and constancy of the repetition interval for the oscillations of the arbitrarily adjusted clock pendulum, are thus found to be consistent, and the 'sidereal day', the interval between successive transits of a star across the meridian,* is in this way established empirically as a provisionally satisfactory unit for the measurement of time (see, however, § 3.5).

Now imagine a similar experiment to be made with the sun, rather than with chosen stars. Obviously the procedure is somewhat different: the great brilliance of the sun has to be overcome, and the time of transit of the centre of the sun has to be deduced from the times of first and last contact of the disk image with the cross-wire in the telescope. But in principle the two experiments are precisely the same. The results, however, are not the same.

---

* This definition is not absolutely correct. In fact no particular star is employed by the modern astronomer for the definition of the sidereal day, but a point in the heavens called the 'vernal equinox' which moves forward against the background of the stars, completing a full circuit in about 25,000 years (see p. 51). This point is occupied by the centre of the sun once each year, when it is exactly 90° from the north celestial pole (i.e. when it is on the celestial equator) in its apparent motion from the southern to the northern celestial hemisphere. (Note the different, though related, uses of the word 'equinox', here and on p. 43). The result of this convention is that the sidereal day of the astronomers' reckoning is shorter than the 'true' sidereal day, as defined by star motions, by about 1 part in $9 \cdot 5 \times 10^6$.

The intervals between successive transits of the centre of the sun across the meridian are found to vary throughout the year, when measured in terms of the accurately controlled, but arbitrarily regulated, pendulum clock. Compared with the average transit-interval for the whole year, the length of the 'solar day' is about 1 part in 4200 shorter in mid-September and about 1 part in 3000 longer in mid-December; it has the mean value, precisely, four times in the year—in mid-February, in mid-May, towards the end of July, and at the beginning of November. Obviously the solar day is not, without further qualification, a satisfactory unit for the measurement of time. If our only concern were with astronomical observations we should not devote further thought to the setting up of a time standard based on the apparent motion of the sun in the heavens. For their own professional purposes, in fact, astronomers reckon by sidereal time, exclusively. They divide the sidereal day into 24 sidereal hours, each of 60 minutes, each subdivided into 60 seconds. The pendulums of their astronomical clocks are adjusted in effective length so that under standard conditions their recurrence interval is some multiple (usually twice) the sidereal second, with as much precision as can be achieved.

But the main business of life takes its rhythms from the sun, not from the stars—and 1 part in 3000 is not a very great variability. It does not intrude into man's consciousness, even though it cannot be tolerated in an age when the well-behaved clock and the almost equally reliable watch have replaced the sundial. For civil purposes, therefore, a 'mean sun' is conceived which moves uniformly in the heavens (as judged by the common testimony of astronomical clocks) along the celestial equator (see footnote, p. 46), completing its yearly retrograde circuit against the background of the stars in the same time as the real sun takes. Now, the real sun crosses this equator twice in the year, at the equinoxes, but it takes nearly 4 days longer to pass from the vernal equinox to the autumnal equinox than it does to return from the autumnal equinox to the vernal equinox again. By definition, the mean sun must take the same time for the two halves of its yearly circuit. Conventionally, therefore, it is decided that the mean sun shall pass through the vernal equinox as far behind the real sun as it is in front of the real sun when it passes the autumnal equinox. In this way the circuit of the mean sun is arranged symmetrically with respect to that of the real sun, the equinoxes being the natural celestial reference

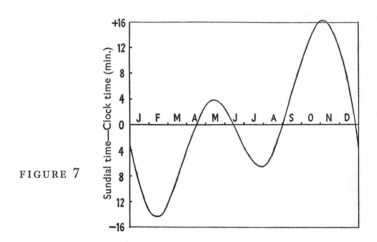

FIGURE 7

points for the latter. The difference in passage times is about 1·9 days at each equinox.

The motion of the mean sun having been thus defined, the mean solar day is the supposedly constant interval between successive transits of the mean sun across the meridian, at any point of observation on the earth's surface. This day, like the sidereal day, is subdivided into 24 hours, 1440 minutes or 86,400 seconds, and the pendulums of our public clocks, and those which physicists use for their measurements, are adjusted to be just so much longer than the pendulums of the astronomical clocks which show sidereal time that their recurrence interval is a whole number of mean solar seconds, as nearly as may be (usually 2 mean solar seconds, for a pendulum of effective length about 100 cm.).

We have said that the mean sun is about 1·9 days behind the real sun in its retrograde motion against the background of the stars at the vernal equinox. This interval being a little more than one two-hundredth part of a full annual circuit, it is obvious that the real sun crosses the meridian at the vernal equinox about $7\frac{1}{2}$ minutes (about 1440/200 minutes) later than mean noon. Similarly, at the autumnal equinox sundial noon is about $7\frac{1}{2}$ minutes earlier than mean (clock) noon. This difference is called, following an old usage, 'the equation of time'. Fig. 7 shows how the equation of time varies throughout the year. It will be noted that the greatest differences occur in mid-February, when the real sun is more than

14 minutes behind the clock and early in November when it is more than 16 minutes ahead of the clock.

3.4. THE CALENDAR

Accurate observations with transit-circles have now been made for some three hundred years. As a result of these the length of the so-called 'tropical' year, the interval of time between successive returns of the sun to the vernal equinox, is known in terms of the mean solar day with high accuracy. It is 365·242195 mean solar days, the last 'significant' figure only being somewhat uncertain.

It is naturally desirable that in any annual calendar the equinoxes should occur at the same date year by year, or at least that they should not move progressively through the civil year, with the passage of the centuries. The seasons of spring, summer, autumn and winter keep in step with the equinoxes, and for convenience the calendar should keep in step with them, too. The most obvious, indeed the only reasonable, expedient is to devise a calendar in which most years contain 365 days, and a smaller number contain 366 days, the incidence of the longer year being predetermined by a simple rule. The simplicity of the rule is perhaps more important than the shortness of its repetition period, though that may also be reckoned an advantage in comparing calendars which are otherwise of similar merit.

For more than 1600 years the countries of the western world generally employed the calendar which was introduced in 46 BC by Julius Caesar on the advice of the Greek astronomer Sosigenes. In this calendar the extra day was included in every fourth year. Sosigenes obviously preferred simplicity to exactitude, for it was known to Hipparchus that the length of the solar year was significantly less than 365·25 days, more than a century earlier. The Julian calendar was in fact already nearly 350 years behind the times at the date of its introduction (it is said that Eudoxus was the first European astronomer to give the length of the year as $365\frac{1}{4}$ days). Yet it continued in use, as we have recorded, for some fifty generations. Its shortcomings were noted by Bede in the eighth century, and by John Holywood (Sacrobosco) early in the thirteenth. Later in that century Roger Bacon (1214-1294) submitted a treatise on the reform of the calendar to Pope Clement IV. The Pope died shortly afterwards, and nothing was done. Two hundred years later calculations were begun as a preliminary to reform,

D

under Sixtus IV, but on this occasion the death of the astronomer Regiomontanus of the plague on 6 July 1476 put an end to the attempt. Another century passed before the matter was reopened, then in 1582 a brief of Gregory XIII abolished the old calendar and substituted in its place a calendar devised by Ghiraldi, a Neapolitan astronomer. Before his calendar was brought into use, however, Ghiraldi also died, and it was left to Christopher Clavius (see p. 21) to make the detailed calculations necessary for its elaboration in relation to the feasts of the Christian year, and its exposition to the world at large. The new calendar was accepted by Spain, Portugal, France and by certain Germanic states within a year of its promulgation, though not by the remaining countries of western Europe until more than a century later. In Great Britain an Act of 1750 established the Gregorian as the official calendar from 14 September 1752.

The Gregorian calendar differs from the Julian in suppressing three 'additional' days in a 400-year period. According to the old calendar each of the century years (1800, 1900, etc.), being 'divisible by 4' would be a 'leap year'; according to the new calendar only those century years which are 'divisible by 400' (2000, 2400, etc.) are leap years. The Gregorian calendar presupposes, therefore, a mean solar year of $365\frac{97}{400}$ or 365·2425 days. Its adoption implies that a period of roughly 3300 years must pass before the dates of the equinoxes change by more than 1 day from their present positions in the calendar in the months of March (21st) and September (23rd). For all practical purposes the calendar has been matched to the seasons.

Here one further comment only is in place. The Gregorian calendar has a repetition period of 400 years. Since, in fact, $\frac{8}{33}=0·2424\ldots$, an equally good stabilisation of the calendar could be achieved on the basis of a repetition period of 33 years (with 8 leap years in this period); furthermore, since $\frac{31}{128}=0·242188$, almost perfect stabilisation (leaving a residual discrepancy of 1 day in about 140,000 years) would result if a 128-year period containing 31 leap years were adopted. But neither of these systems has found favour in the western world; their formulation is not quite as simple as that of the system of Ghiraldi. On the other hand, it is believed that a system with a repetition period of 33 years was introduced into the Persian calendar of AD 1079 by Omar Khayyám. This is but one illustration of the cumulative accuracy of the observations made by the astronomers of the older civilisations through centuries of continuous study, long before the invention of the telescope.

Strictly apart from the problem of the calendar, it is appropriate to remark at this point that, if the tropical year of the modern astronomer contains 365·242195 mean solar days, by definition it contains 366·242195 sidereal days. Thus, the length of the sidereal day is effectively given as 23 hours 56 minutes 4·0905 seconds of mean solar time. In this result we come nearer perhaps than in any other to a direct definition of the mean solar second, the physicist's chosen unit of time measurement, in terms of actual operations. The mean solar second is 1/86164·0905 of the interval between successive transits of the vernal equinox across the meridian.

3.5. COSMOLOGICAL CONSIDERATIONS

It has been stated (§ 3.2) that, in relation to time standards, the physicist's criterion of acceptability is that use of an acceptable standard, along with other standards of measurement, enables the intuitively recognised regularities of the external world to be described in terms of simple quantitative laws. Such a body of laws, when it becomes sufficiently all-embracing, qualifies for recognition as a cosmology. Lack of precisely defined standards did not, however, prevent the ancients from elaborating their fanciful pre-scientific cosmologies, and, in later times, the slow process of refinement of definition of a standard proceeded in parallel with the gradual simplification of the world-picture of the astronomer. It may seem strange, then, that in our account of the former process we have made no reference to the latter. Our restraint has been deliberate: its object has been to show how far the purely descriptive approach may be followed. It has indeed been followed almost to the conclusion of the matter. This is no mere idiosyncrasy in the writer, nor is it so disregarding of history as might be supposed. It should not be forgotten that the phenomenon basically involved in the last refinement of definition described in the footnote on p. 46, the so-called 'precession of the equinoxes' (see § 5.6), was discovered by Hipparchus in 130 BC. Our modern cosmology dates from the sixteenth century AD. However, we cannot proceed to our final discussion until we have at least stated the cosmological beliefs of the present age, leaving some account of their origin for another occasion (§ 7.1). Briefly, then, for our present purposes, they are as follows. The sun differs from any one of the stars only in that it is much nearer the earth, nearer by a factor of 10^5 than the nearest of them. It is enormously larger than the earth, which seen from the sun revolves in a plane orbit around it, at a distance which varies continuously within a range of about 3·3 per cent of the mean during each revolution, the mean distance remaining constant. The earth rotates about an axis which is inclined to the plane of its orbit (the angle between this axis and the normal to the orbit being about 23° 27′), the sense of its rotation being the same as the sense of its revolution about the sun. The rotational axis itself rotates very slowly about a direction normal to the earth's orbit, in the sense opposite to that in which the orbit is described.

Judged against this background of 'theory', the assumption which is basic for our scientific time standard, that the sidereal day is repeated indefinitely as a constant interval, is seen in its 'true' context as the assumption in cosmology that the period of rotation of the earth about its axis is constant. The apparently complete success of Newtonian mechanics, during the two centuries which followed Newton's death, in describing the phenomena of the external world on the basis of this assumption is sufficient evidence of its close approximation to 'truth'. In this last section we have to ask only two questions: firstly, whether there is any recent evidence that the assumption is not strictly valid, and, secondly, whether its acceptance involves any logical inconsistencies. It will be convenient to consider the second of these questions before we consider the first.

Our professed aim is to exhibit the workings of the universe in terms of mathematical laws of universal validity. One of the symbols in our mathematical expressions denotes elapsed time, for which the definition of the mean solar second provides our unit of measurement. The Newtonian system had its origin, and one of its greatest successes, in the attempt to 'explain' the motion of the earth around the sun in terms of general principles (see § 7.3). It can hardly be doubted that, if it is adequate for this, it is similarly adequate for the detailed description of the rotation of the earth on its axis. In fact, the general principles on which it is grounded include precise statements relating to the behaviour of bodies that are freely rotating. Thus it is specifically stated that if a freely rotating body shrinks towards the axis of rotation, without losing any of its substance, its rate of rotation increases, whereas, if it expands, it rotates more slowly (see § 9.6.3). Likewise, Newtonian natural philosophy recognises an effect, to which the name 'friction' is given (see § 13.1), which invariably results in the slowing down of relative motion. Now, the general cosmological ideas to which astronomers have been led carry the assumptions, first, that the earth has probably been, and may still be, subject to shrinkage, and, secondly, that its rotation is subject to a frictional effect arising in the ocean tides. The second assumption, the more difficult to treat mathematically, has indeed been examined in detail on the basis of the Newtonian laws, and an estimate has been made of the rate of reduction of the earth's rotational motion due to this cause. Only this must be noted: in these calculations the symbol for elapsed time can no longer refer strictly to time measured in mean solar seconds. If we had taken our definition of the unit of time with full seriousness, we should have answered, without appeal to experiment or further calculation, the 'rate of the earth's rotation cannot possibly change: our definition precludes that possibility'. We do not, of course, take our definition so seriously, nor is the physicist likely, in the twentieth century, to alter the definition merely to meet this obvious logical difficulty, but the reader will at least see more clearly, with this discussion in mind, why, at the beginning of the modern epoch, Newton himself thought to endow the time symbol in his equations with 'absolute' relevance. In truth we know of no way of defining time absolutely; we must of necessity define our unit with reference to some process in which a material system is involved. On the other hand such a definition disallows certain questions, as prejudged by the act of definition, and to that extent its universal relevance is circumscribed.

Having examined the position in strict logic, we can now return to our first question, whether in fact the most refined of present-day measurements provide any evidence for lack of constancy in the rotation-period of the earth. The simple answer is that they do. A significant advance in the accuracy of the pendulum clock was made in 1924 by the introduction of the free-pendulum arrangement of W. H. Shortt. The 'free' pendulum, which is the essential time-keeper, oscillates in an evacuated case maintained at a constant temperature and has no mechanical connection with the weight-driven slave clock, whose rate it controls through electromagnetic coupling, except that once every half-minute it receives, through the agency of the slave clock mechanism, a small mechanical impulse by which its swing is indefinitely maintained. Somewhat later, even more reliable instruments were introduced, entirely electrical in action except for the time-keeping element (which could be a quartz crystal electrically maintained in visibly imperceptible vibration, or the atoms of a volume of caesium vapour executing in response to electrical stimulation identical internal motions having a characteristic period). The use of these 'clocks' of more advanced design for comparison of transit observations has brought out quite clearly that the clocks are more consistent timekeepers, judged one against another, than is the rotating earth, as judged against the clocks. Moreover, the discrepancies make sense in terms of Newtonian physics. Broadly speaking, they may be understood in relation to the redistribution of the air masses, and the changes in the earth's crust due to changing temperature. In a general way they follow the seasons, and the weather. These discrepancies in sidereal time are of the order of 1/30 second or less, when they are most in evidence.

The discrepancies which we have just noted are of the nature of fluctuations in the rate of rotation; observations with the most accurate clocks provide no answer to the question whether, with the lapse of centuries, this rate has been slowly changing. The latter question may however be answered, with surprising precision, by reference to ancient observations, regarded as providing little more than qualitative information only, as for example the observation that at a particular place, say 2000 years ago, a total eclipse of the sun occurred in the afternoon rather than in the morning. Times of past and future eclipses may be calculated from present knowledge, and total eclipses in a particular locality are sufficiently rare for the supposed 2000-year-old event to be identified without ambiguity. The standard calculation will assume the constancy of the mean solar day. Let us make an alternative calculation on the assumption that the length of the day has been increasing uniformly at the rate of 0·01 second per century. The actual occurrence of the eclipse is determined by the periods of revolution of the earth round the sun and of the moon round the earth, and these are assumed to have been strictly constant. Without significant error we may suppose the length of the day to have been constant throughout each century and equal to its value at the mid-century. Thus, we may take the length of each day to have been 0·01 second shorter throughout the nineteenth century AD than it is at the present time (1958), throughout the eighteenth century 0·02 second shorter, and so on. Since there are approximately $3·65 \times 10^4$ days per century, the accumulated difference between the two calculations, over 2000 years, is given by

$$(1+2+3+ \ldots 20) \times 10^{-2} \times 3·65 \times 10^4 \text{ seconds,}$$

or $3·5 \times 3·65 \times 10^2$ minutes, or about 21·3 hours. Thus the knowledge that a particular eclipse occurred in the afternoon rather than in the morning, some 2000 years ago, fixing the time of day to within 6 hours, let us say, enables us to conclude (unless a much greater rate of variation be accepted) that the length of the mean solar day is not increasing regularly by more than 0·003 second per century. Knowledge of the approximate time of occurrence of other eclipses observed by the ancients enables us to resolve the ambiguity just noted, to rule out, that is, the possibility that the standard calculation is in error by more than a whole day in 20 centuries, and generally to reduce the limits of our final estimate. Moreover, there are early observations of star transits recorded within the last 1000 years which provide further material for analysis. The final conclusion, on the basis of all this information, is that the rate of the earth's rotation is in fact slowly decreasing, though by no more than about 1 part in 10^8 per century (corresponding to an increase of period of rotation of less than 0·001 second per 100 years). It would appear, then, that the various influences, which might produce changes in our standard timekeeper, at this stage in its evolution very nearly cancel one another out. We need not here pursue the matter further.

CHAPTER 4

ONE-DIMENSIONAL MOTION

4.1. KINEMATICS

In this chapter, and in Chapters 5, 6 and 7, we consider motion purely with the object of describing it quantitatively; we do not at this stage consider the motion of actual bodies, and for that reason we are not concerned to enquire into the causes of motion. Such abstract consideration of motion in its own right is the province of kinematics. In this division of our subject we widen the scope of geometry only by introducing the concept of time, and the idea of rate of change of position which follows from this introduction. It may be held that in the actual world our idea of time originally developed out of our experience of change of position, but in kinematics such criticisms are regarded as irrelevant; here we are effectively dealing with the change of position of points or figures in Euclidean space within durations of ideal Newtonian time (see §§ 2.3, 2.4, 3.2). We adopt this approach because it has been established by innumerable investigations that such considerations are closely relevant to the phenomena of the external world: the actual motions of real bodies admit of similar description, at least to a very good approximation. This being assumed, our choice of the types of motion for consideration in the abstract obviously reflects our judgment of the relative importance for our present purposes of the various types of motion of which we have experience in real life. In this chapter, therefore, we deal first of all with motion in a straight line.

4.2. THE DISTANCE-TIME CURVE

The kinematics of the one-dimensional (rectilinear) motion of a point can conveniently be exhibited on a plane (two-dimensional) diagram. Let M be a fixed point in a straight line LMR and P a point which moves in this line. Let P coincide with M at the instant from which lapse of time is reckoned. At a time t later let $MP = s$.

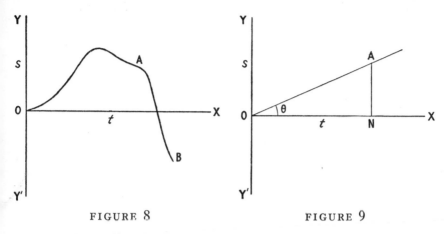

FIGURE 8   FIGURE 9

In fig. 8 let distances measured parallel to the rectangular axes
OX, Y′OY represent, on a specified scale in each case, the elapsed
time t and the distance s characterising the motion of P. Then in
general this motion will be represented on the diagram by a continuous curve such as OAB. Such a curve is referred to as the
distance-time curve for the motion in question. The particular
curve which has been drawn in fig. 8 obviously represents a case
in which P originally moves to the right of M (that is towards R)
reaches a maximum distance in this direction and then returns,
passing through M again and continuing its motion to the left
(towards L) thereafter. In this particular case the distance travelled
in equal intervals of time is not constant, and in fact the direction
of motion is not the same throughout.

4.3. VELOCITY AND ACCELERATION
Geometrically considered, the simplest distance-time curve is a
straight line, such as the line OA in fig. 9. Such a straight line is
said to represent motion with uniform velocity. Clearly, in this
case, if equal intervals of time be taken (however small), the distances travelled by the point P in these equal intervals are themselves equal. The numerical measure of the uniform velocity—in
such a case—is the measure of the distance travelled in unit time.
If the scale of fig. 9 is such that unit distance along OX represents
τ units of time, and unit distance along OY represents σ units of

distance as measured along the line of motion of the point P, v, the measure of the uniform velocity of P is given by

$$v = \frac{\sigma . \text{NA}}{\tau . \text{ON}} = \frac{\sigma}{\tau} \tan \theta \qquad (8)$$

To obtain this result, AN has been drawn parallel to YO from any point A arbitrarily chosen in OA. When the motion of P is uniform, as so defined, clearly v is the measure of the constant rate of change of position of P.

When we consider the second form of equation (8) we see at once how the concept of velocity can be extended to non-uniform motion by use of the distance-time curve. In respect of the uniform motion represented by the straight line of fig. 9, we have seen that the tangent of the angle of slope of this line (with respect to the time-axis OX) is proportional to the measure of the constant velocity of the moving point. It is a natural extension of the velocity concept to define velocity-at-an-instant, in any rectilinear motion, in a similar way, in terms of the slope of the tangent to the distance-time curve drawn through the point on the curve corresponding to the instant in question. This definition, then, specifies a graphical construction by which the velocity at each instant in the course of any rectilinear motion, such, for example, as that represented in fig. 8, may be deduced when the distance-time curve is given. When this information has been derived, it will frequently prove useful to display it graphically. We are led, therefore, to the plotting of curves of velocity against distance or velocity against time. Our choice of independent variable is dictated by convenience, but we may notice that whereas time proceeds inexorably forward, the moving point may return to the same distance from the origin, repeatedly. It would appear, therefore, simpler to choose time as the independent variable, and this we do here (see p. 123). Fig. 10 shows the velocity-time curve corresponding to the distance-time curve of fig. 8. The point starts from the origin with finite positive velocity (in that s increases as t increases). This velocity increases at first, and later decreases, becoming zero when the point reaches its maximum distance from the origin. Further decrease makes the velocity negative (as the point approaches the origin again), and, with variations, the velocity remains negative for the rest of the recorded motion.

Just as we introduced the concept of velocity to provide a

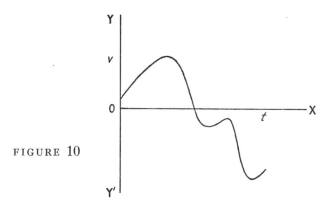

FIGURE 10

numerical measure of rate of change of position, we may now introduce the concept of acceleration to provide a measure of the rate of change of velocity (with time). In this connection the conditions of motion are naturally regarded as simplest when the velocity-time curve is a straight line. In such a case we say that the motion is uniformly accelerated, or that the acceleration is constant, and if ϕ is the angle of slope of the line (with respect to the time-axis) and v and τ are the scale-factors for the velocity- and time-axes, respectively, a, the measure of the uniform acceleration of the point P is given by

$$a = \frac{v}{\tau} \tan \phi \qquad (9)$$

It will be seen that, when the acceleration is constant, the velocity-at-an-instant increases by equal increments in equal intervals of time (however small), and the numerical measure of the uniform acceleration is the measure of the increase of velocity in unit time. As before, we extend this definition, and define acceleration-at-an-instant, in a similar way, in terms of the slope of the tangent to the velocity-time curve drawn through the point on the curve corresponding to the instant in question.

Formally, there is no end to the procedure which we have described with the aid of figs. 8, 9 and 10. Obviously, we could continue, plotting acceleration against time and introducing a new concept providing a measure of the rate of change of acceleration, and so on, indefinitely. We do not do this, however: Newtonian dynamics has developed around acceleration as the central concept.

To carry our present procedure further would prove unprofitable in the outcome. We remain content with these definitions of velocity and acceleration.

4.4. UNIFORMLY ACCELERATED RECTILINEAR MOTION

For the purpose of defining velocity and acceleration in rectilinear motion, we have, in the last two sections, assumed that the distance-time curve is known, and from this we have deduced, consistently with our definitions, velocity-time and acceleration-time curves for such motion of arbitrary character. The problem with which we are now concerned provides a particular example of the reversal of this procedure: we wish to deduce the velocity-time and distance-time curves when the acceleration-time curve is given. In this particular case we are concerned with the simplest situation of this type, that in which the acceleration is constant and the acceleration-time curve is, therefore, a straight line parallel to the time-axis. It will be profitable, however, to consider the general case first.

Suppose that AB (fig. 11) is the acceleration-time curve for a point which moves in a straight line. Let v_1 be the velocity of this point at time t_1, when it is at a distance s_1 from the origin, and v_2 its velocity at t_2, the corresponding distance being s_2. Let the accelerations of the point at t_1 and t_2 be a_1 and a_2, and let us suppose that the interval of time $(t_2 - t_1)$ is so small that the fractional change in acceleration, or velocity, during this interval is very small indeed. Then, if P and Q are the points on AB corresponding to t_1 and t_2, and if PM, QN are drawn parallel to YO, τ and a being the scale-factors for the axes of time and acceleration respectively, we have

$$t_2 = \tau.\text{ON}, \quad t_1 = \tau.\text{OM}$$
$$a_2 = a.\text{NQ}, \quad a_1 = a.\text{MP}.$$

Now, since, in general, acceleration is a measure of the change of velocity in unit time, $(v_2 - v_1)$, the increase of velocity of the point during the interval of time $(t_2 - t_1)$, is intermediate between $a_1(t_2 - t_1)$ and $a_2(t_2 - t_1)$, a_1 and a_2 being, respectively, the smallest and greatest values of the acceleration-at-an-instant during the interval concerned. But

$$a_1(t_2 - t_1) = a\tau.\text{MP}.\text{MN}$$
$$a_2(t_2 - t_1) = a\tau.\text{NQ}.\text{MN}$$

(10)

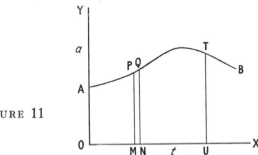

FIGURE 11

and the area PQNMP is itself intermediate between the areas of the rectangles, of common base MN, and heights MP and NQ, respectively, as specified in (10). To a good approximation, therefore, we may write

$$v_2 - v_1 = a\tau \cdot \text{area PQNMP} \tag{11}$$

So far we have derived this result as an approximation, but that it is, in fact, strictly accurate may be seen by imagining the interval $(t_2 - t_1)$ further subdivided, and applying the same argument to deduce the increment of velocity accruing in each sub-interval. When these increments are added together to give $(v_2 - v_1)$, the margin of uncertainty remaining will be found to be smaller, roughly in the ratio $1:n$, where n is the number of sub-intervals employed. Since, in imagination, n may be increased indefinitely, this margin of uncertainty may ultimately be reduced to zero.

Having shown that equation (11) is strictly true in respect of any finite interval of time $(t_2 - t_1)$, we may proceed to apply it generally. Thus, if v_0 is the value of the velocity of the point at the instant from which time is reckoned, v, the velocity at any subsequent time t, is given by

$$v = v_0 + a\tau \cdot \text{area ATUOA} \tag{12}$$

T being the point on the acceleration-time curve (fig. 11) corresponding to t, and the portion AT of the boundary of the area specified in (12) being the segment of that curve between A and T.

By use of equation (12) we may now construct the velocity-time curve for any rectilinear motion for which the acceleration-time curve is given. Once we know the scale of the latter diagram, all that we have to do is to draw in the ordinates corresponding to a succession of suitably chosen times, and to evaluate the areas enclosed by the axes, the curve and each of these ordinates in turn. This construction provides the solution for the first part of the general problem which we set ourselves to solve.

By precisely similar reasoning, a result corresponding to (12) may be derived as a statement of the procedure to be employed in deducing the distance-time curve, when the velocity-time curve for a particular rectilinear motion is given. Remembering that by convention (§ 4.2) we have chosen to reckon time from the instant at which the moving point passes through the origin (which choice involves no lack of generality), this result is

$$s = v\tau \,.\,\text{area ATUOA} \qquad (13)$$

the area specified in equation (13) being the appropriate area under the velocity-time curve concerned. (For convenience we use the same lettering as in (12) to denote this area; it is as if, for our present purpose, fig. 11 were taken to provide the velocity-time curve under consideration.)

In all formal respects, equations (12) and (13) provide full solutions to our general problem; we return, therefore, to the particular problem with which this section was designed to deal. It is to derive the kinematical equations (or the corresponding curves) exhibiting the distance s and the velocity v, in their dependence on elapsed time t, for a point moving in a straight line with uniform acceleration a. As already stated, the acceleration-time curve is, in this case, a straight line parallel to the time-axis. For the purposes of equation (12), therefore, area ATUOA is a rectangle of sides OA and OU, and since $OA = a/\alpha$, $OU = t/\tau$, equation (12) becomes

$$v = v_0 + at \qquad (14)$$

Fig. 12 shows the velocity-time curve corresponding to this equation. To this curve we now apply equation (13). Noting that area ATUOA is here comprised of the rectangle ALUOA together with the triangle ATLA, since $OA = v_0/v$, $OU = t/\tau$, $LT = (v - v_0)/v$, we have

$$s = v_0 t + \tfrac{1}{2}(v - v_0)t,$$

or, substituting for $(v - v_0)$ from (14),

$$s = v_0 t + \tfrac{1}{2}at^2 \qquad (15)$$

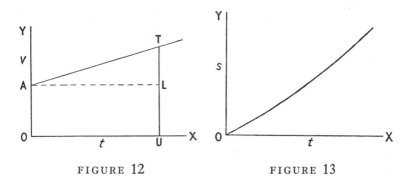

FIGURE 12   FIGURE 13

The distance-time curve corresponding to equation (15) is shown in fig. 13.

It will be remembered that we have already drawn attention to the fact that our choice of time as independent variable is to some extent arbitrary (see p. 58); in this case we may eliminate t, by substitution from (14) in (15), and obtain, as the third kinematical equation for uniformly accelerated rectilinear motion,

$$v^2 = v_0{}^2 + 2as \qquad (16)$$

The derivation of equation (16) completes the solution of our particular problem, and it remains only to comment on the form which the three kinematical equations, (14), (15) and (16), have taken. Equations (14) and (15) provide formulae by which the measures of velocity and distance, respectively, may be calculated. Each formula comprises two terms, and the same statement is true of the formula which equation (16) provides for the calculation of the measure of the velocity through the extraction of a square root. The symbol representing the measure of the acceleration occurs in the second term of each formula, but not in the first. The first term alone, therefore, in each equation, represents the situation when the acceleration is zero (or the velocity constant). When the acceleration is not zero, the second term in (14) gives the measure of the additional velocity which accrues because of the acceleration, and the second term in (15) the additional distance travelled on account of the progressive increase of velocity. A corresponding statement may be made concerning the second term in (16). The fundamental consideration is that in each equation the two terms which are added are measures of the same kind: in equation (14) they are measures of velocity, in equation (16) they are the squares of measures of velocity, in equation (15) they are measures of distance. The equations must remain true whatever self-consistent set of units we use for the measurements concerned. In chapter 2 (§ 2.16) we considered the formulae of mensuration from this point of view, and we concluded that the formulae themselves impose the requisite conditions of self-consistency on the derived units involved. Let us follow through the analogous argument in respect of the derived units of velocity and acceleration, using equation (15) for this purpose.

When the acceleration is zero, equation (15) becomes simply

$$s = v_0 t.$$

Let units of length and time be chosen and let m_1 be the measure of the distance travelled by a particular moving point in a specified interval of time of which the measure is m_2. Then, in terms of the appropriate derived unit of velocity, m_3, the measure of the velocity during this interval is given by

$$m_3 = m_1/m_2 \qquad (17)$$

Now suppose that another unit of length is adopted, f_1 times as large as the former unit, and another unit of time, f_2 times as large as the former unit of time. The measures of the same distance and the same time become

$$\mu_1 = m_1/f_1, \ \mu_2 = m_2/f_2.$$

Also, since we postulate that the kinematical equation shall remain valid, the measure of the original velocity, in terms of the derived unit which is now appropriate, is given by

$$\mu_3 = \mu_1/\mu_2,$$

or, if we substitute for μ_1 and μ_2, by

$$\mu_3 = m_1 f_2/m_2 f_1 \qquad (18)$$

Comparing (18) with (17) we have, finally,

$$\mu_3 = m_3(f_2/f_1) \qquad (19)$$

Equation (19) imposes the condition of self-consistency of units which we have been seeking: it implies that when the size of the unit of length is increased by a factor f_1 and the size of the unit of time by a factor f_2, the size of the derived unit of velocity must be increased by a factor $f_1 f_2^{-1}$. In other words, the dimensions of the unit of velocity are $+1$ in length and -1 in time, or

$$[v] = L^1 T^{-1}.$$

By a similar argument, starting from the simplified kinematical equation

$$s = \tfrac{1}{2}at^2,$$

derived from (15) on the alternative assumption that the initial velocity, v_0, is zero, we obtain the dimensions of the unit of acceleration as $+1$ in length and -2 in time, or, in conventional notation,

$$\lfloor a \rfloor = L^1 T^{-2}.$$

Having deduced the dimensions of the units of velocity and acceleration from first principles, we now note that, in each of the kinematical equations, (14), (15) and (16), each of the terms involves a composite unit having the same dimensions. Thus, in equation (16), obviously the terms v^2 and v_0^2 involve the same composite unit, for each is the square of the measure of a velocity. For these terms we have

$$[v^2] = L^2 T^{-2}.$$

For the term $2as$,we have, correspondingly

$$[as] = L^1 T^{-2}.L^1 = L^2 T^{-2},$$

verifying our assertion. This result is the counterpart of the statement already made, 'the fundamental consideration is that in each equation the two terms which are added are measures of the same kind'. This is a perfectly general result, and in future, when we have occasion to deduce the dimensions of a derived unit newly introduced, we shall not repeat the argument from first principles, as we have done in respect of the unit of velocity, but we shall have recourse to the simple result just verified, that with any valid equation, if we write in the dimensional formula for the unit of each measure involved in the equation in place of the symbol for that measure, and re-interpret the other algebraic symbols on this basis, we obtain individual terms which are the same. This result is said to embody the principle of 'dimensional homogeneity' in

E

relation to the valid equations of mensuration and of physics. For equation (15), for example,

$$[s] = [v_0 t] = [at^2] = \text{L}^1 \tag{20}$$

If the principle of dimensional homogeneity does not hold good for any suggested equation, then, obviously, that equation is irrelevant and meaningless in the context of physical measurements, but use of the principle alone cannot establish unambiguously the validity or relevance of any such equation. The purely numerical constants involved are outside the scope of its verification. In equation (15), so far as dimensional homogeneity is concerned, the last term might be $\frac{1}{2}at^2$ or $\frac{1}{3}at^2$, with equal plausibility: in fact, with one form the equation is valid, with the other it is not. A valid equation must satisfy the principle of homogeneity but not all equations which do so are necessarily valid equations.

4.5. ANGULAR MOTION

In this chapter we have been dealing hitherto with the one-dimensional motion of a point in a straight line. Considered purely on the basis of the mathematical symbolism involved, other types of motion may equally be regarded as one-dimensional. The only necessary condition is that the motion shall be capable of complete description in terms of a single co-ordinate of position, using this phrase in its full generality. The motion of a line in a plane, when one point in the line remains fixed, can be so described; so also can the motion of a solid figure in space, when one finite line in the figure remains fixed in position. In each case the motion is so constrained that it can be described in terms of an angle-time curve, in all respects analogous to the distance-time curve representing the rectilinear motion of a point. When an angle-time curve has been obtained for any such motion, the arguments of §§ 4.3 and 4.4 apply in their new context, and, for angular motion which is uniformly accelerated, we finally obtain kinematical equations, corresponding to equations (14), (15) and (16), in the form

$$\omega = \omega_0 + at \tag{21}$$

$$\theta = \omega_0 t + \tfrac{1}{2}at^2 \tag{22}$$

$$\omega^2 = \omega_0^2 + 2a\theta \tag{23}$$

Taking the particular example of the rotational motion of a line in a plane, if O (fig. 14) is the position in the plane which is occupied by the point in the line which remains fixed throughout the motion, if X'OX is the position of the moving line at the instant from which lapse of time is reckoned, and Y'OY is its position when the elapsed time is t, then θ of equations (22) and (23) is the measure of the angle XOY. The angular velocity of the motion, represented by ω in the

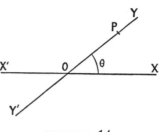

FIGURE 14

equations (with ω_0 as its initial value), is the measure of the rate of change of θ, and the angular acceleration, a, is the measure of the rate of change of ω. Moreover, since we have already noted (§ 2.13) that the measure of an angle is in all cases given by the ratio of two lengths, so that there is no arbitrary unit of angular measurement, the magnitude of an angle being expressible as a pure number, a consideration of equation (22) in respect of the derived units of angular velocity and acceleration leads immediately to the dimensional equations

$$[\omega] = \mathrm{T}^{-1}$$
$$[a] = \mathrm{T}^{-2}.$$

4.6. AREAL VELOCITY

Closely related to the concept of the angular velocity of a line which rotates in a plane about a point which remains fixed both in the line and in the plane, is that of the rate of description of area by a finite segment of the line terminated at one end by the fixed point. Thus if OP (fig. 14) is such a segment of a straight line which rotates about O with constant angular velocity ω, the area swept out by OP in time t is $(\omega t/2\pi) \cdot \pi \mathrm{OP}^2$. In this case we measure S, the constant 'areal' velocity involved, in terms of the equation

$$S = \tfrac{1}{2}\omega r^2 \tag{24}$$

r having been written for the measure of the length OP.

In the example just given we have assumed that the length r remains constant during the rotation of OP. In the general case, r may vary and the angular velocity of OP may not be constant. Even so, as a little consideration will show, equation (24) continues

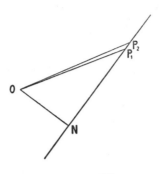

FIGURE 15

consistently to give the measure of S, the areal-velocity-at-an-instant, in terms of ω and r the corresponding measures of the angular-velocity-at-an-instant and the radius, respectively. It may be noted that in thus considering the general case we have in effect shifted the focus of attention from the rotational motion of the segment OP to the plane motion of its extremity P. In fact, r and θ (fig. 14) are now seen as the two-dimensional 'polar' co-ordinates of a moving point P, with respect to a fixed pole O, and OX as reference line, and equation (24) as giving the instantaneous measure of the areal velocity of a point moving in a plane path about a pole.

Strictly, the generalisation which we have just considered transgresses the bounds of one-dimensional kinematics, as our mention of two-dimensional polar co-ordinates makes clear. Let us conclude, therefore, by treating a special case in which the motion of the moving point itself is one-dimensional. We wish to calculate the instantaneous measure of the areal velocity, about any pole, of a point which moves with uniform velocity v in a straight line. Let P_1, P_2 (fig. 15) be the positions of the point at times t_1, t_2, and let O be the pole. Let ON be drawn from O at right angles to NP_1P_2, the straight-line path of the moving point. Then the average value of the areal velocity during the interval between t_1 and t_2 is given by $\dfrac{\text{area } OP_1P_2}{t_2 - t_1}$, or by $ON.P_1P_2/2(t_2 - t_1)$. But $P_1P_2 = v(t_2 - t_1)$, thus the average value of the areal velocity is $pv/2$, $ON = p$. Now, the position of the pole being fixed, this average value is constant, since it is obviously independent of t_1 and t_2. We have, therefore,

$$S = \tfrac{1}{2}pv \tag{25}$$

and the conclusion, in words, that the areal velocity, about any pole, of a point which moves with constant velocity in a straight line, is itself constant, and proportional to the perpendicular distance of the pole from the path.

CHAPTER 5

MOTION IN SPACE

5.1. THREE-DIMENSIONAL MOTION WITH RESPECT TO RECTANGULAR AXES

In Cartesian geometry (René Descartes (1596-1650)) the position of a point in space is uniquely specified in terms of three co-ordinates. If a fixed point O is arbitrarily chosen as origin (fig. 16), and if through O lines X'OX, Y'OY, Z'OZ, are drawn mutually at right angles as axes of reference, the three co-ordinates of any other point P with respect to these axes are the measures of the lengths of the lines ON, NM and MP, respectively. Here PM has been drawn parallel to ZO, and MN, in the plane XOY, parallel to YO to intersect OX in N. These three co-ordinates, x, y and z, thus specify the perpendicular distances of the point P from the three planes YOZ, ZOX and XOY. The co-ordinate x is conventionally considered as positive when P is on the same side of YOZ as is X, y is considered as positive when P is on the same side of ZOX as is Y, z is considered as positive when P is on the same side of XOY as is Z.

Suppose now that the point P moves in space. In general each of the three co-ordinates of P will vary with lapse of time. From this point of view we can describe the motion of P only if we can construct three independent distance-time curves, one in respect of each of the three co-ordinate distances. However, if we possess these curves, we can proceed, as in § 4.3, to define and deduce the values of three velocities-at-an-instant, and three accelerations-at-an-instant, in respect of our moving point. Each of these velocities represents the rate of change of the perpendicular distance of the point from one of the reference planes YOZ, ZOX, XOY; all three are necessary to specify the actual velocity-in-space at the instant in question. Concerning the three accelerations, a similar statement may be made. Because of these considerations we describe the velocities and accelerations derived from the three distance-time curves in this way as the 'component velocities' (or 'com-

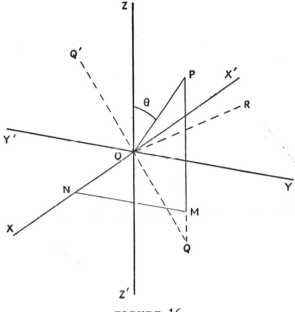

FIGURE 16

ponents of velocity') and 'component accelerations', respectively.
Looking back, we see that the same phraseology can be applied
equally well to the mere change of position of the moving point,
leaving aside all considerations of elapsed time. Thus if the point
changes its position from (x_1, y_1, z_1) to (x_2, y_2, z_2) we say that the
distances (x_2-x_1), (y_2-y_1), (z_2-z_1) are the 'components of displacement' involved. If s is the actual displacement, then clearly

$$s^2 = (x_2-x_1)^2+(y_2-y_1)^2+(z_2-z_1)^2 \qquad (26)$$

(Refer to fig. 16 and imagine that O and P are the initial and final
positions of the point.) Conversely, the component displacements
are given by

$$x_2-x_1 = s \cos \theta_1$$
$$y_2-y_1 = s \cos \theta_2 \qquad (27)$$
$$z_2-z_1 = s \cos \theta_3$$

where θ_1, θ_2 and θ_3 are the angles between the direction of the
actual displacement and the reference axes OX, OY and OZ, respectively. Expressions exactly analogous to (26) and (27) relate the

three components of velocity to the actual velocity, and the component accelerations to the actual acceleration.

From the account which has just been given of the motion of a point in space, in terms of the notation of analytical geometry, it would appear that, though the situation is more complex than it is in rectilinear motion, no essentially new concept is involved. The three components of the motion may be regarded as mutually independent motions, each represented mathematically exactly as if it were motion in a straight line. If we had to deal with uniformly accelerated motion in three dimensions (that is motion in which each of the three components of acceleration is constant), we could deal with it in terms of three sets of kinematical equations precisely similar in form to equations (14), (15) and (16) of § 4.4. All this is self-evidently true, but it does not conclude our discussion; indeed, the analytical method obscures certain aspects of the situation which become all-important when we make the transition from kinematics to physics in Chapter 8. For the remainder of the present chapter, therefore, we shall concentrate attention on these aspects.

5.2. VECTOR QUANTITIES

Following the analytical approach, in the last section we found it natural to lay stress on the components of displacement, velocity and acceleration rather than on the 'actual' values of these quantities. Any particular motion, however, is seen as a continuous process of 'actual' displacement persisting throughout a finite duration of time—or as a series of actual displacements in successive short intervals of time. To enquire what is the actual velocity-at-an-instant, or what is the actual acceleration-at-an-instant, in any such motion, may well be thought to be more realistic than to enquire what the components of these quantities are, for this latter enquiry is meaningless without reference to arbitrarily chosen axes of co-ordinates, whereas one aspect of the former enquiry is independent of any such arbitrary choice. In relation to three-dimensional motion, the quantities displacement, velocity-at-an-instant and acceleration-at-an-instant have two distinct attributes, namely, magnitude and direction. Only the latter attribute requires the adoption of a system of axes-in-space for its specification, the former is expressible in each case, in terms of a predetermined unit, by an appropriate measure, and in this sense is absolute. The three equations (27) show how the specification of displacement, in terms of its 'absolute' magnitude (given by its measure s) and its 'relative' direction (given by any two of the angles θ_1, θ_2 and θ_3 with respect to the three arbitrarily chosen axes of co-ordinates), is correlated with its specification in terms of its components relative to the chosen axes. A precisely similar set of equations applies when the quantity in question is a velocity- or an acceleration-at-an-instant.

Quantities such as displacement, instantaneous velocity and acceleration, for which, in respect of phenomena occurring in three-dimensional space, it is necessary to specify direction if the quantity is to be completely identified, are generally called 'vector' quantities. It is the merit of the synthetic, or unitary, as opposed to the analytical, approach to the problems of motion that it concentrates attention on the kinematical quantities in their vectorial aspects.

5.3. RESOLUTION AND COMPOSITION OF VECTORS

A vector quantity, or more simply, in much of what follows, a vector, has been provisionally defined as a measurable quantity possessing the additional attribute of direction-in-space. Measurable quantities which do not possess this attribute are called 'scalar' quantities, or scalars. Although this distinction assumes full importance only in respect of phenomena in space of three dimensions, the fundamental propositions concerning vectors admit of treatment in two dimensions in sufficient detail for all important results to be apparent. We accept this simplification, therefore, in this section and in §§ 5.4 and 5.5, restricting our consideration essentially to motion in a plane. Finally, in § 5.6 we include a brief treatment of a special case of three-dimensional motion which is instructive because it can be dealt with in terms of a two-dimensional diagram.

We begin with the observation that a vector quantity, of whatever sort, can be represented in a diagram by a straight line of finite length. The only conditions necessary for full representation are that we agree upon a scale by which unit length in the diagram represents a vector of specified magnitude, say a vector of which the measure is f in terms of the units appropriate to the vector in question, and that we adopt a convention by which directions in the space of the diagram represent uniquely directions in the space of 'experience'. The situation is at its simplest when the vector to be represented diagramatically is a displacement: in this case the space of the diagram may be considered as a replica of actual space —we need not, in fact, distinguish between the diagram and the actuality, though it is preferable that we should.

Suppose, therefore, that OP (fig. 17) represents a displacement (the line OP in the figure carries an arrow to avoid ambiguity regarding the two possible directions associated with any straight line, though, to be precise, this ambiguity may be resolved by adoption of the standard convention whereby, in the same figure, 'the straight line OP' always makes an angle of two right angles with 'the straight line PO'). Let any other line OQ be drawn in the diagram, starting from O, together with QP, the third side of the triangle OQP. Let OR be drawn, equal and parallel to QP, and let R be joined to P. As a result we have the parallelogram OQPR, with OP as a diagonal. It will be clear from this figure that, so far as the end-result is concerned (and when a displacement is specified this is all that is implied), the displacement represented by OP is identical with the composite displacement OQ + QP, and identical also with the composite displacement OR + RP. Moreover, OQ and RP themselves represent identical displacements, in the strict sense, since the magnitudes are equal and the directions are the same; similarly OR and QP represent identical displacements. The result which we have reached, then, is that the combined effect of displacements represented by OQ and OR, respectively, is the same in whichever order these displacements are combined, since the combined effect is, in each case, identical with that of the single displacement represented by OP.

Because the order of occurrence is irrelevant to the final result, we may reasonably claim that the result would be the same if the component displacements OQ and OR occurred simultaneously. On this basis we say that any actual (or 'resultant') displacement is in every way equivalent to a combination of two 'component' displacements occurring simultaneously, so long as the resultant and the components are related, in respect of magnitude and direction, in the same way as the diagonal and the two including sides of a parallelogram are related in fig. 17. This important result is known as the parallelogram law for displacements.

Two features of the parallelogram law may be noted at this stage. The first is that it contains within its statement the Cartesian mode of representation as a special case. If in fig. 17, the directions OQ and OR are at right angles, and coincide with the directions of

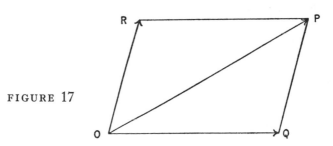

FIGURE 17

arbitrarily chosen (two-dimensional) Cartesian axes, then the component displacements are the distances $(x_2 - x_1)$ and $(y_2 - y_1)$ of § 5.1. The second feature of the parallelogram law is that it may simply be extended to deal with any number of components. The displacement represented by any side OA_n of a polygon may be considered as made up of components represented as to magnitude and direction by the other n sides, OA_1, A_1A_2, . . . $A_{n-1}A_n$. It is easy to see that, in this case, the polygon need not be a plane figure. Moreover, if $n = 3$, we obtain, again as a special case, the three-dimensional Cartesian representation of fig. 16. In that figure ONMPO is a skew polygon of four sides, and, with respect to the axes there chosen, ON, NM and MP are the Cartesian components of the resultant displacement OP.

In our discussion of the resolution of an actual displacement into components, just concluded, the notion of simultaneously effective component displacements was not reached without argument. If, however, we are to extend the application of the parallelogram law to the other vector quantities of point kinematics, that is to velocities and accelerations, the notion of simultaneously effective components must be accepted from the outset. There is no possibility of considering consecutively effective components when the quantity in question is a velocity-at-an-instant, or an acceleration-at-an-instant. This proviso involves no difficulty, but it is worth stating —otherwise our arguments in respect of displacements might appear merely pedantic. The truth is that so far as displacements are concerned the notion of simultaneously effective components adds little to our understanding of the situation, so far as velocities and accelerations are concerned it is all-important. To these remarks, therefore, we need only add the formal statement that the parallelogram law, and its corollary the polygon law, are equally valid for instantaneous velocities and accelerations, as we have shown them to be for displacements.

From the point of view of physics, rather than of kinematics, there is one further general comment. It concerns the complementary aspects of 'resolution' and 'composition' of vectors, as reflected in the heading of this section. In respect of any vector quantity it may be convenient for calculation to resolve that quantity into components (generally into two or three components), and to treat each component separately, combining the results to provide the final answer to the problem in hand. The parallelogram law provides the basis for such resolution and combination, and indicates the infinite choice which lies open, within the limitations which the law imposes, regarding the precise mode of resolution to be adopted. Facility in the solution of problems in mathematical physics frequently depends on the possession of a sure instinct in relation to this choice. In relation to the composition of component vectors there are two points. One of these has already been made, namely that composition is the natural counterpart of resolution, in the last stage of a calculation carried out by the method which has just been described. The other point is more fundamental. It is that the notion of composition reflects a definite element in the physical situation in respect of accelerations which is lacking when velocities or displacements are the vectors in question. According to Newtonian dynamics we are supposed to be able to identify the immediate physical 'causes' of accelerations in a way which we cannot do for velocities and displacements (see § 8.3). If more than one such cause is effective in relation to the motion of a single body, then there is a real physical sense in which the component accelerations of that body are conceptually distinct. These components are given by the situation in the external world, not merely evolved in the mind of the investigator. To obtain the acceleration of the body at an instant they must be compounded, using the parallelogram law.

The parallelogram law for the composition and resolution of the vector quantities force and impulse (see § 8.9) was first explicitly stated by Isaac Newton in 1687, in the first and second corollaries appended to his laws of motion. As we have seen, the parallelogram law is in one sense a generalisation of the analytical method of Descartes, elaborated some fifty years earlier. In spite of this connection, it is very doubtful indeed whether Newton regarded himself, in this respect, as generalising the work of his immediate predecessor; it is much more probable that he was consciously returning to what appeared to him to be the more powerful methods of the Greek geometers. Newton's *Philosophiae Naturalis Principia Mathematica* has very much the superficial appearance of Euclid's *Elements*, though the comparison might be pressed to Newton's disadvantage. We have stated (§ 2.3) that Euclid's great merit was as a systematiser of existing knowledge, rather than as an original contributor. Newton's *Principia*, on the other hand, was an outstanding work of novelty and genius.

5.4. THE HODOGRAPH

The particular type of vector diagram with which we are here concerned was introduced in 1846 by Sir W. R. Hamilton (1805-1865), a Scotsman by parentage, who was born in Dublin, and spent the whole of his life in and around that city. He was appointed professor of astronomy at the age of twenty-two, while still an undergraduate, and made contributions to mathematical physics altogether out of proportion to his academic mobility, or to the degree of recognition which his work achieved in his lifetime.

The hodograph of the plane motion of a point is made thus. Let AB (fig. 18) represent a portion of the path followed by a point which moves in a plane. Let the positions of the moving point at a series of equally-spaced times, t_1, t_2, ... t_n, be noted on the path. In the figure these are represented by the points P_1, P_2, ... P_n. In an auxiliary diagram let a fixed point O be taken as pole, and, a suitable scale having been chosen, let lines, OV_1, OV_2, ... OV_n, be drawn from O representing the velocity of the moving point as it passes through the positions P_1, P_2, ... P_n. Let V_1 and V_2, V_2 and V_3, ... V_{n-1} and V_n, be joined by straight lines. Then, when the constant time interval

$$t_2 - t_1 = t_3 - t_2 = \ldots = t_n - t_{n-1} = \tau$$

is reduced to zero, and the number of reference points, P_1, P_2, ... P_n is correspondingly increased, the smooth curve $V_1 V_2 \ldots V_n$ of the auxiliary diagram is the hodograph of that part of the original motion included in the portion $P_1 P_2 \ldots P_n$ of the path.

The properties of the hodograph may be simply deduced by use of the parallelogram law in the following way. Consider any two adjacent velocity vectors, OV_r, OV_{r+1}, in the auxiliary diagram. These represent the velocities of the moving point at t_r, t_{r+1}, as it

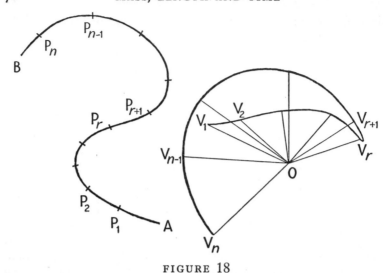

FIGURE 18

passes through P_r, P_{r+1}, respectively. Now $V_r V_{r+1}$ is the vector which compounded with OV_r, according to the parallelogram law, produces OV_{r+1} as resultant. Thus $V_r V_{r+1}$ represents, as to magnitude and direction, the additional velocity which the moving point acquires in the time interval between t_r and t_{r+1}. Further, if a representative point is thought of as moving in the auxiliary diagram in the polygonal path $V_1 V_2 \ldots V_r V_{r+1} \ldots V_{n-1} V_n$, whilst the 'real' point moves in the actual path $P_1 P_2 \ldots P_r P_{r+1} \ldots P_{n-1} P_n$, the average velocity of this representative point in the segment $V_r V_{r+1}$, being given by $V_r V_{r+1}/\tau$, itself represents the average rate of increase of velocity of the real point in the actual path between t_r and t_{r+1}. In the limit, then, when τ is reduced to zero, we have the final result that the velocity of the representative point in the hodograph is representative, as to magnitude and direction, of the acceleration of the real point in the actual path. This is an important result, the power of which was first clearly recognised by P. G. Tait, afterwards professor of natural philosophy at Edinburgh, and Hamilton's chief expositor. The widespread adoption of the hodograph construction is probably to be traced to its original description in *Dynamics of a Particle* by Tait and Steele, the first edition of which was published in 1856. Thereafter its incorporation in Thomson and Tait's *Natural Philosophy* (1867) was a natural sequel.

5.5. UNIFORM MOTION IN A CIRCLE

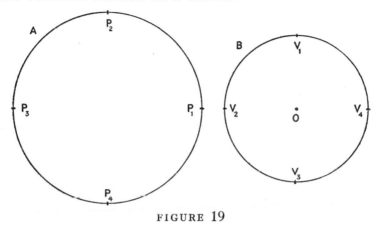

FIGURE 19

When the actual motion of a point is in a closed curve, repeated indefinitely with constant periodic time T, the hodograph of the motion is obviously also a closed curve described in the same time. The simplest case is that of uniform motion in a circle. Let A, fig. 19, represent a circular path of radius r uniformly described. In such a case we cannot say that the velocity of the moving point is constant, only that the magnitude of the velocity is constant; the direction of the velocity is continuously changing. Conventionally, we say rather that the speed of the moving point is constant, distinguishing, by this convention, 'speed', which denotes the magnitude only, and 'velocity' which refers to the vector quantity in its full connotation as a directed magnitude. Then, if v denotes the constant speed of the point moving in A, and if O (fig. 19) is the pole of the hodograph of this motion, the hodograph is obviously the circle B, the radius of which is v in appropriate units. Corresponding to the successive positions, P_1, P_2, P_3, P_4, of the point in the path, the positions of the representative point in the hodograph will be V_1, V_2, V_3, V_4, respectively, where OV_1 is parallel to the tangent to A at P_1, and correspondingly for V_2, V_3, V_4. Now, obviously, the speed of the representative point in the hodograph is constant and is equal to $2\pi v/T$. Thus the magnitude of the acceleration in the path is constant, and its measure is given by this expression. But

$$T = 2\pi r/v,$$

thus

$$a = v^2/r \tag{28}$$

where a is written for the measure of the acceleration. The direction of the acceleration when the moving point is at P_1 is the direction of the velocity of the representative point when at V_1, which is at right angles to OV_1, and towards the left in the figure. Since OV_1 is parallel to the tangent at P_1, the direction of the acceleration at P_1 is along the radius from P_1 towards the centre of A. Clearly, this result is general for any point in the path. Expressed in words, our full conclusion is that the acceleration of a point, which moves in a circle of radius r with constant speed v, is at each instant v^2/r towards the centre of the circle.

We might have described such circular motion equally well in terms of a constant angular velocity ω. In this connection ω is most significantly regarded as the constant angular velocity of rotation of the velocity vector OV which generates the hodograph. In relation to the path A, we may write $\omega = v/r$; in relation to the hodograph B, $\omega = a/v$. Thus equation (28) may be re-written

either as $\qquad\qquad a = \omega^2 r \qquad\qquad\qquad\qquad$ (29)

or as $\qquad\qquad\quad a = v\omega \qquad\qquad\qquad\qquad\;$ (30)

5.6. UNIFORM PRECESSION

In the last section we considered a specially simple case of two-dimensional motion in terms of a necessarily two-dimensional hodograph. But there is one aspect of equation (30) for the consideration of which a third dimension is required, or, at least, for the consideration of which it is necessary to refer to the normal to the auxiliary diagram through O, the pole of the hodograph. This normal is the axis about which the velocity vector OV rotates, with angular velocity ω. When we have thus specified this axis of rotation, we may express equation (30) in words as follows: if a point moves in a plane so that the direction of its velocity rotates with constant angular velocity ω about an axis at right angles to the plane, whilst the magnitude of the velocity remains constant, the acceleration of the point is at each instant at right angles both to the direction of the velocity at that instant and to the axis about which this latter direction rotates, and the measure of the acceleration is given by $a = v\omega$, where v is the constant measure of the velocity of the point. It must be admitted that this statement is somewhat more cumbersome than the more familiar alternative statement given in § 5.5, but, as there implied, it may be claimed that it is more significant. For the details of the path of the point are not now specifically referred to; though the path may be shown to be circular, the magnitude of the radius is of no importance for the new statement. Moreover, though the new statement has been given here in relation to the acceleration involved when a linear velocity changes direction uniformly in a plane, obviously the result is a general one, capable of expressing the instantaneous rate of change of any vector quantity when its direction rotates about a fixed axis at a constant rate. In this section it is proposed to apply the result when the vector quantity involved is an angular velocity. But first, since the question has not previously been raised, we should investigate the assertion, not immediately self-evident, that angular velocity is in fact a vector quantity.

The first question at issue is whether or not a direction in space can be uniquely associated with a motion of pure rotation. In respect of motion about a point in a plane we have already provided a partial answer to this question at the beginning of this section. The line through the centre of rotation at right angles to the plane is unique as axis of such motion. Similarly, in § 4.5 it was pointed out that, when a solid figure simply rotates in three-dimensional space, one line in the figure remains fixed in position. To make these partial answers complete we require a convention assigning a positive direction along the unique axis in each case. When this has been devised, angular velocity can be recognised as a physical quantity having not only magnitude but unique direction in space. The convention which is generally adopted is referred to as the right-handed screw convention. It may be stated as follows: the vectorial direction of a rotation is that direction along the axis of the rotation which is related to the direction of rotational motion about the axis in the same way as the direction of forward motion of a right-handed screw turning in a fixed nut is related to the direction of rotation of the screw about its axis. Thus the direction OZ (fig. 16) is the vectorial direction of the rotation through one right angle which would bring OX into coincidence with OY, and OZ' is the vectorial direction of the reverse rotation in the plane XOY which would bring OY into coincidence with OX.

We return, then, to the problem of applying equation (30) to the motion of a solid figure which rotates with constant angular speed

F

ω about an axis fixed in the figure, whilst the direction of this axis itself rotates in a plane fixed in space with constant angular velocity Ω. According to (30), a, the instantaneous angular acceleration of the motion, is given by

$$a = \omega\Omega \tag{31}$$

the axis of this acceleration being at right angles both to the instantaneous direction of the axis of rotation of the figure and to the fixed line (the normal to the plane mentioned above) about which the latter axis is rotating. Referring to fig. 16 once more, if OZ is the vectorial direction, fixed in space, of the rotation, with angular velocity Ω, of the axis of rotation of the solid figure concerned, then, when OX is the vectorial direction of the rotation of the figure, OY is the vectorial direction of its angular acceleration.

The motion which we have just considered provides the simplest example of a situation in which the axis of rotation of a solid figure itself rotates in space. Such motion is referred to as 'precessional' motion. In our example, Ω, the angular velocity of precession was assumed to be constant, and the axis of precession to be at right angles to the axis of rotation of the figure. We wish now to generalise equation (31), so as to make it applicable when the axis of uniform precession is inclined at an arbitrary angle θ to the axis of rotation.

Equation (31) gives the measure of the angular acceleration about OY (fig. 16) when OX is the instantaneous position of the axis of rotation of the solid figure, and this axis is instantaneously approaching OY with angular velocity Ω about OZ. It will facilitate further consideration of the more general case if we write ω_1 for the instantaneous angular velocity of the figure about OX, and Ω_3 for the angular velocity of precession about OZ. This choice of subscripts will be recognised as the appropriate one in relation to the cyclic order of axes in the diagram. Now imagine that, in addition to the motion already specified, the solid figure has a component of instantaneous rotation about OZ, ω_3 being the measure of the angular velocity concerned. Then, if this axis of instantaneous rotation of the figure is itself precessing in the positive direction about OX with angular velocity Ω_1, it is instantaneously receding from OY at this angular rate. In that case there are two components of angular acceleration about OY, and, taking count of their directions, their resultant is given by

$$a = \omega_1\Omega_3 - \omega_3\Omega_1 \tag{32}$$

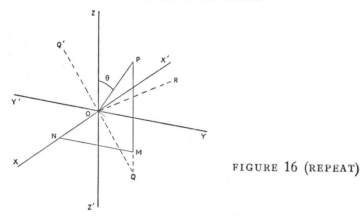

FIGURE 16 (REPEAT)

The solution to the problem of uniform precession about an axis arbitrarily inclined to the axis of rotation is derived when we are able to insert appropriate values of ω_1, ω_3, Ω_1, Ω_3 in equation (32).

Let OP (fig. 16) be the position occupied, at a particular instant, by the axis about which the solid figure rotates with angular velocity ω. Let OZ be the axis of precession, the angular velocity of precession being Ω, and let $\angle ZOP = \theta$. We suppose that θ remains constant throughout the motion, so that the axis of rotation of the figure generates a cone of semi-vertical angle θ about OZ. Let PM (perpendicular to the plane XOY) be produced to Q so that $\angle POQ = \pi/2$, and let OR be drawn (in the plane YOX') at right angles to the plane POQ. Then the three lines OQ, OR, OP constitute the most convenient set of rectangular axes in relation to which to discuss the instantaneous motion of the rotating figure. In this connection the subscripts 1 and 3 of equation (32) refer to motions about OQ and OP, respectively, and OR is the axis of the resultant angular acceleration α. Having made this identification, we obtain the following results.

(a) $\omega_3 = \omega$. This is stated explicitly: the solid figure rotates with instantaneous angular velocity ω about OP.

(b) Since the axis of rotation of the figure precesses with angular velocity Ω about OZ, it may be regarded as rotating with instantaneous angular velocity $\Omega \sin \theta$ about QOQ'. Thus $\Omega_1 = -\Omega \sin \theta$.

(c) But the axis of rotation of the figure is supposed to remain fixed in the figure, thus the instantaneous angular velocity of the figure about OQ is equal to the instantaneous rate of precession of the axis of rotation about this line. Thus $\omega_1 = \Omega_1 = -\Omega \sin \theta$.

(d) The axis of the angular velocity ω_1, which coincides instantaneously with OQ, rotates about OP at an angular rate given by the component of precession about OP. Thus $\Omega_3 = \Omega \cos \theta$. Substituting these results in equation (32), we then have

$$a = -\Omega \sin \theta . \Omega \cos \theta + \omega \Omega \sin \theta,$$

or $\qquad\qquad a = (\omega - \Omega \cos \theta)\, \Omega \sin \theta \qquad\qquad\qquad (33)$

It will be noted that, when $\theta = \pi/2$, equation (33) reduces to (31), which it must do, and that in any case the axis of angular acceleration remains, throughout the motion, at right angles to the plane containing the axis of rotation of the figure and the axis of precession.

5.7. RIGHT-HANDED AND LEFT-HANDED AXES

In discussing rotational motion in the last section we introduced the right-handed screw convention, and we also made considerable use of the three-dimensional rectangular axes of Cartesian geometry, which we originally introduced, in our initial considerations of the motion of a point in space, in § 5.1. It has already been pointed out (p. 81) that, according to the right-handed screw convention, the vectorial direction of the rotation from X to Y in the plane XOY of fig. 16 is OZ. Similarly, the vectorial direction of the rotation from Y to Z in the plane YOZ is OX, and the vectorial direction of the rotation from Z to X in the plane ZOX is OY. In fig. 20 (a) we reproduce the three-dimensional rectangular axes of fig. 16 for which these statements are true. In fig. 20 (b) a second set of three-dimensional rectangular axes is shown for which, on the basis of the right-handed screw convention, these statements are not true. They would be true only if we were to change our convention so that the vectorial direction of a rotation became that direction along the axis of the rotation which is related to the direction of rotational motion about the axis in the same way as the direction of forward motion of a left-handed screw turning in a fixed nut is related to the direction of rotation of the screw about its axis. It is natural, therefore, that we distinguish between the two sets of rectangular axes shown in fig. 20, by referring to the set (a) as right-handed axes and to the set (b) as left-handed axes. Since we are to adopt the right-handed screw convention generally in this book, we shall also use right-handed three-dimensional rectangular axes without exception.

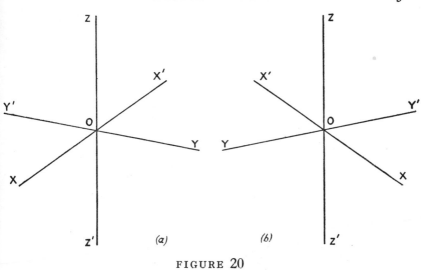

FIGURE 20

A little consideration will show that the arrangements represented by (*a*) and (*b*), fig. 20, exhaust the possibilities of drawing
three lines through a fixed point so as to be mutually perpendicular,
also that the two sets of axes there represented stand to one another
in the same relation as do an object and its image in a plane mirror.
In fig. 20 the plane mirror may be thought of as being normal to
the diagram and midway between its two halves.

CHAPTER 6

SIMPLE HARMONIC MOTION

6.1. SIMPLE HARMONIC MOTION GEOMETRICALLY DEFINED

Consider a point P which moves with constant speed u in a circle, of centre O and radius A. Let the time, t, be reckoned from the instant of 'first' passage of P through the fixed point X (fig. 21)

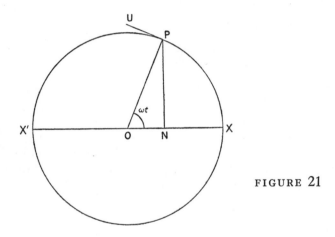

FIGURE 21

Then if $\omega = u/A$, $\angle XOP = \omega t$. Let PN be drawn from P to be perpendicular to X'OX, the diameter of the circle which passes through X. Then, as P moves round the circle, the point N moves back and forth along this diameter, from X to X' and back to X. This back-and-forth motion of N, which is repeated indefinitely (and which is assumed already to have been in progress for an indefinite time at $t = 0$), is referred to as simple harmonic motion. If ON $= x$, then x is defined as the measure of the instantaneous displacement of N, and A (x varies between $+A$ and $-A$) as the measure of the 'amplitude' of the motion. The periodic time of the motion is given directly by

$$T = 2\pi/\omega \qquad (34)$$

In relation to the simple harmonic motion of N, the motion of P may be referred to as motion in the auxiliary circle. In this circle the angle XOP is said to determine the 'phase' of the motion of N at time t. Because the phase of the motion is determined by an angle, ωt is sometimes referred to as the phase angle. The 'frequency' of the simple harmonic motion is the number of complete back-and-forth oscillations in unit time. Thus

$$f = 1/T = \omega/2\pi.$$

Now, at time t the direction of the instantaneous velocity of P is along PU, the tangent to the auxiliary circle at P, also the direction of the instantaneous acceleration of P is along PO (§ 5.5), and its measure is $\omega^2 A$ (equation (29)). If, therefore, v is the measure of the velocity, and a the measure of the acceleration, of N at this time, we have, regarding the direction OX as positive,

$$x = A \cos \omega t \tag{35}$$

$$v = -\omega A \sin \omega t \tag{36}$$

$$a = -\omega^2 A \cos \omega t = -\omega^2 x \tag{37}$$

6.2. ALTERNATIVE DEFINITION AND GENERALISATION

Equation (37), in its second form, provides the basis for an alternative definition of simple harmonic motion in which the use of the auxiliary circle is not required. It will be noted, in fact, that A, the measure of the amplitude of the motion (previously identified with the radius of the auxiliary circle), does not occur in this equation. The conclusion must be that the two results (37) and (34), namely,

$$a = -\omega^2 x$$

and $$T = 2\pi/\omega,$$

are mutually consistent whatever the amplitude. The quantity represented by ω^2 can, therefore, no longer refer to any particular auxiliary circle and we may emphasise this independence by denoting it instead by the symbol μ. We may then adopt the equation

$$a = -\mu x \tag{38}$$

as defining a whole family of linear simple harmonic motions, of different amplitudes perhaps, but all having the same periodic time, T, given by

$$T = 2\pi/\sqrt{\mu} \tag{39}$$

Our new definition may be expressed in words: a point is said to move with simple harmonic motion in a straight line if at each instant the acceleration of the point is proportional to its distance from a fixed reference point in the straight line and is directed towards this point. The conclusion implicit in equation (39) can similarly be expressed: whatever the amplitude of the motion, the periodic time is determined only by the measure of the acceleration at unit displacement.

Hitherto we have considered only simple harmonic motion in a straight line. It is obvious, however, that equations (38) and (39) might equally well refer to angular motion: if in any case the angular acceleration is proportional to the angular displacement and is oppositely directed, the motion in angle is simple harmonic, and the period is independent of the angular amplitude. The concept can be further extended, even to the exclusion of the idea of motion in space altogether (though such extension strictly removes it from the province of kinematics). Thus equation (35) may be found to apply to the periodic variation in time of any physical quantity, say the electric charge on a condenser, the difference of temperature between a point at the surface of the earth in any locality and a point some distance underground, the excess pressure at a point in the atmosphere when a sound wave is passing. In such a case it is natural to describe the variation of the physical quantity as simply harmonic. Finally, the independent variable in equation (35) need not necessarily be the measure of the time. In certain situations in physics the measure of a physical quantity may be simply harmonic in distance rather than in time. To all these various cases the mathematical results of this chapter apply, when suitably interpreted.

6.3. DIMENSIONAL CONSIDERATIONS

At this stage we are able to give the first example of a more-than-trivial use of the principle of dimensional homogeneity (see p. 65). We start from equation (38) as defining simple harmonic motion in a straight line, and, making certain generally admissible assumptions, we deduce the result that the periodic time must be independent of the amplitude, and that its dependence on the quantity μ must be essentially as given by equation (39).

Applying the principle of dimensional homogeneity to equation (38) we have, first of all,

$$[\mu] = L^1 T^{-2}/L^1 = T^{-2}.$$

We now assume that the periodic time cannot depend upon any characteristic of the motion other than the acceleration constant μ and the amplitude A, and we suppose that this dependence is given by

$$T = c \mu^k A^l,$$

c being a numerical constant and k and l indices of simple numerical form. Finally, we apply the principle of dimensional homogeneity to this equation and obtain

$$T^1 = T^{-2k} L^l,$$

whence we deduce $l = 0$, $k = -\frac{1}{2}$, establishing the results which we sought.

6.4. COMPOSITION OF SIMPLE HARMONIC MOTIONS

6.4.1. In our discussion of the parallelogram law for the composition of vector quantities it has already been pointed out (p. 76) that the procedure for the composition of accelerations reflects a definite element in the physical situation which is lacking when the corresponding procedure is applied to other vector quantities. According to Newtonian dynamics the immediate physical causes of accelerations are supposed to be identifiable: composition of accelerations, therefore, is the natural procedure for compounding the effects of separate causes acting on a single system.

Now, according to equation (38), simple harmonic motion is motion in conformity with a particular law specifying the acceleration in its relation to the displacement. If there occur situations in the external world in which accelerations so specified can be attributed to identifiable causes (and we should not be discussing simple harmonic motion in its kinematical aspects if this were not so), then the composition of simple harmonic motions takes on a very real significance as the natural procedure for compounding the effects of such causes. In the present section we consider various examples of this procedure.

6.4.2. *Composition of two Simple Harmonic Motions about the same point and in the same straight line with the same period.* Simple harmonic motions having the same period can differ only in amplitude and in phase. Suppose, therefore, that the amplitudes, A_1, A_2, of two simple harmonic motions are represented by the lengths of the lines OP_1, OP_2 drawn from a fixed point O (fig. 22).

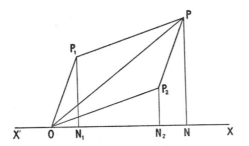

FIGURE 22

Suppose that the difference between the phase angles for the two motions is δ, the first motion leading. Let the two lines be so drawn that $\angle P_2 OP_1 = \delta$, and let them be considered to rotate together in an anti-clockwise direction in the figure, with constant angular velocity ω, about O. Let $\omega = 2\pi/T$, T being the periodic time common to the two motions. Then, if P_1N_1, P_2N_2 be drawn perpendicular to the fixed line $X'OX$, the motions of N_1 and N_2 in this line represent the two simple harmonic motions to be compounded, for they are of the same periodic time T, they have amplitudes A_1 and A_2 according to the scale of the diagram, and the first motion leads the second by the phase angle δ.

Since the motions are about the same point in the same straight line, x, the resultant displacement at any instant, is given by the sum of x_1 and x_2, the displacements due to the two motions separately. Now x_1 is represented by ON_1, and x_2 by ON_2, in the diagram. If, then, we complete the parallelogram P_1OP_2P, draw in the diagonal OP, and make PN at right angles to $X'OX$, we see that x is represented by ON. For P_2P being equal and parallel to OP_1, $N_2N = ON_1$, therefore the sum of x_1 and x_2 is represented by $N_2N + ON_2$, which is ON, as stated. We conclude, then, that the resultant of the two simple harmonic motions of the same period, specified by the projections on the same straight line $X'OX$ of the rotating vectors OP_1, OP_2, is similarly specified by the projection of the vector OP on that line, OP being obtained from OP_1, OP_2

by use of the parallelogram law. The length of OP thus represents the amplitude of the resultant motion.

If A is this amplitude, we have, since $\angle OP_2P = \pi - \delta$,

$$A^2 = A_1{}^2 + A_2{}^2 + 2A_1A_2 \cos \delta \tag{40}$$

Also, if the resultant motion leads the lagging component (represented by OP_2) by the phase angle $\varDelta$, then

$$\sin \varDelta = \frac{A_1}{A} \sin \delta \tag{41}$$

Here we have obtained the solution to our problem by graphical means: it could, of course, equally well have been obtained analytically. Starting from equation (35) as the basic representation of simple harmonic motion, we should have written

$$x = x_1 + x_2 = A_1 \cos (\omega t + \delta) + A_2 \cos \omega t,$$

which we should have proceeded to reduce to the form

$$x = A \cos (\omega t + \varDelta) \tag{42}$$

with A and $\varDelta$ given by (40) and (41) as before.

6.4.3. *Very nearly equal periods*: *Beats*. According to equation (40) the amplitude of the resultant motion in the situation last considered is greatest when $\delta = 0$, and least when $\delta = \pi$. In the former case the two component simple harmonic motions are sometimes referred to as being 'in phase', in the latter case as being 'out of phase'. When the components are in phase the amplitude of the resultant is the sum of the amplitudes, A_1, A_2, of the components, when they are out of phase it is $|A_1 - A_2|$, the difference.

Let us now consider two collinear simple harmonic motions, of amplitudes A_1 and A_2, and frequencies f_1 and f_2, nearly, but not quite, the same. Over a long time-interval t, these two motions come into phase on $|f_1 - f_2|t$ occasions regularly spaced in time. On an equal number of intermediate occasions the motions are out of phase. The resultant amplitude, in fact, rises and falls periodically in time with repetition frequency $|f_1 - f_2|$, or repetition period $T_1T_2/|T_1 - T_2|$. We may write

$$A^2 = A_1{}^2 + A_2{}^2 + 2A_1A_2 \cos 2\pi |f_1 - f_2|t.$$

These alternations in amplitude are referred to as 'beats', the phenomenon being most familiar in respect of musical notes of nearly equal pitch sounded together.

6.4.4. Composition of two Simple Harmonic Motions with the same period in mutually perpendicular directions about the same point. Let

X'OX, Y'OY (fig. 23) represent the two mutually perpendicular directions through O, the common origin, of the simple harmonic motions of amplitudes A and B and the same periodic time T. Let the rectangle KLMN, centred at O, have sides MN, NK the lengths of which represent, on the scale of the diagram, $2A$, $2B$, respectively. Then, taking X'OX, Y'OY as rectangular axes of co-ordinates, the displacements in the component simple harmonic motions may be written (compare equation (35))

$$x = A \cos (\omega t + \delta)$$
$$y = B \cos \omega t \tag{43}$$

if $\omega = 2\pi/T$, and δ is the phase angle by which the x-component motion leads the other. The displacements being in directions at right angles, their instantaneous resultant is represented by the line OP, wholly within the rectangle KLMN, (x, y) the co-ordinates of P being given by equations (43).

Let us suppose, first of all, that $\delta = 0$, then $x/y = A/B$, the representative point P moves back and forth along the diagonal MOK, and the resultant motion is seen to be a linear simple harmonic motion, making an angle $\tan^{-1}(B/A)$ with the x-component, and of amplitude $(A^2 + B^2)^{\frac{1}{2}}$. Again, when $\delta = \pi$, the situation is precisely similar, only the direction of the resultant motion is along the diagonal NOL.

Let us next suppose that $\delta = \dfrac{\pi}{2}$, or $\delta = \dfrac{3\pi}{2}$. In the first case $x = -A \sin \omega t$, in the second case $x = A \sin \omega t$. In either case, combining equations (43), we have

$$\frac{x^2}{A^2} + \frac{y^2}{B^2} = 1 \tag{44}$$

Equation (44) is the equation of an ellipse referred to its principal axes as axes of co-ordinates, and a little consideration will show

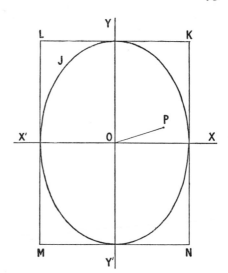

FIGURE 23

that this ellipse (J, in the diagram) is described in a clockwise direction if $\delta = \dfrac{3\pi}{2}$ and in the opposite direction if $\delta = \dfrac{\pi}{2}$.

In considering these special cases, in which $\delta = 0$, π, $\dfrac{\pi}{2}$, $\dfrac{3\pi}{2}$, we have, perhaps, been unfortunate in our emphasis. In fact, a statement can be made which is valid whatever the difference of phase of the component motions. It is that the resultant motion is an ellipse, described in an anti-clockwise direction when $0 < \delta < \pi$, and in a clockwise direction when $\pi < \delta < 2\pi$. In the diagram the representative ellipse, of necessity, is always entirely contained within the rectangle KLMN, and in general its principal axes do not coincide with the axes of co-ordinates. When δ has an arbitrary value its equation is

$$\frac{x^2}{A^2} - \frac{2xy \cos \delta}{AB} + \frac{y^2}{B^2} = \sin^2 \delta \; .$$

Substituting $\delta = 0$ or $\delta = \pi$ in this equation, and simplifying, we have $x/y = \pm A/B$: the ellipse degenerates into a straight line, as we have already stated. In these circumstances the statement regarding the direction of description of the ellipse is ambiguous, but it is also meaningless.

Hitherto we have supposed that the periodic times of the two component motions are the same, and therefore that δ is constant in any relevant case. Obviously, as in § 6.4.3, we could treat the case of component motions of very slightly different periods or frequencies by imagining δ to change slowly and at a constant rate. We should then conclude that the resultant motion would pass through a continuous succession of aspects, from being the rectilinear simple harmonic motion represented by MOK in fig. 23, through widening ellipses to attain the smallest eccentricity as at J in the figure, afterwards, through continuously narrowing ellipses again, collapsing to the rectilinear motion represented by NOL, then returning, though the reverse sequence to the initial rectilinear aspect, with opposite rotation. The repetition frequency of these cyclic changes would be $|f_1 - f_2|$, as in the previous example, f_1 and f_2 being the frequencies of the component motions. To be quite precise, we should note that in such a case the 'instantaneous' aspect of the resultant motion cannot strictly be specified as elliptical: the path is of continuously varying parameters, no portion of it is ever exactly retraced—unless f_1 and f_2 are numerically commensurate. Clearly, the description which we have given approximates ever more closely to the truth as $|f_1 - f_2|$ becomes smaller in relation to f_1 or f_2.

6.5. RESOLUTION OF UNIFORM CIRCULAR MOTION INTO SIMPLE HARMONIC COMPONENTS, AND RELATED CONSIDERATIONS

According to equation (44), if we combine two linear simple harmonic motions of the same period, and phase angle difference $\dfrac{\pi}{2}$ or $\dfrac{3\pi}{2}$, the two motions being about the same point and in directions mutually at right angles, the resultant motion is in a circle, if the amplitudes of the component motions are equal. If we write A for the measure of this common amplitude, the equation of the circle is

$$x^2 + y^2 = A^2.$$

That this circle is described with uniform angular velocity will be seen from equation (36). If $\delta = \dfrac{\pi}{2}$, the component velocities are given in terms of this equation as $-\omega A \sin\left(\omega t + \dfrac{\pi}{2}\right)$ along OX and

$-\omega A \sin \omega t$ along OY. Remembering that the time t is reckoned from the instant at which the point has its maximum positive displacement along OY (fig. 23), these components obviously combine to give a velocity of ωA the direction of which is along the tangent to the circle drawn in an anti-clockwise direction as already concluded. A similar result is obtained with $\delta = \dfrac{3\pi}{2}$, except that the direction of rotation is reversed. In either case the measure of the constant angular velocity in the resultant circular motion is ω.

Quite clearly the converse of the general statement which we have just made is equally true: if a point moves in a circle of radius A with constant angular velocity ω, the motion may be resolved into component simple harmonic motions of periodic time $2\pi/\omega$, occupying any two diameters of the circle which are mutually at right angles, the difference of phase of the component motions being $\dfrac{\pi}{2}$ or $\dfrac{3\pi}{2}$ according to the direction of rotation in the original circle. In this statement the phrase 'occupying any two diameters' is intended to define both the direction and the amplitude of each component: simple harmonic motion which is bounded by the ends of a diameter is obviously of amplitude equal to the radius, and has the centre of the bounding circle as origin.

This converse statement may be generalised in relation to elliptical motion as follows. The auxiliary circle to any ellipse is defined as that circle which has the major axis of the ellipse for a diameter, and corresponding points on the circle and the ellipse are those which lie on the same straight line at right angles to this common diameter. If, then, X'OX (fig. 24) is the common diameter, and Q and P are corresponding points on QN, if $\angle XOQ = \phi$, obviously

$$ON = x = A \cos \phi.$$

Then, from equation (44),

$$NP = OM = y = B \sin \phi,$$

PM being at right angles to Y'OY, the direction of the minor axis of the ellipse. Suppose now that P moves round the ellipse. Then the motion of P may be resolved into simple harmonic motions

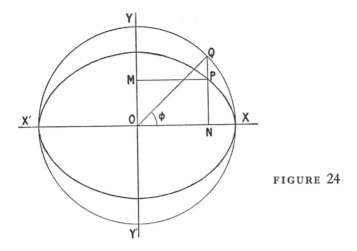

FIGURE 24

along X'OX and Y'OY if, and only if, $\phi = \pm \omega t$. For only in that case do we obtain, for x and y, expressions of the requisite form, namely,

$$x = A \cos \omega t$$

$$y = \pm B \sin \omega t.$$

It will be observed that the amplitudes of the component motions are the lengths of the semi-principal axes of the ellipse, and that the ambiguity of sign reflects the dual possibility as to the direction of rotation in the elliptical path. Our conclusion may, therefore, be stated in words: if a point moves in an ellipse of semi-principal axes A and B in such a way that the corresponding point describes the auxiliary circle with constant angular velocity ω, the motion may be resolved into component simple harmonic motions, of periodic time $2\pi/\omega$, occupying the major and minor axes of the ellipse, the difference of phase of the component motions being $\dfrac{\pi}{2}$ or $\dfrac{3\pi}{2}$ according to the direction of rotation in the original path.

The statement just made is indeed not as general as it might have been. Though we shall not pursue the matter in detail here, it can be proved that provided the angular velocity in the auxiliary circle is constant, the motion of a point in an ellipse may be resolved into component simple harmonic motions about the centre along any two lines mutually at right angles. In this general case, α and β, the amplitudes of the x- and y-components, are given in terms of A and B, the lengths of the semi-major and semi-minor axes of the ellipse, and θ, the angle between the direction of the x-component and the major axis, by the equations

$$\alpha^2 = A^2 \cos^2\theta + B^2 \sin^2\theta,$$
$$\beta^2 = A^2 \sin^2\theta + B^2 \cos^2\theta,$$

and δ, the difference of phase of the component motions (the x-component leading), is given by

$$\tan \delta = -\frac{2AB}{(A^2 - B^2)\sin 2\theta}.$$

In all these equations we assume $-\frac{\pi}{4} \leqslant \theta \leqslant \frac{\pi}{4}$, as a matter of convention. It will be observed that when $\theta = \pm\frac{\pi}{4}$, $\alpha = \beta$ whatever the eccentricity of the original ellipse. In this case

$$\tan \delta = -\frac{2AB}{A^2 - B^2}.$$

We have, therefore, the following conclusion in words: any elliptical motion of a point, for which ω, the angular velocity in the auxiliary circle, is constant, may be resolved into simple harmonic motions of equal amplitude about the centre of the ellipse, the directions of these component motions bisecting the angles between the principal axes of the ellipse. The periodic time of these component motions is $2\pi/\omega$, and the difference of phase is determined by the eccentricity of the ellipse and by the direction of rotation of the moving point in it.

As a final example of the resolution of simple periodic motions, we consider here the resolution of simple harmonic motion in a straight line into two oppositely directed uniform circular motions of equal radius. We have already concluded that motion in a circle of radius A with uniform angular velocity ω can be resolved into component simple harmonic motions in directions mutually at right angles, the phase angle difference being $\frac{3\pi}{2}$ or $\frac{\pi}{2}$ according as

G

the rotation in the circle is clockwise or anti-clockwise. To be precise, the component motions, in these two cases, are represented by

$$x_1 = A \cos \left(\omega t + \frac{3\pi}{2} \right) \quad \text{and} \quad x_2 = A \cos \left(\omega t + \frac{\pi}{2} \right)$$

$$y_1 = A \cos \omega t \qquad\qquad y_2 = A \cos \omega t.$$

Suppose now that these two circular motions are compounded.

We have

$$x = x_1 + x_2 = 0$$

$$y = y_1 + y_2 = 2A \cos \omega t.$$

The resultant motion is simple harmonic motion along the y-axis, and of amplitude $2A$. We may formulate the converse result, therefore, as follows: any linear simple harmonic motion may be resolved into oppositely directed uniform rotations in two equal circles centred on the origin, the radii of the circles being half the amplitude of the original simple harmonic motion, and the common period the same as the period of that motion.

CHAPTER 7

PLANETARY MOTION

7.1. HISTORICAL

In the last three chapters we have considered, in the abstract, certain simple types of motion, avoiding the basing of our discussion on particular instances of observed motion in the real world, on the assumption that, when we come to make the transition from kinematics to physics, we shall find in nature abundant examples of the types of motion which we have considered. We have also made, and repeated, the assertion that we shall then find the concept of acceleration to be unique amongst the kinematical concepts in its relation to the realities of phenomena. In this chapter, whilst still treating the matter as a question of kinematics rather than physics, we consider a particular class of real motions, namely the motions of the planets. It is a fact of history that over a period of some thousands of years these motions were so treated: they were not understood within the context of terrestrial physics —if, indeed, there was such a science—until they were interpreted by Newton in terms of a universal gravitational attraction in the seventeenth century AD. In the course of that interpretation the uniqueness of acceleration among the kinematical quantities also received its first clear enunciation. For that reason alone this particular example of real motion merits separate treatment: it does so, also, because for a period of two hundred years it remained, as an isolated example, in a class by itself. Not until, at the other extreme of the scale of relative magnitudes, the motion of electrons in atoms began to be considered mathematically, was another general situation recognised to which the same mathematical results might apply. And, in the upshot, this application was in fact found to be fraught with many and great difficulties—but that is another story which cannot be told here.

The history with which we are concerned in this section is that of the development of the kinematical description of planetary motion during the millennia preceding the birth of Kepler (1571).

In our catalogue of the basic facts of observational astronomy as known to the ancients, we have already stated (p. 41), 'except for a very few "wanderers", the stars keep their relative positions constant night after night. . . .' The 'wanderers' referred to in that statement are the planets. There is no written account of the astronomical knowledge of early man in any part of the world which shows him lacking in appreciation of the peculiar characteristics of 'the five stars called "planets" '. The emperor Yao, whose accession the traditional chronology of the Chinese places in the year 2317 BC, and in whose reign the length of the tropical year was officially accepted as $365\frac{1}{4}$ solar days (see p. 24), recalled his astronomers to the sterner disciplines of earlier times and ordered them to be diligent in observing the motions of the sun and the moon, of the planets and the stars. Again, the first known mention of Babylon is in a dated tablet of the reign of Sargon of Akkad (about 3800 BC), yet records of the same reign imply an expert and detailed knowledge of the heavens.

In Egypt, the priest-astronomers of a past age achieved a bold synthesis in classing together the five planets with the sun and the moon: all are indeed wanderers against the background of the stars (we have considered the wanderings of the sun in detail in § 3.3). In that way, it has been said, the names of the days of the week had their origin. Saturn, Jupiter, Mars, Sun, Venus, Mercury, Moon: this was the supposed order of decreasing distance from the solid ground of Earth. If we go through this list cyclically, taking one and missing two until all the names have been used, we recognise, either in English or in French, the proper names of the seven days. In Egypt and the East this seven-day 'week' was already an independent calendar unit more than three thousand years before the birth of Christ.

We have referred to the five planets of the ancient astronomers. Today, of course, it is common knowledge that there are others, but it should not be forgotten that the first of these, Uranus, was not discovered until 1781, not until William Herschel had greatly improved the optical power of the Newtonian telescope. There are only five 'naked-eye' planets, and the antiquity of knowledge concerning them is certainly in large measure explained by a curious fact. Following the classification introduced by Hipparchus in the second century BC, the brightness of a star is reckoned in 'magnitudes'. Hipparchus placed six such magnitudes within the compass of naked-eye visibility, and the curious fact is that in favourable circumstances each of the five planets of the ancients exceeds in brightness a standard first-magnitude star. At its brightest—for this brightness varies, as we shall see—each is a conspicuous object in the night sky. It is surely curious that, over the much wider range from the second to the sixth magnitude, inclusive, this small class of wanderers has no single representative. (Modern, more exact, definition of star magnitudes may place Uranus, at its brightest, in the sixth magnitude, and acute observers have claimed to have seen it with the naked eye, but the statement which we have made is not seriously misleading.) The upshot is the situation that we have noted: five 'wandering stars' were recognised as soon as men turned intelligently to the contemplation of the heavens, beyond those five their number received no addition for five thousand years.

This part of the story ends, as we shall discover, in 1609. In 1609 the complexities of the apparent motions of the 'naked-eye' planets were finally elucidated by Kepler, and in that year, also, by a strange coincidence, Galileo (1564-1642), happening to be in Venice, heard that, in Holland, Lippershey, Metius and others had independently discovered the properties of certain combinations of two lenses, and in so doing had invented the first practical telescope. With the invention of the telescope naked-eye astronomy virtually came to an end, but Kepler's mathematical work is a fitting commentary on the unremitting labours, and a tribute to the skill, of the last and in some ways the greatest of the long succession of observers who measured the sky without optical aid, Tycho Brahe (1546-1601), a Danish nobleman. For a short time Kepler was assistant to Brahe, and without his master's observations his own attempts at systematisation would have been of no avail.

It has been stated that the ancient Egyptians arranged the planets, with the sun and moon, in order of supposed distance from the earth: the moon was the nearest, then Mercury and Venus, next the sun, and beyond that Mars, Jupiter and Saturn. We have to see on what evidence this order was decided. We have described the apparent motion of the sun against the background of the stars (§ 3.3): steadily throughout the year it appears to move from west to east through the constellations of the zodiac, completing the cycle in a little more than 365 days. The apparent motion of the moon is in many ways similar, though it is much more rapid, a period of 27·3 days sufficing for a full revolution. In general the planets, too, move from west to east in relation to the stars, but once each year there is for each a phase of retrogression, when the apparent motion is in the reverse direction. It is the nature of this retrogressive phase which provides a ready-made basis of classification—Mars, Jupiter and Saturn in the one class, and Mercury and Venus in the other. For the three first-named the rate of retrogression is greatest at the time when the planet crosses the southern meridian at midnight, for the other two it is greatest when it crosses the meridian at noon (in the nature of things this last conclusion is based on an interpolation of observations). Let us, then, consider the question of distance in relation to these two classes separately.

First, in relation to the class of three: the overall rate of progression through the zodiac provides a suitable ground of comparison. This is least for Saturn (roughly 12 degrees of arc per annum) and greatest for Mars (some 200 degrees per annum). We recognise here the facts upon which intuition operates and builds its case: Saturn is 'obviously' the most distant, Mars the nearest of the three. Then the relative variations of brightness, to which we have already referred: these are most pronounced for Mars, least pronounced for Saturn. For all three planets, however, the main rhythm is an annual one, the time of greatest brightness coinciding roughly with the time of most rapid retrogressive motion. Intuition accepts these further differences as corroborative of an earlier conclusion.

With the second class of two the situation is different, and the evidence more confusing. The overall rate of progression of Mercury and Venus through the zodiac is strictly the same: it is the sun's rate precisely: these planets appear to swing back and forth continuously, now leading now following the sun in its eastwards movement in relation to the stars. They are the evening and morning 'stars': they never cross the southern meridian at midnight. If, intuitively, we seek for a periodic time, it is the period of one complete cycle with respect to the sun (rather than the stars) which we may take for comparison. For Venus this period is 584 days, for Mercury it is 116 days. Intuitively, though perhaps now on more slender grounds, we place Venus farther from us than Mercury. But we (or rather the ancient Egyptians) placed the sun in the mid-position between the two groups of planets, and we notice, with some misgiving, that Mercury appears to keep closer to the sun than Venus does. For Mercury the maximum 'elongation' is about 23 degrees of arc, for Venus it is 46 degrees. But the order has been written down: in a simple order one cannot have it both ways. Moreover, if we were to consider the matter of brightness we should only be still further confused: with both Mercury and Venus, as the time of most rapid retrogressive motion is approached the brightness decreases: the maximum occurs at a point in the motion which, in terms of apparent velocity or position in relation to the sun, has no simple specification.

Finally, we have only the moon. As appropriate to the wanderer of most rapid motion, and possibly because we can make out its 'features' with the naked eye, we place it closest to ourselves—then to explain its regularly varying aspects we call in the priest and the poet—for we are still, in imagination, in the land of the Pharaohs.

This, then, is the system of the ancient cosmology, but it was obvious to the early Greeks that it would not work. Plato (427-347 BC) pointed the problem of the kinematic description which would accurately 'preserve the appearances of phenomena'; after him Eudoxus (c. 370 BC) made the first sustained attempt to meet the challenge. The earth is at the centre, certainly, fixed and immobile, with the stars revolving in unison in the outer firmament. Taking their motions as the simplest and most perfect (or, as we should say, the most fundamental), and with the ancient cosmology as background recognising that a single rigid rotating 'crystal sphere' could be made their vehicle, Eudoxus attempted to describe the motions of the wanderers also in terms of sets of variously rotating spheres peculiar to each. Twenty-six spheres were required in all; three each for the sun and the moon, and four for each of the planets. According to Eudoxus, all these spheres were centred in the earth. For each wanderer one sphere had a motion of rotation essentially the same as that of the firmament of the stars. The others were contained within this, each rotating about an axis carried round by the sphere immediately outside it, the relative orientations of the axes, and the speeds of rotation, being suitably chosen. The wanderer—planet, sun or moon, as the case might be —was itself carried round in the equatorial plane of the innermost sphere of its own set.

We recognise in this description the earliest attempt at the systematic resolution of motions, the precursor of methods such as those we have described in Chapter 6 (§ 6.5). As we shall see, Eudoxus's system, and its derivatives, dominated astronomical thought for nineteen centuries, but we should note that it was not the only system to be proposed and to be seriously discussed by astronomers in the days when Greece was the centre of the civilised world.

Eudoxus had adopted the ancient view that man is at the centre of his universe: in the first place, therefore, we should note those other systems which differed from his in certain respects but were geocentric, nevertheless. Some authorities have believed that the Pythagoreans in the second half of the fifth century BC showed preference for a heliocentric system. If that is so, there is no clear record to establish their case. But it seems fairly certain that, in the following century, Hicetas of Syracuse, a contemporary of Eudoxus, and Ecphantus, taught that the earth rotates on its axis: at least the common motion of the stars could thus be explained. Then Heraclides of Pontus (c. 388-315 BC), a disciple of Plato's old age, not many years later, suggested that Mercury and Venus revolve round the sun (which, in the orthodox tradition, he still supposed to revolve round the earth).

These were the variants on orthodoxy; in relation to them all the system of Aristarchus of Samos (c. 310-230 BC) was certainly unorthodox, in the estimation of some it was heretical. We know little of Aristarchus's life other than that he was active in Alexandria in the period 280-264 BC. A mathematical school had been founded there, not long previously, by Euclid (see p. 6), and a school of astronomy, which was destined to retain its pre-eminence for close upon five hundred years, was already vigorous in its early fame. Aristarchus put forward the view that the sun is at the centre of things and that the earth revolves round it, as the planets do. It should not be thought that this possibility was ignored as unworthy of serious consideration by other astronomers. Archimedes, as a young man, spent some time in Alexandria studying mathematics and astronomy (c. 265 BC), and on his return to Syracuse, in a small treatise addressed to the king's son, he referred to Aristarchus's system only to dismiss it as unsatisfactory. In Athens it became a subject of debate, sufficiently important, it would appear, to incur the judgment of impiety from Cleanthes the Stoic, head of that school of philosophy during the period 264-232 BC. Condemned by the greatest physicist of the day and by the most austere moralist, the heliocentric system might well have been forgotten, but such was the intellectual climate of the age that a century or so later it received favourable notice from the Babylonian astronomer Seleucus, and a new attempt was made to commend it to the philosophers. This again was of no avail: it was not accepted even by Hipparchus (see p. 106); thereafter science slowly hardened into dogmatism and nothing more was heard of this far-reaching notion for another sixteen hundred years.

It must be confessed that the objectors to Aristarchus's system had good reason for their doubts: once it was accepted that the earth revolved in an orbit round the sun, the common motion of the stars, the simplest and most perfect motion of all, was the more difficult to understand. For there was no experimental basis of knowledge of astronomical distances, and the idea that most stars might be a million times farther away than the sun (see p. 52) had no place in the ancient cosmologies. It is to the further credit of Aristarchus, therefore, that, over and above his heliocentric system, he provided the first estimate of relative distances founded on a simple and unexceptionable hypothesis. In order to consider it, let us merely assume that the moon, spherical in shape as the other heavenly bodies are, shines by light reflected from the sun, then, whatever be the system of orbits and motions, when the moon is exactly at 'first quarter' or 'last quarter', that is with disc half-illuminated, the line from the centre of the sun to the centre of the moon is at right angles to that from the centre of the moon to the centre of the earth. Suppose that, at that instant, the angular separation of sun and moon as seen from the earth is θ, and that R and r are their distances, respectively. Then, obviously, $r = R \cos \theta$, in our modern notation. We have, of course, assumed that light travels in straight lines, but this has been implicit in all our considerations, and we have neglected small effects due to the finite size of both the sun and the earth as seen from the moon. These imperfections in the argument need not detain us. In principle, at least, Aristarchus's method is valid: if we can measure θ we can calculate R/r. In practice the method is difficult to apply. The instant of half-illumination is not easy to determine, and great accuracy in the measurement of θ is necessary for success. The actual value of θ is about 89° 51' (R/r about 400); Aristarchus believed it to be about 87°, and so concluded that the distance of the sun is some 20 times greater than that of the moon. Even this conclusion, so far from the truth, must be accounted a notable advance from speculation, a first step towards incontrovertible fact. Some forty years later Eratosthenes (276-196 BC), royal librarian at Alexandria, added another such fact to astronomical knowledge, calculating, with fair exactitude, the circumference of the earth from the lengths of the noontide shadows (see p. 40) at Alexandria and Syene (Assuan).

But we must return to the history of our main concern. Within some thirty years of its formulation, the original system of Eudoxus had been further elaborated by Callippus of Cyzicus, and by Aristotle (384-322 BC). Here speculation entered once more, only to complicate the picture. Eudoxus had attempted merely to describe the motions of the wandering stars; Aristotle aspired to interpret them. Wishing to 'explain' why the motions of the wanderers were independent one of another, he was compelled to postulate a series of 'compensatory' spheres so arranged as to prevent movement being transmitted from the more distant wanderers to the less distant: in the end fifty-five spheres were involved. It is noteworthy—even fortunate—that in this instance, at least, the opinions of the great philosopher were not accepted without question by those who followed him. Quite apart from the heterodox Aristarchus, whose ideas they discarded, Apollonius of Perga (born c. 262 BC), the mathematician, and Hipparchus, famous alike as mathematician and practical astronomer, restored the emphasis on description, eschewing speculation. Hipparchus, in particular, regarded it as essential that the astronomer should adopt the simplest hypothesis which it is possible to entertain in face of ascertained fact. Moreover, being possessed, through his own labours (on the island of Rhodes from 161 to 126 BC), of observations in greater variety and of greater accuracy than any of his predecessors had been, he was eminently well-placed to honour this principle.

Yet the situation was not itself as simple as it might appear. It is an ascertained fact that the earth does not fly to pieces. The question may be asked whether it is possible to entertain the hypothesis of its axial rotation in face of this fact. Some of the ancients held that it is not. Obviously, in such circumstances, the criterion of simplicity is not entirely distinct from the criterion of plausibility. For Hipparchus, at least, whatever his reason, simplicity was not to be sought in other than a fixed-earth system. But he replaced the spherical rotations of Eudoxus by uniform circular motions—and he was strictly honest in his conclusions. He was satisfied that the apparent motions of the sun and the moon could be represented by this method, if the centres of their circular orbits were supposed displaced from the centre of the earth, but he was less satisfied in relation to the five planets. This device of 'eccentrics' was certainly not adequate, nor was that of concentric deferents and epicycles which Apollonius had introduced entirely satisfactory, in respect of their more complicated motions. (Apollonius had imagined the combination of two uniform circular motions, the centre of the circle of smaller radius, the epicycle, being carried with uniform speed round the deferent, or larger circle, which was centred in the earth.) For the planets, according to Hipparchus, the simplest description must involve epicycles moving round eccentric deferents.

Another two and a half centuries passed before this orthodox geocentric cosmology was further systematised. Then in the period AD 127 to 151, in Alexandria, Claudius Ptolemy did for astronomy and trigonometry what Euclid had done, in the same city more than four hundred years earlier, for abstract geometry. His *Syntaxis*, in thirteen books (*Almagest*, its alternative designation, derives from the fact that the work has come down to us chiefly through its Arabic translations of the ninth and tenth centuries), summarised and codified the knowledge and accepted belief in these two subjects as it stood at the end of the classical era. And so Ptolemy's great work remained, unquestioned, the standard authority on each for fourteen centuries. Modern trigonometry is indeed securely built on the foundations which Hipparchus and Ptolemy laid down, and if modern cosmology bears little trace of the geocentric system elaborated in such detail by the successive contributions of these two men, as a faithful description of the motions of the wandering stars that system provided all that was needed by the navigator (and the astrologer) long after Columbus reached the New World—and for a hundred years after Copernicus at long last, had given the world of learning another chance to reassess the alternative hypothesis, that the motions of the planets are sun-centred, not earth-centred as the critics of Aristarchus had so successfully maintained.

Nicolaus Copernicus (1473-1543) was not a professional astronomer. He studied mathematics at the university of Cracow, canon

law at Bologna and medicine at Padua. Then, in 1505, at the age
of thirty-two, a young man of immense learning, he returned to
his native Poland and spent the rest of his life in ecclesiastical
duties. From 1512 until his death he was canon of the cathedral of
Frauenburg. As a student in Italy he had sensed the excitement of
the reawakening of the spirit of critical enquiry in Europe: the
doctrines of Aristotle and Ptolemy were at last subject to fresh
scrutiny; his own attitude to them was plainly that of disbelief. He
had become convinced that in cosmology a much simpler system
could be devised, a system in which spherical bodies rotated as a
consequence of their sphericity (so that the earth could not be
fixed and immovable) and in which the sun, not the earth, was at
the centre of things. He had examined the writings of the ancients
—such as were available to him—to discover whether similar views
had previously been entertained. In the eighth book of the *Satyricon*
of Martianus Capella, written in Carthage in the early years of the
fifth century, he had found reference to the ascription of heliocentric motion to Mercury and Venus, which hypothesis we have
attributed to Heraclides (see p. 104), though some have regarded
the Egyptians as its originators. But it is reasonably certain that in
his search he missed any record there might have been of Aristarchus and his fully heliocentric system: to all intents that had
gone out through Babylon more than sixteen centuries earlier. So
far as we know the only place where he might have found mention
of it was in Archimedes's small treatise *Sandreckoner* (*Arenarius*)
(see p. 104), but, in spite of Eutocius's commentaries of the sixth
century, the writings of the great man of Syracuse were still lost in
general oblivion; they were not rescued for western civilisation
until they were printed at Basle in 1544 by Hervagius.

So Copernicus returned to Poland, and for seven years, as private
physician to his uncle the bishop of Ermeland, he had leisure to
mature his ideas. When he moved to Frauenburg their formulation
was essentially complete. But they were not fully committed to
paper for another eighteen years, and not published for thirty-one.
During the intervening period of thirteen years (1530-1543), in the
universities of central Europe, the new cosmology became more
widely known, largely through oral transmission. At an early
stage, it is true, and with papal approval, an official request for full
publication had been made by Cardinal Schönberg, but this had
produced no response. It remained for a young German, George

Joachim (Rheticus), appointed professor of mathematics at Witten-
berg in 1537, to resign his professorship two years later and devote
four years of his life as Copernicus's disciple at Frauenburg, to
bring the matter to issue. Ultimately, the first printed copy of *De
revolutionibus orbium coelestium* came from the press only a few
weeks before its author died, on 24 May 1543. The whole strange
episode provides many parallels with that of Newton and Halley
and the publication of the *Principia,* to which we shall later have
occasion to refer (p. 203).

Copernicus's system, though heliocentric, was essentially classical
in structure. We have seen that he attached peculiar significance
to the 'perfection' of spherical form. He likewise accepted, even
more explicitly than the ancients, the analogous 'perfection' of
circular orbits uniformly described. On this basis he could not
hope to reconstruct the apparent motions of the sun, the moon and
the planets without the device of eccentrics, though it was the sun
not the earth which was now out of centre in the planetary orbits—
and he could not avoid the use of epicycles, though the planetary
retrogressions were now reproduced without their aid. He had
reduced the neo-Ptolemaic total of eighty independent motions to
thirty-four; he had produced a system simpler than the classical
system, indeed, but it was not one which carried instant conviction
by its stark simplicity. That task was beyond him: if he was
temperamentally unsuited to it, it is also fair to say that the
observations at his disposal—for he relied essentially on the same
observations as Ptolemy had used—were insufficiently detailed to
sustain it. Fifty years later Tycho Brahe had made and recorded
the necessary observations; not long after that Kepler had produced the cosmological system towards which the mathematical
astronomers of two thousand years had been groping in vain.

As we have noted (p. 101), Tycho Brahe was born three years
after Copernicus's *De revolutionibus* was published. He was fortunate, as Copernicus had been, in being able to follow academic
studies in many centres of learning, Copenhagen, Leipzig, Witten-
berg, Rostock and Augsburg, continuously over many years. He
was reading Ptolemy in Latin at the age of fifteen, and two years
later, when he should have been studying law, he was already
spending his nights making observations on the heavens. When he
returned to Denmark at the age of twenty-five he set up a modest
observatory in his uncle's castle at Herritzvad. Before he was

thirty he had secured the patronage of the king. Money was avail-able without stint, and Brahe rapidly assembled at Uraniborg the instruments for an observatory conceived on a scale grander than anything which had been attempted since Hulagu Kahn had equipped the observatory at Maraga for the Persian astronomer Nasir-ud-din (1201-1274) three centuries earlier. For his purely 'visual' observations—for it must be repeated that the telescope had yet to be invented—he had arranged to have constructed a quadrant of 19 ft. radius, and his other instruments were of com-mensurate size. Brahe made systematic observations in every field of naked-eye astronomy at Uraniborg for twenty-one years. He left Denmark in 1597, his former patron having died and the new king proving less well disposed towards his science and his person, and after two years moving from place to place (though still observing) he finally settled near Prague. The emperor Rudolph II had now befriended him, granting him the castle of Benatky for his resi-dence and his observatory. There his instruments were re-assembled towards the end of 1599. But Tycho died on 24 October 1601, having achieved little in the country of his adoption—except the accession of Kepler as his assistant.

Tycho Brahe was essentially an observer, with a sound know-ledge of the physics, and the chemistry, of his day. He was lucky in the time at which he lived. There can have been few occasions in history when a new star ('nova') of the brightness of that which appeared in November 1572 was available for observation, and hardly more on which a comet as spectacular as the great comet of 1577 provided unusual opportunity for measurement and specula-tion. Brahe seized these opportunities and profited by them: the ancient theory of the 'perfection' of the heavens did not survive the conclusions which he drew from the observations which he made in these two 'miraculous' years. In private conviction he was no Copernican: he believed that the earth was fixed and that the stars revolved daily in the firmament, but he accepted a heliocentric arrangement for the planets, believing them to revolve in orbits round the sun, as the sun circled the earth. Here, however, we are not concerned with his individual essay in cosmology; we need only record the fact that as a result of his patient observations he corrected the value of almost every accepted astronomical datum, leaving this vast material in perfect order for his successors. That is sufficient title to enduring fame.

7.2. KEPLER'S LAWS OF PLANETARY MOTION

The advantages of wealth and good family, which Copernicus and Brahe had enjoyed as young men, Johann Kepler did not possess. He was born of feckless and ill-educated parents (when he was nearly fifty he had to exert all his influence to secure the release of his mother, who, as an old woman, had been arrested as a witch). He survived smallpox in infancy, to be permanently maimed as a result. He had little formal education until he was placed in a seminary at the age of twelve. Growing to manhood, he for a time accepted the vocation chosen for him, and not until he was twenty-two did he finally abandon it. The intervening years, however, had shaped his future: he had obtained admission to the university of Tübingen as a foundationer, and, outside his classical and theological studies, he had become a pupil of the astronomer Maestlin. From Maestlin he had appropriated the view that astronomy was ripe for radical renovation, and it was the faint chance that he might be able himself to contribute to this end that had led him to renounce the ministry. This happened in 1594, when he was offered the professorship of astronomy in the Lutheran gymnasium at Gratz.

In 1596 Kepler published a fanciful dissertation in which he described a complicated figure wherein the five regular polyhedra, octahedron, icosahedron, dodecahedron, tetrahedron and cube, were built together in that order (from the centre outwards), so scaled that the circumscribed sphere of the octahedron was the inscribed sphere of the icosahedron, the circumscribed sphere of the icosahedron was the inscribed sphere of the dodecahedron, and so on. In respect of this figure he claimed that the radii of the four 'cementing' spheres and of the fifth (the circumscribed sphere of the cube) were in proportion as the mean distances of the five planets from the sun. This essay in geometrical mysticism brought him the gratifying reward of correspondence with Galileo and Tycho Brahe—and it did more for him than that, as we have already seen. In the following year Brahe started on his wanderings from Uraniborg in search of a new patron, and by the time that he had found one, and his observatory had been re-built at Benatky, Kepler also was in straitened circumstances under a new ruler. Soon after his accession in 1598 the archduke Ferdinand had issued a decree of banishment against Protestant professors, and, although Kepler was spared immediate exile as a result, he was glad to accept Brahe's offer of employment in 1599 as his personal assistant. After Brahe's death in 1601 the emperor appointed Kepler to succeed him. From that time, until the end of his life, at least he had no lack of observational material on which to work, and against which to test one speculative hypothesis after another.

For our present concern Kepler's contribution was complete by 1619, but long before then, his salary from the imperial treasury having fallen into great arrear, he had been forced into the first of a series of moves designed either to offer less gloomy prospects of financial return, or merely to escape the wars. So he transferred himself, his work and his family, from Prague to Linz, from Linz to Ulm, from Ulm to Sagan, and he died at Ratisbon (Regensburg) on 15 November 1630 appealing against the injustice of yet another move in prospect, to a professorship at Rostock, with which the duke of Friedland, his employer at the time, was preparing to 'compensate' him for monies due. It is not the least of the wonders of his very considerable output of important original work that it was achieved amidst these vagaries and that it was continued until his death.

Brahe had been the first to make systematic observations on the planets throughout the whole year, and year after year, continually. He had observed the apparent motion of Mars in this way for thirteen years, that is over some seven circuits of the zodiac (p. 102). Kepler was well advised (probably at the instigation of Brahe himself) to concentrate attention on these observations in his attempt to reduce them to simple formulation. If he were unable to describe the motion of Mars, concerning which the information was so nearly complete, obviously he could not hope to succeed with the other planets. In fact, it was nearly ten years before he reached his limited goal. Having postulated one shape after another for the orbit, and one law of velocity after another, at last he came upon assumptions which fitted the observations to his complete satisfaction. He tested his assumptions on the earth, and again they were satisfactory. This was confirmation indeed. He had now succeeded in explaining the apparent motions of Mars and the sun as seen from the earth on the assumption that the sun is at rest and that these two Copernican planets revolve around it in orbits having the same mathematical specification. He did not wait to confirm that the motions of the other planets could be similarly described. He assumed that that must be so—and time proved him to be right. In 1609 he published *De motibus stellae Martis*, wherein, along with much else that is quaint and much that is significant, appear the first and second laws essentially as we know them today:

1. Each planet moves in an ellipse with the sun at one focus.
2. For each planet the line from the sun to the planet sweeps out equal areas in equal times.

Kepler's third law was formulated in 1619. It appeared in *Harmonice mundi*, published at Augsburg and dedicated to James I of England. It may be stated in modern terms:

3. The squares of the periodic times of the planets are as the cubes of their mean distances from the sun.

Before he could formulate this empirical law, Kepler had to consolidate the observations of Brahe on the more distant planets Jupiter and Saturn, and those on Venus and Mercury, verifying the first and second laws for these four bodies as he went along. His final success provided the first real demonstration, intuitive rather than logical though it may be, that the system of Aristarchus and Copernicus is something more than the most convenient representation of the planetary motions: a system which is articulated in so simple a manner as the third law describes must certainly correspond with reality in some very intimate way. But the full kinematic simplicity of this law had to wait for the work of Newton to reveal it. Kepler's own presentation was still encumbered with the fantastic extravagance of his mysticism.

7.3. NEWTON'S ANALYSIS OF KEPLER'S LAWS

Copernicus, as we have noted, followed the Greeks in their insistence on the 'perfection' of uniform motion in a circle. In the classical tradition he sought to describe the heliocentric motions of the planets in terms of component motions which were 'perfect' (see p. 107). Kepler, the mathematician, is more likely to have considered this perfect figure as a degenerate ellipse, one in which the two foci are coincident; in any case, his first and second laws certainly describe a general situation which admits of uniform circular motion as a limiting case. It is interesting here to remark how closely in fact the planetary orbits approximate to circles, and how, in this respect, the two-thousand-year history, which traces

H

the development of systems from the deferents and epicycles of Apollonius to Kepler's ellipses, is the history of small discrepancies only. Mercury's orbit departs most from the perfect figure, but the major and minor axes of the ellipse differ by a mere 2·2 per cent; for the orbit of Venus the corresponding difference is no more than 2·3 parts in 10^5. It is not surprising, therefore, that the first attempts to understand the implications of Kepler's third law, which undoubtedly posed a new question for the natural philosophers of the time, should have been based on the approximation that the first and second laws could be replaced by the ancient assumption in its simplest form—namely that the orbits are circular and uniformly described. This was the approximation which Newton used in his earliest speculations on the subject in the summer of 1666.

An expression for the acceleration in uniform circular motion had been deduced by Christiaan Huygens (see p. 43), probably in 1659, though it was not published by him until 1673, when it appeared in an appendix to *Horologium oscillatorium*. Huygens sent a copy of this work to Newton, who, in thanking him for it, 'gave those rules in the end thereof a particular commendation for their usefulness in Philosophy', indicating his own previous acquaintance with them by numerous examples. Newton, in fact, had discovered Huygens's result independently when he first began to speculate on the possible significance of Kepler's 'sesquialterate proportions'. These speculations can be very simply formulated if we write our previous equation (29) in the form

$$a = \left(\frac{2\pi}{T}\right)^2 r.$$

Here a is the acceleration towards the centre of a circular orbit, of radius r, which a planet describes with periodic time T. If two planets are considered, then, by an obvious extension of notation, we have

$$\frac{a_1}{a_2} = \frac{r_1}{r_2}\left(\frac{T_2}{T_1}\right)^2.$$

But by Kepler's third law we have, also,

$$\left(\frac{T_2}{T_1}\right)^2 = \left(\frac{r_2}{r_1}\right)^3.$$

Thus

$$\frac{a_1}{a_2} = \frac{r_2{}^2}{r_1{}^2},$$

or the ratio of the (supposedly constant) magnitudes of the accelerations of the two planets is equal to the inverse ratio of the squares of their (supposedly constant) distances from the sun. Newton did not publish this result at any time—for it was a result based on a blatant approximation—but twenty years later, in the *Principia*, he gave a full analysis of the three laws which justified the intuition informing his earlier speculations. We proceed, therefore, to give the gist of his later analysis without further ado.

Our starting point is Kepler's second law: for each planet the areal velocity about the sun is constant. Now we have shown (§ 4.6) that in uniform rectilinear motion the areal velocity about any point is constant. Suppose that we approximate to the continuous orbit of the planet by assuming that the orbit is made up of successive rectilinear segments described in equal short intervals of time, each segment being traversed with uniform velocity. If, ultimately, the chosen time interval is indefinitely decreased (and the number of segments correspondingly increased) this approximation can be made as close to reality as we please. Let S (fig. 25) represent the centre of the sun, and a portion of the actual path of a planet be represented approximately by the segments AB, BC, traversed, during successive equal intervals of time, each with uniform velocity. Then, because of Kepler's second law, area SAB = area

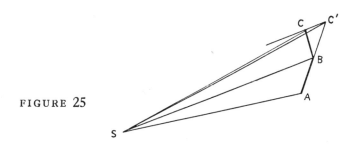

FIGURE 25

SBC. Now let AB be produced to C', so that BC' = AB. Then, if the velocity of the planet had been the same (in magnitude and direction) during the second interval as it was during the first, the position of the planet at the end of the second interval would have been as represented by C′ rather than C. Moreover, the motion in this case being rectilinear and uniform, area SAB = area SBC′. Thus, in fig. 25, area SBC′ = area SBC; and, these being the areas of triangles on the same base SB, we conclude that C′C is parallel to BS. Now, fig. 25 has been drawn to represent displacements in equal time intervals. It may equally well, therefore, represent velocities. On this interpretation BC′ represents in magnitude and direction the velocity of the planet during the first, and BC its velocity during the second, of the equal intervals of time which we have considered. Furthermore, the vectors BC′ and BC are drawn from the same point. Thus C′C is the vector which represents the change of velocity between the one interval and the other. Ultimately, when the length of the time interval is indefinitely decreased, obviously C′C represents in direction the instantaneous acceleration in the orbit. Since we have shown that C′C is parallel to BS, we conclude that at every point in the orbit the acceleration of the planet is directed towards the centre of the sun.

Once Newton had obtained the result which we have just deduced, he proceeded to show that Kepler's first law implies that the acceleration of the planet, throughout its elliptic path, is in magnitude inversely proportional to the square of the planet's distance from the sun. This deduction was made geometrically, in two ways, but neither is sufficiently simple to be in place here. We must content ourselves with indicating Newton's mode of approach to the problem (by one route)—and by giving an incomplete treatment of our own.

Newton first deduced a very general result. He showed that if two geometrically identical orbits are described in the same periodic time, in the one orbit the direction of the acceleration being towards one fixed internal point throughout the motion, and in the other towards another fixed internal point continuously, then the magnitudes of the accelerations at geometrically corresponding points in the two orbits stand in the same ratio as two volumes specified in terms of the instantaneous distances of the moving points from the corresponding centres of acceleration and the skew distances from these centres to the instantaneous tangents to the orbits, the skew distance in each figure being measured in the direction corresponding to the instantaneous radius vector of the other. He then noted that a point may describe an ellipse, not

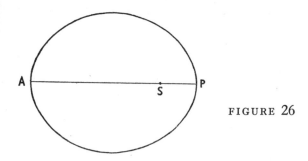

FIGURE 26

only as a planet describes its orbit but also under conditions whereby the acceleration is always directed towards the centre of the ellipse and proportional to the distance from the centre. We have given the condition for such a motion in § 6.5: it is that the angular velocity of the point in the auxiliary circle is constant. Comparing this case with the former case, in which the acceleration in the ellipse is towards a focus continuously, Newton finally obtained the result quoted: the acceleration of the planet is inversely proportional to the square of the instantaneous distance from that focus. The whole deduction was a consummate piece of geometrical kinematics; in bringing it to a successful conclusion Newton had solved a problem which had completely baffled the greatest mathematicians in Europe over a period of close on seventy years (see p. 201).

Having achieved a distant glimpse of Newton's genius, let us consider the problem with the more modest aim of comparing the accelerations of the planet at two particular points in its orbit—the points at which it is nearest to and farthest from the sun, respectively. These points (perihelion and aphelion) are the extremities of the major axis of the planetary ellipse. Let them be represented by P and A (fig. 26), S representing the position of the sun. The points we are considering are the only points in the orbit at which the velocity of the planet is instantaneously at right angles to the line joining its centre to the centre of the sun; they are also the points at which the magnitude of this velocity is instantaneously constant, being a maximum at perihelion and a minimum at aphelion. Let v_1 and v_2 be the measures of these maximum and minimum speeds, r_1 and r_2 the perihelion and aphelion distances, and a_1 and a_2 the measures of the acceleration at perihelion and aphelion, respectively. Then, from Kepler's second law (see equation (25)),

$$\tfrac{1}{2}r_1 v_1 = \tfrac{1}{2}r_2 v_2.$$

Also $a_1 = v_1^2/R_1$. $a_2 = v_2^2/R_2$. where R_1 and R_2 are the radii of curvature of the orbit at the points in question. But, from the symmetry of the ellipse, $R_1 = R_2$ (see fig. 26), thus

$$\frac{a_1}{a_2} = \frac{v_1^2}{v_2^2} = \frac{r_2^2}{r_1^2}.$$

Here we have deduced the inverse-square relation for the special case: we did not set our aim higher than that.

Accepting now Newton's analysis of Kepler's first two laws, we have, for any one planet, that the acceleration is directed towards the centre of the sun continuously, and that its magnitude is given by $a = \mu/r^2$, r being the distance from planet to sun and μ being a constant. Let us consider, dimensionally, how on this basis the periodic time depends upon μ and upon the size of the orbit. Our method is precisely the same as that which we employed in the case of simple harmonic motion in an earlier section (§ 6.3). If T is the measure of the periodic time, we write

$$T = ck\mu^x d^y.$$

In this equation c is a numerical constant, k is a pure number characterising the shape of the ellipse, and d is the measure of a characteristic length representing its size. From the equation defining μ we have

$$[\mu] = \mathrm{L}^1\mathrm{T}^{-2}.\mathrm{L}^2 = \mathrm{L}^3\mathrm{T}^{-2}.$$

Then applying the principle of dimensional homogeneity to our trial equation for T, we obtain

$$\mathrm{T}^1 = \mathrm{L}^{3x}\mathrm{T}^{-2x}.\mathrm{L}^y,$$

whence $3x + y = 0$, $2x = -1$, or $x = -\tfrac{1}{2}$, $y = \tfrac{3}{2}$. We conclude, therefore, that the periodic time in elliptical motion under the inverse square law of acceleration is given by an equation of the form

$$T = ckd^{\frac{3}{2}}/\mu^{\frac{1}{2}} \tag{45}$$

—and if there are two planets moving in such orbits we have, in obvious notation,

$$\left(\frac{T_1}{T_2}\right)^2 = \left(\frac{d_1}{d_2}\right)^3 \left(\frac{k_1}{k_2}\right)^2 \frac{\mu_2}{\mu_1}.$$

But by Kepler's third law, in its original form,

$$\left(\frac{T_1}{T_2}\right)^2 = \left(\frac{d_1}{d_2}\right)^3,$$

d_1 and d_2 being identified as the mean distances of the planets from the sun. Moreover, we have seen (p. 114) that the shapes of the planetary orbits are in fact very nearly the same: they are circles, to a reasonable approximation. If we are content with this double approximation, then we conclude that $\mu_1 = \mu_2$ without further enquiry. Newton was not content, as we have already implied in relation to the reverse argument based upon circular orbits (p. 114), but he was able to deduce equation (45) in explicit form. He found, in fact, that the shape constant k is unity—the shape of the ellipse is immaterial—and the size factor d is the measure of the length of the semi-major axis of the ellipse, exactly. With this result accepted, and Kepler's third law re-worded (as it could well be without significant change) 'The squares of the periodic times of the planets are as the cubes of their major axes', the conclusion $\mu_1 = \mu_2$ is inescapable.

Newton, then, had provided a full and convincing analysis: if Kepler's laws are a correct representation of reality, the acceleration of any planet in its orbit is at all times directed towards the sun, and its magnitude is determined by two quantities only, the distance between the centre of the planet and the centre of the sun and a quantity μ, the same for all planets. In algebraic form

$$a = \frac{\mu}{r^2} \tag{46}$$

It is important to realise that this analysis implies that the acceleration of a planet does not depend in any way upon its size or shape or constitution, so that, for example, if the planets Mars and Saturn were to interchange positions and velocities, Mars would continue in the present orbit of Saturn precisely as Saturn would have done had the switch not taken place, and *vice versa*. Indeed, the satellites of the planets, the first of which—other than the moon—was discovered by Galileo a few months after Kepler's first and second laws were given to the world, as they revolve around their primaries, revolve also around the sun, and they do so each with precisely the same period as the planet to which it belongs.

CHAPTER 8

THE CONCEPTS OF FORCE AND MASS

8.1. THE MOTIONS OF REAL BODIES

In the last four chapters we have been considering motion in its own right: only in the last of the four have we based these considerations on an actual example of motion in the real world. Henceforward we shall be concerned with real motions exclusively, that is with the subject kinetics rather than with kinematics. The word kinetics implies that the concept of force is fundamental to our enquiry: force in relation to motion.

The idea of force has a long history. It arose, no doubt, from the consciousness of the muscular effort required to lift heavy bodies from the earth's surface. Such bodies are 'heavy' in that they tend to fall to the ground, unless supported in some way; moreover, it requires muscular effort to set them in motion in the reverse direction, to lift them. Also, in general experience, it requires muscular effort to move a body over the surface of the earth; if that effort is relaxed, the body comes to rest. But it was not until the seventeenth century that this intuitive idea of force was given the precision of a scientific concept.

It is not surprising, perhaps, that in the physics of Aristotle terrestrial motions and celestial motions were regarded as in separate categories. The heavenly bodies were not regarded as subject to the same laws as determine the motions of earthly bodies. Only the continuance of motion had to be explained in each case: the condition of rest was regarded as the natural condition of bodies everywhere. The motions of the heavenly bodies were 'perfect', these bodies were carried around by the transparent spheres, each moved by a 'soul' which was of its essential nature. Near the earth's surface heavy bodies sought the centre of the universe in the depths below, similarly following the dictates of their own natures. Other terrestrial motion was 'violent' motion: it continued only so long as an operative cause persisted. This hypothetical cause had often to be sought in the medium through which the body moved, in the disturbance of the air or the water, as the case might be, transmitting continuing motion to the moving body. 'Violent' motion was unthinkable in a vacuum (therefore, the argument ran in part, there could be no such thing as empty space). Butterfield has written (*The Origins of Modern Science*) 'A universe constructed on the mechanics of Aristotle had the door half-way open for spirits already . . . the modern theory of motion is the great factor which in the seventeenth century helped to drive the spirits out of the world and opened the way to a universe that ran like a piece of clockwork'.

But the attempt to drive these particular spirits out of the world had in fact been made much earlier than the seventeenth century, though it had not been very successful. About the middle of the fourteenth century, in Paris, first Jean Buridan (who was born in the last decade of the thirteenth century and became Rector of the University of Paris in 1327), and later Nicolas Oresme (who became bishop of Lisieux in 1377) and Albert of Saxony (bishop of Halberstadt, 1366-1390), taught that persistence of 'violent' motion is due to 'impetus' or 'impetuosity' acquired in the original process of projection, and in the fall of heavy bodies continuously acquired. In motion under terrestrial conditions, the impetus of a moving body, if not renewed, gradually weakens, so these philosophers taught, 'just as a poker grows cold when taken from the fire'. This doctrine of impetus continued to be taught in Paris for nearly two hundred years, Leonardo da Vinci (1452-1519) found it spoken of in Pavia in 1490, and its influence on the early thinking of Galileo (1564-1642) can be discerned in his writings. By that time, however, the doctrine had served its purpose; the experiments which Galileo performed in Pisa in the years 1589 to 1591 gave a new turn to his thought, and the doctrine of impetus became the principle of inertia, at least in a limited field of application.

Galileo Galilei entered the University of Pisa in 1581 as a medical student. He was already well versed in the classics, well known as a musician, and was showing promise as a painter. But his father had chosen medicine for him as a career, 'having had personal experience of the unremunerative character both of music and mathematics'. This choice, however, though clearly prudent, was not for long effective; the young Galileo abandoned medicine for mathematics, and it might appear as the swift retribution of fate that in 1585 he had to leave the university, through lack of funds, without a degree. Undeterred by this misfortune, however, he continued to follow his own inclinations, and within three years he had made such a name for himself by his writings that, no longer a student, he found himself called to the staff of the university as lecturer in mathematics. His tenure of this appointment was brief: within a further three years he had aroused so much enmity by the sharpness of his tongue that he wisely resigned his post. But he was not long out of employment: in 1592 he was appointed professor of mathematics at the University of Padua, and there he remained for eighteen years. In 1610, at the height of his fame, he retired to Florence, endowed with the emoluments of his professorship for life, and the lucrative sinecure of philosopher and mathematician extraordinary to the grand-duke of Tuscany. Then, again, the sharpness of his tongue and the pungency of his writings brought him trouble. For us it would take too long to record the history of Galileo's conflict with the Church, a conflict which started in 1613, came to a crisis in 1632 following the publication of his *Dialogues on the Two Systems of the World*, and was resolved before the Inquisition on 22 June 1633 in the church of Santa Maria sopra Minerva in Rome. The story has often been told in the histories of science, embroidered by invention or simplified by omission. As a corrective it will be sufficient to quote the more recent verdict of Whitehead (*Science and the Modern World*): 'In a generation which saw the Thirty Years' War and remembered Alva in the Netherlands, the worst that happened to men of science was that Galileo suffered an honourable detention and a mild reproof, before dying peacefully in his bed.' Galileo died on 8 January 1642, in his villa at Arcetri to the south-east of Florence. He had lived there, virtually under house-arrest, since the time of his sentence, but his scientific activities had been undiminished to the end, and the recapitulation of the results of his early experiments in mechanics, and his considered views on the principles of that subject, which were published under the title *Dialogues on the New Sciences* in Leiden in 1638, constitute a work of timeless importance.

As has already been indicated (p. 121), it is Galileo's early experiments in Pisa (1589-1591) which chiefly concern us here. Modern scholarship discounts the frequently repeated story of his demonstration of the equality of times of fall of light and heavy bodies by dropping a muket-ball and a cannon-ball simultaneously from the top of the Leaning Tower (an inconclusive experiment of this nature was, in fact, performed by Stevinus and de Groot at Delft in 1590), but the conclusions which he drew from his experiments with inclined planes indicated that such indeed would be the result of an ideal experiment of that nature, if the retarding effect of the air could be eliminated. His conclusions, however, were more detailed than that, and basically more important. Galileo conceived of free fall and free horizontal motion (near the surface of the earth) as extreme cases of motion down a perfectly smooth inclined plane, the inclination in the first case being 90°, and in the second case zero. For him there was a difference in degree, not in character, between these two types of motion, and, in thought, a continuous gradation, as he imagined the inclination of an ideal plane decreased from 90° to zero. In practice he was able to convince himself that the motion of metal balls on the polished and grooved surfaces of the wooden planes which he had at his disposal was sufficiently near to the ideal to be significant for detailed study. From the results of this study Galileo deduced three important conclusions, one of them quantitative and the other two qualitative in form of expression.

The quantitative conclusion concerned the manner in which the speed of the body increases throughout its motion, in the type of motion he was considering. Here the recognition that the characteristics of free fall are to be found, modified only in scale, in motion down an inclined plane under ideal conditions, was essential for the generality of his conclusions. Galileo's water-clocks were not sufficiently sensitive instruments for the timing of free fall under laboratory conditions, but they sufficed for the observations which he made on motion down inclined planes of small inclination. Assuming that the law of increase of velocity could be expressed in a simple mathematical formula, he considered the two simplest possibilities, that the instantaneous velocity is proportional to the distance moved from rest, and, alternatively, that it is proportional to the elapsed time. It is not surprising that he ran into difficulties in considering the first possibility (according to this law, in fact, the body would never start from rest), for the calculus had not then been invented, and the notion of velocity-at-an-instant was itself a novelty. But, on the basis of the second possible law, Galileo deduced (which we have done by a simple graphical treatment in § 4.4) that the distance moved should be proportional to the square of the elapsed time. His experiments showed that this was precisely the situation in fact: his intuition regarding mathematical simplicity had been justified, and, extrapolating to the case of free fall, his quantitative conclusion could be expressed 'in free fall under gravity the distance travelled from rest is proportional to the square of the time of fall'. However, it is the mathematical insight behind the quantitative conclusion which is the essential contribution of Galileo at this point: in such motion, in particular in free fall under gravity, the velocity increases linearly with the time. Indeed, the modern concept of acceleration entered physics at this juncture, exemplified in the uniform acceleration of a body falling freely in 'local motion' near the surface of the earth.

The first of Galileo's qualitative conclusions can now be simply expressed: the accelerations of different bodies, down a fixed inclined plane, are the same under ideal conditions. Here we need not labour the description of the experiments by which this limiting result was 'deduced' from actual observations under conditions which were not perfectly ideal—obviously the intuition of the observer must come into play before such an assertion can ever be made. But in these experiments at least we find the laboratory counterpart of the experiment from the Leaning Tower, with which his first biographer, Vincenzio Viviani, credited Galileo (as he falsely credited him with the invention of the microscope) and which later historians were not slow to embellish with colourful detail. We merely remark that this first qualitative conclusion marks the initial acceptance of 'the acceleration due to gravity', as a geophysical constant of real significance.

Galileo's second qualitative conclusion was fundamentally more important than the first. He carried out experiments in which two inclined planes were set facing one another, making a shallow V, and he concluded that, under ideal conditions, a ball which had rolled freely down one plane would roll up the other losing speed, as it had previously gained speed in descent, until it came to rest, momentarily, at a height above the horizontal which was equal to the height from which it had started. Under ideal conditions the slope of the second plane was immaterial, if the ball was always released from the same point on the first plane, it would travel along the second plane until its velocity became instantaneously zero when it had reached its original height above ground. From this point of view only the vertical component of the motion was important. Moreover, in the limiting case in which the second plane was itself horizontal, under ideal conditions the ball, never able to regain its original height, would travel forwards indefinitely with undiminished velocity. This is Galileo's novel contribution to the foundation of dynamics, deduced from experiment through the intuition of genius. The slowly dying impetus of the Parisian philosophers was seen as essentially inexhaustible, except by the action of resistive forces. On a horizontal plane, in the ideal situation, rest, and uniform motion in a straight line with any velocity, were equally 'natural' conditions for a material body. The principle of inertia took shape in this statement.

We have spoken of 'local motion near the surface of the earth' (p. 124). The title of one of Galileo's *Dialogues* was, in fact, *Mechanics and Local Motion*, and it is just this preoccupation with terrestrial motion which prevented him from formulating the principle of inertia in its final simplicity. On a scale larger than 'local', Galileo imagined his horizontal 'plane' encircling the earth along a great circle. He assumed that rest or uniform motion with any velocity, along such a plane, was equally natural. He could not know, directly from his experiments, that if the velocity of the body along the plane were greater than a limiting value the body would leave the plane and travel off into space. So he regarded uniform circular motion about the centre of the earth, with any velocity, as exemplifying the new principle. In this he was mistaken, but he had, at least, disproved, to his own satisfaction, the doctrine of decaying impetus, and in the modern principle of inertia Galileo's contribution is clearly manifest. Only, now, the last relics of his earth-centred bias have been removed, and rest or uniform motion in a straight line—anywhere in the Euclidean universe—is taken as the natural condition for a body wholly free of influence from outside.

The generalisation which we have just described first became part of an acceptable system of dynamics with Newton, but it should be stated as a fact of history that it was earlier formulated as an element in the speculative cosmology of Descartes (see p. 70), effectively as an intuitive notion, not derived from experiment, its explicit statement appearing first in *The Principles of Philosophy* published in Amsterdam in 1644. And, as we have seen (p. 114), at least independently of Newton and probably before him, Christiaan Huygens (with whose father Descartes had corresponded during his residence in Holland) realised very clearly that if unaccelerated motion is the norm in the absence of external force, then uniform motion in a circle is not free motion, for it is definitely accelerated.

8.2. NEWTON'S LAWS OF MOTION

Newton had more than the experimental results of Galileo and the speculations of Descartes to build on when in 1685 he began to set out in formal fashion the elements of his own system on Halley's instigation (see p. 203). There had been much experimenting on the collisions of hard spherical bodies moving as pendulums or on smooth horizontal planes, by Rev. John Wallis, by Sir Christopher Wren and independently by Huygens, and these three had communicated their results to the Royal Society in London in the three consecutive months of November and December 1668 and January 1669. Also, in 1676, Robert Hooke had published, albeit as a Latin cryptogram, his law of the deformation of spiral springs under load. Forces other than the force of gravity had thus been brought under study. The result of Newton's consideration of Galileo's principle of inertia in the light of this whole body of evidence led him to introduce into physics, as we shall now describe, a new concept 'mass', closely related to 'weight', but essentially distinct from it. As long as motion under gravity alone was in question, the disentangling of these two concepts was indeed difficult in the extreme.

Galileo had recognised the weight of a body as a force accelerating its motion towards the earth. 'The propensity of a body to fall is equal to the least resistance which suffices to support it,' he wrote, and he knew that the less the inclination of an inclined plane the less the resistance necessary to prevent the body sliding down the plane. Stevinus had established the mathematical relation between the slope and the necessary resistance in 1586 (see p. 142), and Galileo had derived the same result by another method (p. 165) when he was at Padua. He had also found, many years earlier, that the acceleration down an inclined plane is less, the less steeply the plane is inclined. But, when he came to put all these matters together, at the end of his long life, he missed the point that for a given body the ratio of the measures of the acceleration down the plane and the resistance necessary to prevent sliding, under ideal conditions, is constant whatever the inclination—equal, in fact to the ratio of the measures of the acceleration of the body in free fall under gravity and its weight. If he had seized upon this point—if his experimental results had been sufficiently precise for it to have been immediately obvious—he might well have been led to the concept of mass before Newton.

For Newton the situation was in some degree less perplexing. The experiments on impact had shown that when two hard spherical bodies are in direct collision the ratio of the measures of the changes of velocity which they suffer, respectively, is determined by two factors, one the inverse ratio of the measures of the volumes, and the other a factor depending upon the materials of which the bodies are made. Thus, if two identical spherical bodies are in direct collision, the changes of velocity which they suffer are equal in magnitude; if the bodies are of the same material, but the radius of the first is n times the radius of the second, then the magnitudes of the velocity changes are in proportion as $1:n^3$; finally, if the bodies are of different materials, the proportion may be written as $\rho_2:n^3\rho_1$. In this last expression, ρ_1 and ρ_2 represent the measures of the 'densities' of the two materials concerned. 'Density' itself is a new concept: it refers to mass per unit volume.

Having indicated very briefly, as we have just done, the additional observational material which Newton had for consideration in 1685, without further preliminaries we shall merely state the laws of motion as he formulated them, for however much we may work over the experimental results beforehand, we cannot deduce the laws by rigorous argument. There is much intuition in them, even some obscurity, and they stand to be tested in the light of subsequent experience, not to be passively accepted as established on the basis of previous knowledge—as indeed do all the laws of physics. In the next section we shall attempt their logical appraisal. Here we give a modern rendering of the original Latin.

Definition 1. Quantity of matter, or mass, is the measure of it given by the product of the measures of density and volume.

Definition 2. Quantity of momentum of a body is the measure of it given by the product of the measures of its velocity and its mass.

Law 1. Every body perseveres in its state of rest, or of uniform motion in a straight line, except in so far as it is compelled to change that state by forces impressed on it.

Law 2. The rate of change of momentum of a body is proportional to the moving force impressed on it, and is effective in the direction in which that force is impressed.

Law 3. An action is always opposed by an equal reaction; or, the mutual actions of two bodies are always equal and act in opposite directions.

We have not given Newton's formulation here in its entirety. There were, in all, eight definitions, and to the three laws were appended six corollaries (see p. 76). But what we have given is sufficient for our immediate considerations.

8.3. APPRAISAL OF NEWTON'S LAWS

In the Introduction to this book we made the distinction between 'quantitative definitions' and 'laws of nature', pointing out that one of the criteria which a law of nature must satisfy is that the statement 'it might have been otherwise' is true of it. As we have seen, Newton also made the formal distinction between definitions and laws, and it is now pertinent to enquire whether we can accept his assignments. Let us examine each of the five statements of the last section—the two 'definitions' and the three 'laws'—in turn.

Newton's first 'definition' certainly leads to a quantitative specification of density, if mass is known. We have, using the accepted symbols for the measures of the three quantities involved, $\rho = m/V$, but mass itself is defined here only as the quantity of matter in a body. This statement gives no clue to the method by which mass may be measured. It has been maintained, and it may be true, that Newton held the extreme view that all matter is made up of identical elementary sub-atomic particles, differently arranged in the atoms of different substances, so that for him the quantity of matter in any body had a definite meaning in terms of the number of such particles which it contained. But this explanation does not alter the situation in respect of measurement, which is our present concern: in that connection Newton's first 'definition' is not at the same time a valid definition of both density and mass. We shall assume that, in fact, it leaves mass undefined.

Newton's second 'definition' is obviously a valid definition of momentum, if mass is known. Writing P for the measure of the momentum of a body, we have $P = mv$. But we must remember that mass has not as yet been satisfactorily defined. Moreover, there is nothing in the other six definitions, which have not been quoted hitherto, to clarify the concept of mass any further. We are compelled to seek such clarification in the so-called laws.

Newton's first 'law' is hardly distinguishable, except in grammatical construction, from his fourth definition, which we now quote for comparison:

Definition 4. An impressed force is an action exerted on a body, tending to change its state either of rest or of uniform motion in a straight line.

We are tempted to conclude that Law 1 contains nothing of importance besides that which is contained in this definition. But this is, perhaps, too hasty a judgment. Newton's third definition may be freely translated:

Definition 3. All matter has the quality of inertia, whereby every body, so far as depends upon itself, perseveres in its state, either of rest or of uniform motion in a straight line.

We are on safer ground if we assert that the first law states nothing which is not stated in one or other of these definitions. We may, in fact, paraphrase the 'law' as follows:

Law 1 (*paraphrase*). If at any instant the velocity of a body is changing, in magnitude or direction or both, then at that instant the body is acted upon by a force having its origin outside the body.

The phrase, 'having its origin' is admittedly vague, but the general intention of this paraphrase is clear: Law 1 is no more than a qualitative definition of force, a specification of the circumstances in which we say 'there is force acting there'. We were obviously committed to this view, once we had asserted the identity of content of Law 1 and Definitions 3 and 4. There is nothing in any of these statements describing a characteristic of the real world which might have been otherwise, if the pattern of the universe had been different from what it is.

Newton's second 'law' clearly provides the basis for a quantitative definition of force, and, equally clearly, it has no other significance, except that by its specification of direction it emphasises the fact that both force and momentum are vector quantities. If the unit of force is suitably chosen, the constant of proportion-

I

ality in the defining equation may be made equal to unity. Then F, the measure of the mean force acting on a body in rectilinear motion, between times t_1 and t_2, when P_1 and P_2 are the respective measures of the momentum of the body, is given by

$$F = \frac{P_2 - P_1}{t_2 - t_1} \qquad (47)$$

Equation (47), appropriately generalised for non-rectilinear motion and so as to give force-at-an-instant rather than mean force, contains the whole content of the second law; we see that it merely carries forward the definition contained in Law 1, giving it numerical precision. It is certainly not a law of nature as we understand that term. And we must not forget that we do not yet know how to assign a measure to momentum, for mass has not as yet been satisfactorily defined. Indeed, we have now traversed the first and second of the three 'laws' of Newton, and we have still to discover a true law of nature, or any further clarification of the concept of mass.

The essence of Newton's whole system of dynamics is to be found in the third 'law'. Even at first sight this law appears to assert something regarding the real world, something that has been inferred from experiment, something which in its generality future experiment may confirm or deny. Here is an assertion that in general the real world has such-and-such characteristics: in fact, the world may have these characteristics, or they may be slightly different—they could conceivably have been utterly different. We accept Law 3 as a law of nature, therefore, but to appreciate its true content we must again paraphrase. To do this we note that, according to Definition 4, 'action' is synonymous with 'force', and we translate 'force' according to the definitions contained in Law 2 and Definition 2. We note, also, that 'rate of change of velocity' is 'acceleration' (§ 4.3). Then we have:

> Law 3 (*paraphrase*). In an isolated system of two bodies the instantaneous accelerations of the bodies are always oppositely directed, and their magnitudes are in a constant ratio. This ratio is the inverse ratio of the masses of the bodies.

We have already accepted Law 3 as a law of nature; we now realise that, taken together with the rest of Newton's formulation, it provides a practical definition of mass, also. Using an obvious notation, successive steps in the argument leading to our paraphrase of the third law may be sketched thus:

$$F = F' \quad \text{(Newton's assertion, Law 3)},$$

therefore

$$\frac{P_2 - P_1}{t_2 - t_1} = \frac{P_2' - P_1'}{t_2 - t_1} \quad \text{(from equation (47))},$$

or

$$\frac{m(v_2 - v_1)}{t_2 - t_1} = \frac{m'(v_2' - v_1')}{t_2 - t_1} \quad \text{(from Definition 2)},$$

or

$$\frac{a}{a'} = \frac{m'}{m} \quad \text{(from § 4.3)}.$$

The ratio of the masses is the inverse ratio of the accelerations produced by equal forces.

It will be noted that the third law deals specifically with the behaviour of two bodies considered in isolation from the rest of the world. Newton speaks of 'the mutual actions of two bodies', and in our paraphrase, to give added point to this limitation, we refer to 'an isolated system of two bodies'. Now, in practice, there is no such thing as a perfectly isolated system of bodies of whatever specified number. And Newton gives no hint how, amidst the welter of interactions between the many bodies in the world, he is able to disentangle the mutual actions of any pair of them. These remarks merely serve to emphasise the depth of his intuition, and the magnitude of the claim which, by implication, the third law makes concerning the order of the world. In effect, the claim is as follows. If the instantaneous accelerations of all the bodies in the world—say N of them, an astronomically large number—could be determined at any time, there would be one way, and one way only, in which these accelerations could be resolved, each into $(N-1)$ components, so that the $N(N-1)$ component accelerations would constitute $\frac{1}{2}N(N-1)$ pairs, oppositely directed along the lines joining the N bodies each to every other, the magnitudes of these paired components being such that N mass-constants, $m_1, m_2, \ldots m_r,$ $m_s, \ldots m_N,$ would relate them, in the sense that $_r a_s$, the measure of the component acceleration of body r towards body s, and $_s a_r$, that of the component acceleration of s towards r, would satisfy $_r a_s /_s a_r = m_s / m_r$, and similarly for all possible pairs. When the statement is truly made that Newton's laws were in fact found adequate for the description of motions in the real world with entire fidelity over a period of more than two hundred years, it is tacitly implied that this far-reaching claim was essentially well founded.

In the present chapter we have accepted the ideas of space and time, which we have discussed in some detail already, and, following Newton, we have been led to the ideas of mass and force from a consideration of the motions of bodies in the real world. We have just stated that Newton's laws, in which these latter ideas were first expressed, proved uniformly successful as tested by experimental results over more than two hundred years, and we have pointed out that this in great measure justifies our acceptance of the new concepts of mass and force as valid concepts in relation to reality. But it should also be clear that the success of the Newtonian formulation indicates that our basic ideas of space and time are justified in like measure. We have raised doubts on this point, pointing out some of the difficulties, at various stages in our earlier discussion (§§ 3.1, 3.2, 3.5). We shall not refer to these again in detail here: it will be enough to mention one of them (p. 38) of which Newton himself was well aware. This is the doubt concerning the notion of 'absolute rest'.

It is true that Galileo, first, and Newton more systematically, later, disposed of the idea that the condition of a body 'absolutely' at rest is in any way different, kinetically, from that of a body in uniform rectilinear motion. But this did not settle the philosophical difficulty, which arises from the suspicion that any statement regarding motion implies knowledge of a reference point at rest. If Newton's laws, which treat of motion, are in any sense 'absolutely' true, then there must inevitably be a standard of absolute rest in the universe. On this point Lamb has written, 'By "motion" we mean of necessity motion relative to some frame of reference which is conventionally spoken of as "fixed". . . . As a first step we adopt a system of rectangular axes whose origin is fixed in the earth, but whose directions are fixed by relation to the stars; in the planetary theory the origin is transferred to the sun, and afterwards to the mass-centre of the solar system; and so on. At each step there is a gain in accuracy and comprehensiveness; and the conviction is cherished that *some* system of rectangular axes exists with respect to which the Newtonian scheme holds with all imaginable accuracy' (*Encyclopaedia Britannica*, 11th edition, 1911). Lamb's remarks are characteristic of the general scientific attitude at the end of the 'period of more than two hundred years' to which we have already referred—the period during which Newton's laws proved entirely adequate for the description of the physical situation as known at the time. For the purposes of the present volume Newton's laws remain entirely adequate today, but we have to record the fact that for the less familiar phenomena which involve very high velocities —velocities comparable with the velocity of light—modifications are now known to be necessary. These are the modifications introduced in the theory of relativity of Einstein. It is characteristic of this theory that a new attitude towards absolute rest is taken: effectively it is held that the notion is meaningless for the physicist—he should rid himself of his 'cherished conviction' that there is any system of axes with respect to which the Newtonian laws are 'absolutely' true. At the best they are an approximation, albeit a most useful one. Having registered this caveat, we shall proceed throughout the rest of this book to accept the Newtonian laws as valid: the approximation which they represent is entirely satisfactory for our purposes.

8.4. CONSERVATION OF MASS

It is a fundamental attitude of the physicist that he does not accept a new concept as satisfactorily defined until a recipe has been formulated on the basis of which a measure may be assigned to the magnitude of the corresponding physical quantity. In the last section we have concluded that Newton's third law of motion provides that recipe in relation to the concept 'mass'. The assertion of that law, as we have paraphrased it and explained its implications, is that, measured in terms of an invariable unit, the mass of any body which retains its identity throughout time remains constant. If, therefore, the physical universe consists entirely of identifiable bodies, then the total mass of the universe remains constant indefinitely. This is a statement about the universe, and, in so far as it is true, it is a law of nature. It is the first of the conservation laws, and for our purposes we accept its validity.

Newton also spoke of mass as the quantity of matter in a body, and there is the suggestion (p. 128) that he thought of this as expressible, in the ultimate analysis, in terms of the number of identical sub-atomic particles making up the substance of the body. From this point of view, the law of conservation of mass implies the permanence of these sub-atomic particles through all vicissitudes, and the indestructibility of matter in general. Here we impinge on the province of the chemist. For the chemist, however, the universe does not consist of isolated bodies which are permanently identifiable: substances may be made to react so that macroscopic identity is lost—red mercuric oxide powder has none of the obvious characteristics of the silver-grey liquid mercury and the colourless gaseous oxygen out of which it is formed. It is not surprising, therefore, that in spite of the overwhelming success of Newtonian physics, nearly two hundred years after the death of Newton chemists should still be submitting the hypothesis of the indestructibility of matter to the stringent test of precise experiment. Throughout the first hundred years of this period the dominance of earlier views was such, and the lack of accurate gravimetric analyses so nearly complete, that little progress was made. The atomic hypothesis of Dalton was not formulated until 1805— and another century had to pass before the work of Landolt showed that under favourable conditions it is possible to account for all the matter entering into a chemical reaction to within one part in ten million, the ultimate refinement of the experimental method. Though it is never possible to establish exact equality by direct observation, at this stage at least it appeared that there was no reason to doubt the mass-conservation law in respect of either physical or chemical changes.

Landolt's experimental results were published in 1908. Three years earlier Einstein's theory of relativity had been advanced in order to explain certain puzzling experimental results in pure physics, and to resolve a number of philosophical difficulties to which reference has already been made (p. 133). It is an interesting coincidence that during the same few years in which the chemists were finally convincing themselves that mass is indeed conserved within the accuracy of their means of estimation, experimental and theoretical physicists were demonstrating that it is not basically invariable, as Newton had supposed, but increases with increasing velocity, and, by implication, that every chemical reaction involves a small change of mass. We are not going to be concerned with these refinements in this book: we can safely disregard them, for the velocity-dependence of mass is appreciable only at velocities comparable with the velocity of light, and there are not many chemical reactions in which the mass-change is as great as one part in ten thousand million (compared with the one part in ten million of Landolt).

8.5. CONSERVATION OF LINEAR MOMENTUM

Newton's third law of motion involves a second conservation law, the law of conservation of linear momentum. We may formulate this law as follows:

> For any isolated system of particles, the resultant compounded of the instantaneous (linear) momenta of the individual particles remains unchanged (in magnitude and direction) with the passage of time.

Or alternatively:

> For any isolated system of particles, the instantaneous vector sum of the (linear) momenta of the individual particles remains constant.

Linear momentum, a vector quantity, the measure of which is defined by Newton's second definition (p. 127) as the product of the measures of the scalar quantity, mass, and the vector quantity, linear velocity, is such that for any particle its rate of change is the measure of the resultant force acting on the particle (Law 2). Let us begin, then, with the isolated system of two particles postulated in our paraphrase of Law 3 (p. 130). Instantaneously, the only forces that there can be constitute an equal and oppositely directed pair. These forces may change with time but at each instant they are equal and oppositely directed. In each elementary duration, therefore, the rate of increase of the linear momentum of the one particle is equal and opposite to the rate of increase of the linear momentum of the other. Over any finite time, in consequence, the change of linear momentum of the one particle exactly counterbalances the change of linear momentum of the other. For these two particles, then, linear momentum is conserved. It is a simple matter to extend this argument to an isolated system containing any number of particles, say N of them. In such a system the components of force consist of $\frac{1}{2}N(N-1)$ equal and opposite pairs (p. 131). In any finite time the net momentum generated by any one of these pairs of force components is zero, thus the resultant momentum of the whole system remains unchanged. And the same result is true for an isolated system of bodies, for each body may be regarded as constituted of a large number of individual particles to which Newton's third law applies (see, also, § 9.6.3).

8.6. COMPARISON OF MASSES: THE BALLISTIC BALANCE

Galileo's ideal, a perfectly smooth plane surface, was one on which, when it was horizontal, and in the absence of air resistance, a body would travel freely, without change of velocity. In this case the force between the surface and the body is normal to the surface, supporting the body in opposition to its weight (p. 126). A perfectly smooth surface is incapable of generating, through contact of another body with it, any force parallel to its plane. Imagine, then, a perfectly smooth concave surface in the form of a portion of a circular cylinder of radius R, as shown in vertical section in fig. 27, and let the cylindrical axis, passing through O, be horizontal and perpendicular to the diagram. Let a small body be placed on the surface at P. According to Galileo's observations with inclined planes of various inclinations (the present situation is novel only in that the inclination of the cylindrical surface varies continuously), in the ideal case the body would oscillate backwards and forwards between P and P' (PP' being horizontal), and the speed of the body as it passed through A, the lowest point in its path, would be the same as it would have acquired in free fall from N to A. If g is the measure of the acceleration of free fall (acceleration due to gravity), and v that of the velocity of the body at A, if $NA = h$, $PN = NP' = x$, we thus have

$$v^2 = 2gh \text{ (from equation (16))}$$

and, from the geometry of the circle,

$$x^2 = h(2R-h),$$

therefore

$$v = x\left\{g \Big/ \left(R-\frac{h}{2}\right)\right\}^{\frac{1}{2}} \tag{48}$$

In the limiting case, when h is very small compared with R, equation (48) becomes

$$v = x(g/R)^{\frac{1}{2}} \tag{49}$$

In practice it is impossible to realise Galileo's ideal of a perfectly

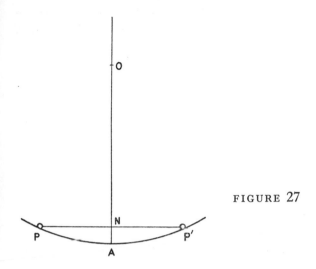

FIGURE 27

smooth surface with complete fidelity. On the other hand, by a
different arrangement, we can in fact approximate very closely
indeed to the type of motion which we have just described. Suppose
that our small body, instead of being constrained to move along the
circular arc PAP' by virtue of its being supported on the concave
surface previously specified, is attached to a fixed support at O by
an inextensible weightless string of length R, the concave surface
being removed. Then the body must move in a circular arc as
before, and the force normal to the surface in the first arrangement
is replaced by a force along the string in the second. For corresponding positions of the body these forces are in the same direction in the two cases. Indeed, the motion of the body is precisely
the same in the two arrangements: the same geometrical constraint
is achieved throughout, thus the forces must be the same, though
they are differently produced. For small vertical displacements,
equation (49) applies as previously: v, the velocity of the body at
the lowest point of its motion, is proportional to x, the distance
through which it is withdrawn sideways before being released, or
through which it will afterwards move before coming momentarily
to rest. In relation to the ideal of unresisted motion, surface resistance has been eliminated and only air resistance remains, however
a new feature of complication has been introduced in the form of
the string. No string, in fact, can be perfectly inextensible and

perfectly weightless. It can only be repeated that on balance the gain is greater than the loss: the pendulum arrangement is both more convenient and intrinsically more nearly perfect than the Galilean arrangement of the concave cylindrical surface. It has been mentioned already (p. 126) that many experiments on collisions were made by the two-pendulum method, notably by Sir Christopher Wren, in the period which elapsed between the publications of Galileo's *Dialogue*, in 1638, and Newton's *Principia*, in 1687.

Hicks's ballistic balance represents a refinement of the two-pendulum arrangement, giving greater flexibility. Its principle can be understood initially without reference to that refinement, as follows. Let two small spherical bodies, X and Y, of masses m_1 and m_2 respectively, be supported with their centres in the same horizontal plane from rigid supports separated by a horizontal distance AB (see fig. 28) equal to the sum of the radii of the spheres. Let the vertical distance from AB to the line of centres of the spheres be R. Let the body X be drawn aside through a horizontal distance x_1 (to the left in the figure), let it be released, and, after collision with the stationary Y, let it move forward (to the right in the figure) through a horizontal distance x_1' before itself coming momentarily to rest. Similarly, let Y move through a horizontal distance x_2' (of necessity $x_2' \geqslant x_1'$) before it in turn comes momentarily to rest after the collision. Then, if v_1 is the measure of the velocity of X before the collision, and v_1' and v_2' are the measures of the velocities of X and Y after the collision, respectively, and if the direction of the original motion of X is regarded as positive throughout, we have, from (49), certainly as long as x_1, x_1' and x_2' are all small compared with R,

$$v_1 : v_1' : v_2' = x_1 : x_1' : x_2'.$$

Also, from the principle of conservation of linear momentum, we have

$$m_1 v_1 = m_1 v_1' + m_2 v_2'.$$

Thus

$$\frac{m_1}{m_2} = \frac{v_2'}{v_1 - v_1'} = \frac{x_2'}{x_1 - x_1'} \qquad (50)$$

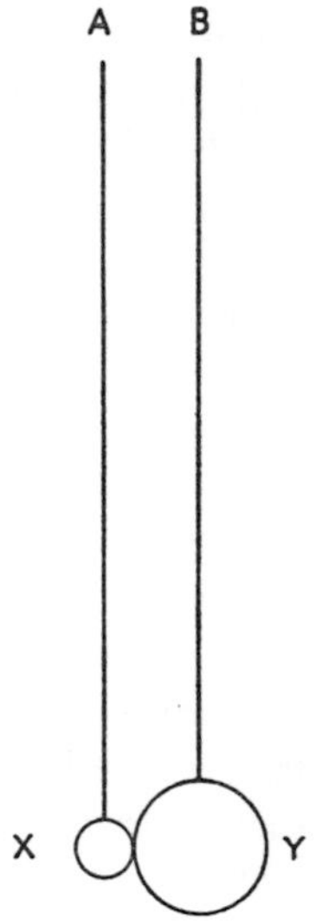

FIGURE 28

In the special case in which the bodies stick together on collision, obviously $x_1' = x_2'$, and in this case, therefore,

$$\frac{m_1}{m_2} = \frac{x'}{x_1 - x'} \qquad (51)$$

where $x' = x_1' = x_2'$. Equation (51), or equation (50), provides a basis for the comparison of the masses of two spherical bodies in terms of an experiment in which the only measured quantities are the magnitudes of the sideways displacements involved. Clearly the validity of either equation is not restricted to the case of two spheres, and Hicks's ballistic balance provides the physical conditions in which the experiment can be carried out for bodies of arbitrary shape.

The ballistic balance consists of two exactly similar wooden platforms, so suspended by multifilar suspensions that they remain essentially horizontal for small sideways displacements, and provided with sharp spikes on their opposing faces ensuring that they stick together on collision, also with means of securing on their upper surfaces the experimental bodies of which the masses are to be compared. Pointers attached to the platforms move over horizontal scales, so enabling the initial and final displacements to be easily observed. Obviously, two sets of observations are required in order that the (equal) masses of the platforms may be eliminated from the calculations. Thus, if μ be the mass of either platform, an experiment in which one platform is loaded with the first body, whilst the other platform is unloaded, will enable the ratio m_1/μ to be determined, and a similar experiment using the second body only will yield the ratio m_2/μ. The required ratio m_1/m_2 may then be obtained by division.

Alternatively, if a graded series of reference masses is available ('box of weights'), the two experiments might consist in the loading of one platform with each of the experimental bodies in turn, and in each case loading the other platform with a selection of reference masses so chosen that $x' = \frac{1}{2}x_1$, as nearly as may be arranged. Then, according to equation (51), in each case the colliding bodies must be of effectively equal mass, that is, in each case the mass of the experimental body on the one platform must equal the total of reference masses on the other. If we imagine the reference masses to be exactly similar units of any convenient size, clearly the ratio of the masses of the two experimental bodies is given in terms of the numbers of reference-mass units required for 'balance' in each experiment. The accuracy of this comparison is determined by the patience of the observer, and by size of the reference-mass unit at his disposal. Obviously, the smaller this unit is, in relation to the mass of either experimental body, the more accurate is the best comparison that can be made with a given apparatus—at least until the limit fixed by the accuracy in the measurement of displacement is reached.

It will be common knowledge that the masses of bodies are not generally compared by use of a ballistic balance. The method of weighing, to be discussed in the next section, is in fact susceptible of enormously greater accuracy than the method we have just described, but the concept 'mass' was introduced into physics through Newton's third law, and the ballistic balance has at least the merit that it operates primarily and essentially within the field of this law. It is true that in practice use is made of the fact that the acceleration due to gravity is the same for all bodies in a given locality (compare equations (49) and (50)), but this assumption is not basic for the operation of the ballistic balance as it will be found to be for the operation of weighing using a beam balance of conventional type.

8.7. WEIGHT

Galileo recognised that, for all bodies in the same locality, the acceleration of ideally free fall is the same. He also recognised the property of heaviness, or weight, as measured by the least force necessary to prevent the fall of a body. A body supported against the action of its weight is in equilibrium under equal and opposite forces: when the supporting force is withdrawn, the weight, that is the natural force due to gravity, produces the acceleration. Accepting the quantitative definition of force provided by Newton's second law, we have, if m is the mass of a body and W is its weight in a locality where the common acceleration due to gravity is g,

$$W = mg \qquad (52)$$

Equation (52) shows that we can compare the masses of two bodies by comparing their weights, or the forces necessary to support them against the pull of gravitational attraction, in the same locality on the earth's surface. The beam balance, the operation of which we shall be considering in greater detail in a later section (§ 9.10), provides a method of matching two bodies, or two sets of bodies, so that the forces necessary to support them are equal. We balance each experimental body in turn against an appropriate selection of reference masses ('weights'), effectively in the same manner as we considered in the last section in relation to the second method of using a ballistic balance—though by a much less tiresome and more accurate procedure.

For our present purposes it need only be stated that the beam balance consists fundamentally of two exactly similar scale pans freely supported one from each end of a beam which is itself supported symmetrically so that it is free to turn about a horizontal axis at right angles to its length. The forces necessary to support the scale pans and their contents act vertically upwards through the points of attachment of the pans to the beam. Through these same points equal and opposite forces act downwards on the beam. If the beam is in equilibrium in a horizontal position when the pans are empty, one may conclude from the symmetry of the arrangement that the beam will also be in equilibrium in the same position when the pans are loaded with bodies whose weights (and, therefore, whose masses) are the same. The criterion of equality of loading of the pans—apart from a minor complication arising from the buoyancy of the air—is, therefore, that the beam shall be in equilibrium when it is horizontal, or that in this position it shall show no tendency to tilt either to the right or the left.

The experiments of Landolt to which reference was made in § 8.4 were made with a beam balance. It was there stated that an accuracy of one part in ten million was attained in favourable circumstances. This was a particular example: it may be asserted more generally, with equal truth, that the process of weighing is intrinsically one of the most accurate of the processes of measurement in physics. In practice, therefore, whenever this is possible the masses of bodies are compared by weighing them in turn on a beam balance.

In the last section we defined a perfectly smooth plane surface as incapable of generating, through contact of another body with it, any force parallel to its plane. If, therefore, a body is placed on a perfectly smooth inclined plane surface, an external force parallel to the surface must be applied to prevent the body sliding downwards. It has been stated, in § 8.2, that Stevinus solved the problem of relating this force to the weight of the body in 1586.

Recognising the fact that force is a vector quantity, we should, nowadays, simply resolve the weight of the body into components, $W \cos \theta$ normal to the surface and $W \sin \theta$ parallel to the direction of steepest slope of the surface, W being the weight and θ the inclination of the surface to the horizontal (see §§ 9.2, 9.5 for full justification of this statement). We should note that the normal reaction on the body must be $W \cos \theta$, since it can have no acceleration at right angles to the surface, whatever its motion parallel to it may be. And we should note that the body would have an acceleration parallel to the surface unless the weight component $W \sin \theta$ were opposed by an equal and oppositely directed external force. This situation is represented diagrammatically in fig. 29, the body being shown separated from the plane for convenience only.

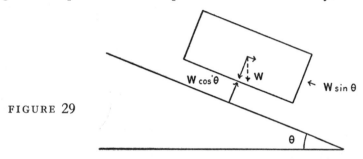

FIGURE 29

In Stevinus's time the procedure of resolution of vectors had not been devised, thus it is instructive to follow the argument which led him to the result which we have just derived. Stevinus considered a uniform heavy flexible band supported on a triangular prism having one face horizontal. Figure 30 represents the arrangement in principal section. Suppose that the inclined faces of the prism, represented by AC, BC in the figure, are perfectly smooth and that their inclinations are θ_1 and θ_2 as indicated. Then it is contrary to experience and to reason, Stevinus held, that, in such an ideal arrangement, the band should start to move, if it were initially at rest. Moreover, the portion of the band below the prism must hang symmetrically, so that lack of movement (acceleration) cannot be ascribed to the balancing of forces resulting from the asymmetrical configuration of the upper part of the band (the part lying on the inclined faces of the prism) by forces arising from a compensating asymmetry of the lower part—for there is no such asymmetry. Therefore, that part of the band actually in contact

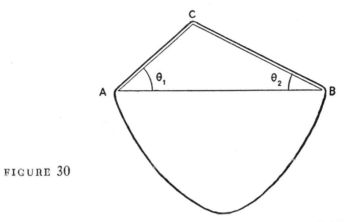

FIGURE 30

with the prism is itself in equilibrium; that is, the force necessary
to prevent the portion in contact with CB moving down the plane,
as it would do if it were unsupported, is equal to the force necessary to prevent the portion in contact with CA moving down CA,
each of these forces being provided by the tension in the band at
the point where it passes over the ridge of the prism. This tension
cannot have different values at a single point. Because the band is
supposed uniform, if W_1, W_2 are the weights of the portions in
contact with CA and CB, respectively, of necessity, from the
geometry of the triangle,

$$\frac{W_1}{\sin \theta_2} = \frac{W_2}{\sin \theta_1},$$

or $\qquad\qquad W_1 \sin \theta_1 = W_2 \sin \theta_2 \qquad\qquad\qquad (53)$

Clearly, the force necessary to prevent motion of either portion of
the band will be proportional to its weight, and will depend upon
the inclination of the plane on which it rests. Further, we have
just concluded that, in the arrangement considered, these forces
are the same for the two portions of the band resting on CA and
CB, respectively. Equation (53) shows that of necessity the product

(weight of portion of band $\times$ (sine of angle of
in contact with plane)   inclination)

is the same for the two portions of the band in question. This
product fulfils the condition that it is proportional to the weight
and dependent upon the inclination; moreover, for a vertical plane,
$\sin \theta = 1$, and in that case the product is simply the weight, as we

know the external force necessary to prevent motion must be when the plane provides no support at all. Thus we conclude that the minimum external force necessary to prevent motion, for any body of weight W placed on a perfectly smooth inclined plane of inclination θ, is $W \sin \theta$, if it acts in the direction of steepest slope of the plane.

At a later stage, when we come to consider the law of moments (§ 9.4), we shall show how Galileo deduced this simple but fundamental result by an entirely different argument, some few years after Stevinus had developed the 'proof' which, in modern idiom, we have just attempted to reproduce. It was the case in the sixteenth century, and it is even more obviously the case in the twentieth, that new results in physical science appear frequently at about the same time in different places, as the inevitable products of a ferment of ideas at work in many schools over relatively long periods of apparent inactivity.

8.8. STANDARDS OF MASS

In the last two sections we have discussed in some detail two methods of comparing the masses of bodies. On the basis of either method we have a workable procedure; if, in addition, we specify a unit of mass, we have a complete system of mass-measurement, fully defined.

In the British system, the unit of mass, the avoirdupois pound, is realised in a cylindrical standard made of platinum in 1844 and designated the Imperial Standard Pound in terms of the Weights and Measures Act, 1856. As with the yard, the unit was given more precise definition by the Act of 1878 of the same title. The height of the standard is about 3 cm., and its diameter somewhat less than this, and it has a shallow groove round its cylindrical surface, near to one end, for ease of manipulation, for which purpose an ivory lifting-fork is used. The edges of the standard are rounded as a precaution against damage. There are five 'parliamentary' copies, as with the standard yard.

In the metric system the unit of mass is the kilogramme. Following the failure of an earlier attempt to relate this unit to a volume of pure water (p. 34), the kilogramme was defined, in 1889, as the mass of a cylindrical standard of platinum-iridium alloy, designated the International Prototype Kilogramme. The diameter of the standard is equal to its height (just less than 4 cm.), and the edges are sharp. A determination made at the National Physical Laboratory in 1933 gave the result 1 lb. $= 0.453592338$ kg., a figure which we quote here chiefly as indicating a precision in weighing, in the very favourable case of the comparison of standards, some fifty times greater than that claimed by Landolt in his classical experiments on the conservation of mass in chemical reactions.

With these definitions we have now completed our specification of the units of length (§§ 2.8, 2.10), time (§ 3.2) and mass, as currently used as the basis of accurate measurement in physics. In respect of the units of length and time, we have already discussed in some detail the difficulties in the way of the satisfactory definition of the units, and their realisation in invariable standards. It might appear that, fundamentally, such difficulties are less acute in relation to the units and standards of mass. To some extent this is true: the great accuracy of which the procedure of weighing is susceptible makes possible a check on the constancy of the masses of bodies, under ordinary conditions of use, to a very high order. In so far as the Newtonian idea of mass, as the quantity of matter in a body, is valid, it is necessary only to insure that our standard of mass is protected from all actions which would alter that quantity, in order that its mass should remain constant in perpetuity. It must be protected against mechanical actions such as abrasion which would decrease, or the adherence of dust or dirt which would increase, its mass; it must be proof against the oxidation of its surface layers which would add matter to its bulk. These requirements are obvious enough; they explain the choice of a heavy metal capable of receiving a high polish, highly resistant to all ordinary chemical reagents, for the fabrication of the standard. And they explain why the primary standard is brought into use so infrequently; say once in ten years for comparison with its copies. For all practical purposes the precautions and cross-checks which have been instituted are highly effective.

But, as illustrating the dictum that nothing is as simple as it seems, it is worth remarking that there is one agency with which the standard-makers of the nineteenth century did not reckon, for it has been recognised only in the twentieth. Their precautions did not include shielding against the cosmic radiation. It is an academic, rather than a practical, point, but we now know that in any material exposed to the cosmic radiation—and all bodies on or near the surface of the earth are so exposed, to greater or lesser

K

degree—processes occur from time to time in which atomic nuclei are transformed. To this minute—altogether negligible—extent the matter constituting our standards of mass does not remain for ever the same, even though they remain sealed, in vacuum, as objects of veneration rather than of use. And, as the matter of the standard is thus transformed, now one atom, now another, so, as strict purists, at least, we must believe that its mass changes. As practical scientists, however, we dismiss any doubt from our minds. Accepting 1 part in 10^9 as the ultimate precision of mass-comparison, we estimate that the present rate of change due to cosmic-ray bombardment would have to continue for more than 10^{10} years before its effects became manifest.

These last are modern considerations; it remains only to refer briefly to the history of standards of mass, as we have referred to the history of the material standards of length, in order to make our treatment of the subject complete. For this purpose it is convenient to adopt the old sub-unit, the grain, still legally defined as $\frac{1}{7000}$ of the pound avoirdupois, as the basis of comparison. The kilo-gramme is about 15432·4 grains. Also, it is necessary to note that before Newton there could, strictly, be no standards of mass, though there were standard 'weights' in plenty, two thousand years previously. From very early times the beam balance, in primitive form, was employed for the comparison of these weights, and for the weighing of small articles of trade, objects of gold and silver, precious stones and incense. For many centuries the assumption that by this procedure the intrinsic quantities of material were compared was intuitive rather than explicit. Moreover, with the introduction of coinage in the countries bordering on the eastern Mediterranean, in about the eighth century BC, the distinction between standard weights and coins tended for some hundreds of years to become indefinite and blurred. Even today occasions for confusion still remain: in Britain the troy ounce of 480 grains (relic of the 12-ounce troy pound of 5760 grains) is the legal unit for the sale of the noble metals and precious stones. In Saxon times the moneyers' pound was of approximately 5400 grains, and the troy pound, already in use for more than a century previously, suc-ceeded this unit in 1527. Meanwhile, in 1270, a separate merchants' pound of about 6750 grains was legalised, and in 1303 the avoir-dupois pound was introduced for all the normal purposes of commerce. By the time of Elizabeth I the legal standard had very closely its present value (7002 grains). In France the kilogramme replaced a pound of about 7555 grains in 1801.

The names of our units, ounce and pound, derive directly from those of the units of imperial Rome, where pounds of twelve and sixteen ounces were variously used. We shall not, however, attempt to trace here any direct line of descent from Roman times. It will suffice to maintain that, over a period of three thousand years or more, units of about the magnitude of the pound and the kilogramme have been in common use in one dominant civilisation or another. From Egypt of the sixth century BC, Athens adopted the mina of about 6700 grains, of which the hundredth part was the drachma, and, some hundreds of years earlier, the greater maneh of the Assyrians, the equivalent of 60 greater shekels, averaged 15,500 grains on the evidence of the weights of haematite and bronze which ancient sites have yielded to the archaeologist's spade. So little do the basic needs and inclinations of man change with the centuries.

8.9. IMPULSE, WORK, ENERGY, POWER

The fundamental concepts peculiar to the subject of kinetics are force and mass. These we have discussed in full in the previous sections of this chapter, elaborating the Newtonian scheme by which magnitudes may be assigned to the physical quantities concerned. In the course of that discussion we have also introduced momentum as a physical quantity. In the present section we deal briefly with four other quantities which it is convenient to define as we develop the subject.

Impulse is defined as a change of momentum. On the basis of this definition, a constant force F, acting for a time t, generates an impulse $I = Ft$, along its line of action (see equation (47)). Obviously, it would hardly be profitable to have a separate name for this quantity, if it were not characteristic of certain situations of common occurrence. This is in fact the case: in a collision between two bodies the time over which the force acts on either body is very short, and its magnitude varies from zero at the instant of first contact, through a maximum, and back to zero again at the instant of final separation. Only the overall change of momentum is easily measured, and the magnitude of this change is the same for each body. In such a case the magnitude of the impulse generated in the collision is evidently a significant magnitude. To be precise, the two bodies involved in the collision experience oppositely directed impulses of the same magnitude. Knowing the common magnitude of the impulse, if we can estimate the duration of the collision, we can deduce a mean value of the force developed. Because of its importance for the discussion of collision processes, the quantity impulse is frequently, though rather loosely, defined as a change of momentum produced by a large force acting for a short time.

Just as the quantities momentum and impulse are measured in the same units, so the quantities work and energy are essentially of the same character. Consider the kinematic equation (see § 4.4)

$$v^2 = v_0{}^2 + 2as,$$

as it refers to the uniformly accelerated rectilinear motion of a particle of which the mass is m. Let us multiply each term of this equation by $m/2$, re-arrange the terms,

$$\tfrac{1}{2}mv^2 - \tfrac{1}{2}mv_0{}^2 = mas,$$

and attempt to interpret the equation so obtained as an equation in kinetics. The product ma, on the right-hand side of the equation, is the measure of the constant force F which must act on the particle to maintain the acceleration a. Therefore

$$\tfrac{1}{2}mv^2 - \tfrac{1}{2}mv_0{}^2 = Fs \qquad (54)$$

Now, the left-hand side of equation (54) clearly represents the change in a physical quantity specified by half the product of the measure of the mass of the particle and the square of the measure of its velocity. We define this quantity as the kinetic energy of the particle, and we interpret equation (54) as indicating, in terms of this definition, that the effect of an unopposed force F, acting on a particle over a distance s, is to increase the kinetic energy of the particle by an amount of which the product Fs is the measure. Furthermore, recognising that the force F must have its origin in some physical system unspecified in our description of the situation hitherto, we say that, in the process considered, the unspecified system, through the force F, does work of which the product Fs is equally the measure. And we find it convenient to generalise this definition, and say that, when a body moves in any way under the action of any number of external forces, each force does work in amount given by the product of its measure and the measure of the distance in the direction of its line of action through which its point of application moves.

In a situation in which more than one force is involved, clearly the motion of the point of application will sometimes have a positive, sometimes a negative, component along the forwards direction of the force considered. We distinguish, therefore, between work done by a force, in the former case, and work done against a force, in the latter. When only one force is involved, equation (54) exhibits this distinction in its simplest form. When F and s have the same sign, $v > v_0$, work is done by the force, and this work appears associated with the particle as additional energy of motion. When F and s have opposite signs, $v < v_0$, the kinetic energy of the particle diminishes, and work is done against the force in amount equal to the decrease in energy.

Power is defined as the rate of doing work. As we have already indicated, the phrase 'work done by a force' is the conventional abbreviation for the more precise expression 'work done through the agency of the force by the physical system in which the force originates'. The quantity power, on the other hand, is generally regarded as an attribute of a physical system, explicitly: we speak of the power of an engine when the forces which its operation brings into play do work at a specified rate.

In § 8.3 we concluded that momentum and force are vector quantities: equally clearly, mass is a scalar quantity. The question now arises, what is the status of the quantities impulse, work, energy and power? Obviously, impulse is a vector quantity, for it is defined as an increment of momentum. As regards work and energy, which are of the same nature, kinetic energy is given by half the product of mass and the square of a velocity. Now, mass is a scalar quantity, as we have just decided, and, in one-dimensional motion, the square of a velocity v is indistinguishable from the square of $-v$. If in one-dimensional motion, therefore, the direction of the velocity is immaterial when the corresponding kinetic energy is in question, it cannot be that, in three-dimensional motion, direction in space is any more involved in the specification of that energy. There is nothing, then, in the expression $\frac{1}{2}mv^2$ to which to attach the idea of direction, and kinetic energy is a scalar quantity. If kinetic energy is a scalar quantity, so is work, but the expression Fs represents the product of the measures of two vector quantities, force and displacement. We conclude, then, that the product of two vector quantities, in this instance, is itself a scalar quantity. As a later discussion will show, this is not always the case when the product of the measures of two vector quantities enters as a term in an equation of physics. However, it is always the case when the physical situation is such that, for their product to be significant, the two vectors must have the same direction. In Fs, the expression for the work done, the displacement s is measured in the direction of action of the force F: the product, giving the measure of the work done, is then spoken of as the scalar product of the vectors concerned. Work, then, is a scalar quantity, and power, which is rate of doing work, is a scalar quantity, also.

Finally, to summarise the position in relation to the kinetic quantities which we have now defined, we give in tabular form the dimensions of the various quantities, and the units in which they are measured in the British and metric systems, respectively. For the metric system we give two sets of units for sake of completeness. The metric system, by past scientific usage, has generally been referred to as the centimetre-gramme-second (c.g.s.) system, but, as we have seen, the primary standards of length and mass are the metre and the kilogramme—the centimetre and the gramme are strictly sub-units—and the more directly defined metre-kilogramme-second (M.K.S.) system is gaining favour for some purposes.

Quantity	Dimensions	British unit	K.S. metric unit	c.g.s. metric unit
Mass	M^1	pound	kilogramme	gramme
Momentum Impulse	$M^1L^1T^{-1}$	—	—	—
Force	$M^1L^1T^{-2}$	poundal	newton	dyne
Work Energy	$M^1L^2T^{-2}$	—	joule	erg
Power	$M^1L^2T^{-3}$	—	watt	—

In the table we give the names of units only when these are individual to the quantity concerned. When no name is given it implies that the unit is specified, according to the appropriate dimensional formula, in terms of the individually named units involved. On this basis the unit of power in the British system is 1 foot poundal per second (conventionally the foot, rather than the yard, is taken as the basic unit of length), and the unit of momentum on the c.g.s. metric system is 1 dyne second (or 1 gramme centimetre per second).

CHAPTER 9

MOMENTS OF FORCE AND
MOMENTS OF INERTIA

9.1. INDEPENDENCE OF MOTIONS OF TRANSLATION AND ROTATION

In our development of Newtonian kinetics hitherto, and in particular in our discussion of the law of conservation of linear momentum (§ 8.5), we have concentrated attention on the kinetics of particles. We have stressed the generality of the Newtonian laws, and we have indicated how the motions of rigid bodies of finite extension can be treated by regarding them as made up of great numbers of particles. But we have not as yet made effective use of this idea; in confining our discussion to the motions of particles we have been able to avoid the problem of rotation. Ideally, the only motion of which a point-mass is capable is motion of translation. We must now deal with the motions of extended bodies, and specifically with their motions of rotation. To do this in full we must obviously consider the behaviour of rigid bodies in three dimensions, but much can be learned from considerations of two-dimensional motions, and for this purpose we introduce the idea of the 'lamina', a uniform plate of arbitrary shape, of negligible thickness but finite mass, an ideal two-dimensional rigid body.

In order to fix the position of a lamina in two-dimensional space, we need only specify the positions in space of two points in the lamina. Any displacement of the lamina may therefore be described in terms of the displacements of the two points concerned. As we shall see, it may also be described as compounded of two component displacements, one of pure translation and the other of pure rotation. By pure translation we mean motion in which every point in the lamina moves through the same distance in the same direction; by pure rotation the only type of motion which is possible in two-dimensional space when one point in the lamina is fixed. Let A, B (fig. 31) represent the initial, A′, B′ the final, positions in space of the two chosen reference points in a particular displacement. Let Aa, bB be drawn parallel to A′B′, and A′a′, b′B′ parallel to

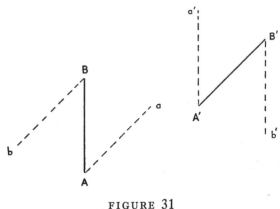

FIGURE 31

AB. Then, clearly, the displacement of the lamina may be described either as the purely translational displacement of AB to A′a′ followed by the clockwise rotation of A′a′ to A′B′, or as the translational displacement of AB to b′B′ followed by the clockwise rotation of B′b′ to B′A′. Alternatively, the order of the translational and rotational components of displacement may be reversed in the description, the translation Aa to A′B′ following the clockwise rotation AB to Aa, or the translation bB to A′B′ following the clockwise rotation BA to Bb. Whichever of these equivalent descriptions is employed, the magnitude of the rotational component of displacement is the same: as a result of our construction of parallels, the four angles, ∠ABb, ∠BAa, ∠a′A′B′, ∠b′B′A′, are obviously equal. Indeed, we may go further, we may say that this particular displacement of the lamina may be described as a pure rotation, about an identifiable point in space, of this same magnitude. In order to establish this twofold assertion let AB, A′B′ (fig. 32) represent the initial and final positions of the lines joining the reference points of the lamina, as before. Join AA′, BB′, and let CE, DE, the perpendicular bisectors of AA′, BB′, meet in E. Then

$$\triangle ABE = \triangle A'B'E,$$

for $$AB = A'B',$$

the lamina being rigid,

$$AE = A'E,$$

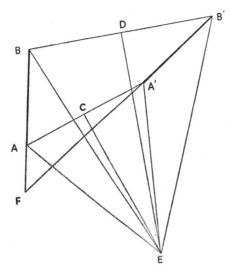

FIGURE 32

CE being the perpendicular bisector of AA',

and $\qquad$ BE = B'E, similarly.

Thus, the displacement of AB to A'B' may be regarded as resulting from the pure rotation about E of the triangle ABE into coincidence with its congruent, $\triangle$A'B'E. The first part of our assertion is thereby established: the point E has been identified, a pure rotation about which describes the displacement AB to A'B'. In order to establish the second part of our assertion, we have to show that, if BA and B'A' produced meet in F, so that $\angle$AFA' (fig. 32) = $\angle$a'A'B' (fig. 31), then $\angle$BEB' = $\angle$AFA'. We have

$$\angle BEB' + \angle EB'B + \angle B'BE = 2 \text{ right angles.}$$

But $\qquad$ $\angle EB'A' = \angle EBA,$

thus $\quad$ $\angle BEB' + \angle A'B'B + \angle B'BA = 2$ right angles

(we have subtracted $\angle$EB'A' from $\angle$EB'B, and added $\angle$EBA to $\angle$B'BE).

However $\angle AFA' + \angle A'B'B + \angle B'BA = 2$ right angles,

thus $\quad$ $\angle BEB' = \angle AFA'$, as was to be proved.

We conclude, therefore, that, for any finite displacement of a lamina in two-dimensional space, there is in general a perfectly definite finite component of rotation, of the same magnitude about whatever point in the lamina we choose to reckon it, and that there is one point, fixed with respect to the lamina, of which the initial and final positions in space are the same.

If, instead of a finite displacement, we consider a displacement which is infinitesimally small, it should be clear that, whilst our analysis provides no basis for the definition of a unique instant-aneous velocity of translation of a moving lamina, it provides a direct and obvious basis for the definition of a unique instantaneous angular velocity of rotation of the lamina. Furthermore, it leads directly to the concept of an instantaneous centre of rotation—the point with reference to which the infinitesimal displacement of the lamina appears as purely rotational. Following the motion of the lamina throughout a finite time, we shall in general find that the position in space of the instantaneous centre of rotation changes continuously, whilst its position in the lamina—that is, the position in the lamina of the point which is instantaneously at rest in space—also changes in a continuous manner. The locus in space of the instantaneous centre of rotation is generally referred to as the 'space centrode' of the motion; the corresponding locus in the lamina as the 'body centrode'.

At a later stage (§ 9.5) we shall return to the question whether any conventional significance can be given to the concept of an instantaneous velocity of translation of a moving body (lamina or solid body), meanwhile, having recognised the uniqueness of the rotational component in two-dimensional motion, we shall deal with motions of pure rotation. We shall consider these motions in two dimensions only, noting that there is no significant loss of generality in so doing: a solid body rotating about an axis may clearly be regarded as made up of a large number of laminae rotating with a common angular velocity. As a preliminary to this general consideration, in the next section we clarify certain aspects of the problem of the equilibrium of rigid bodies acted upon by external forces.

9.2. SOME PROBLEMS OF EQUILIBRIUM

In specifying the conditions of application of an external force to a rigid body we need to know only the magnitude of the force and

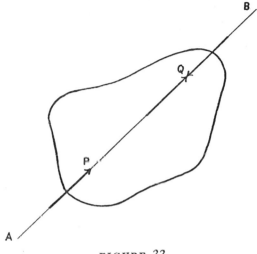

FIGURE 33

its line of action. It is superfluous to enquire what its point of application is. We may justify this assertion by reference to fig. 33. Let P, Q be two points, in the rigid body represented in the figure, lying in the straight line AB. Then the effect on the body of a single force F acting along AB at P is obviously the same as that of three forces each of magnitude F, one acting along AB at P and the other two acting at Q, one along AB and the other along BA (this system is indicated in the figure). For, in the second case, the two forces acting at Q cancel directly. But, since the body is a rigid body, so that no application of external forces can alter its shape or size, we can equally consider the force F acting at P as cancelling the oppositely directed force of the same magnitude acting at Q. In that event we are effectively left with a single force F acting along AB at Q. Our previous statement of equivalence then becomes, 'the effect on the body of a single force F acting along AB at P is the same as that of a single force F acting along AB at Q (P and Q lying in AB)'. Thus the line of action of the external force, not its point of application, is significant.

Consider now two forces acting on a rigid body along lines which intersect. Since the points of application are immaterial, the forces may be considered as applied at the point of intersection of their lines of action. In that case the parallelogram construction may be employed to determine their resultant. This statement remains true, in the limit, when the lines of action are parallel. We shall derive the construction for the resultant of two parallel forces by following its implications.

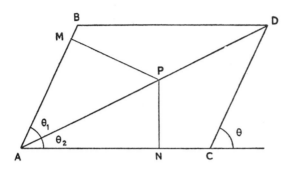

FIGURE 34

In fig. 34, let ABDC be the parallelogram representing the composition of two forces, F_1 and F_2, of which the lines of action are represented by AB and AC, respectively. Then AD represents the line of action of the resultant, and its magnitude F is given by

$$F^2 = F_1{}^2 + F_2{}^2 + 2F_1F_2 \cos \theta \qquad (55)$$

where $\angle CAB = \theta$, as indicated in the figure. Let $\angle CAD = \theta_2$, $\angle DAB = \theta_1$, and from P, any point in AD, let PM, PN be drawn perpendicular to AB, AC. Then, in $\triangle ADC$, $CD = AB$ and $\angle ADC = \theta_1$, thus

$$\frac{F_1}{F_2} = \frac{AB}{AC} = \frac{CD}{AC} = \frac{\sin \theta_2}{\sin \theta_1} = \frac{PN}{PM},$$

or $\qquad\qquad F_1.PM = F_2.PN \qquad\qquad\qquad (56)$

In the limit, when the forces are parallel, equation (55) reduces to

$$F = F_1 + F_2,$$

the perpendiculars from P on the lines of action of the forces become collinear, and equation (56) specifies the position of the line of action of the resultant according to the new construction. Fig. 35 illustrates this construction, which we may describe in words as follows. Let parallel lines of lengths F_1 and F_2 be drawn representing the two forces to be compounded. Let M, N be two points, one in each of these lines, such that MN is perpendicular

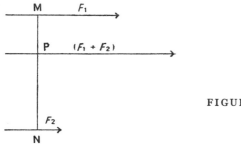

FIGURE 35

to their common direction. If P is the point in MN for which
$F_1.PM = F_2.PN$, then a line of length $F_1 + F_2$ drawn through P,
and at right angles to MN, represents the resultant force as to
line of action and in magnitude.

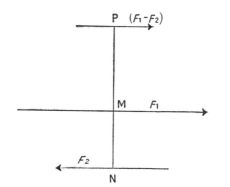

FIGURE 36

In the foregoing analysis we have considered only parallel forces
acting in the same direction. The analysis may be repeated, with
entirely obvious modifications, for the case in which the forces act
in opposite directions. If, in that case, $F_1 > F_2$, the magnitude of
the resultant is $F_1 - F_2$ and its line of action is given by the construction illustrated in fig. 36. Again, $F_1.PM = F_2.PN$.

Let us review the position which we have now reached. In relation to co-planar forces acting on a rigid body we have shown that
equation (56), when appropriately interpreted, is true whether the
co-planar forces are parallel or not. In order to understand this
equation it is only necessary to note that, in each case considered,

P is any point on the line of action of the resultant of the forces F_1 and F_2, and PM, PN are the perpendicular distances of P from the lines of action of these two forces, respectively. Moreover, reference to figs, 34, 35 and 36 will show that, if the forces F_1 and F_2 are considered in relation to possible rotation of the body about P (or, more precisely, about an axis through P perpendicular to the plane of the forces), the rotation-producing actions of the forces are oppositely directed. Suppose, now, that the axis through P perpendicular to the plane of the forces is fixed in space, so that the only motion of which the body is capable is rotation about this axis. Since P is a point on the line of action of the resultant of the forces F_1 and F_2, the resultant passes through the axis of rotation, and the forces F_1 and F_2 as applied to the body cannot have any rotational effect about the axis in question. Equation (56), in fact expresses the condition of equilibrium, in respect of rotation, of a rigid body acted on by two forces in a plane at right angles to a fixed axis—when appropriately interpreted. In this connection the most obvious interpretation is that the equation expresses the equality of the turning efforts of the forces, these efforts being oppositely directed, as we have noted already. We conclude, therefore, that the turning effort of a force F, applied to a rigid body in a plane at right angles to a fixed axis, is measured by the product Fd, where d is the measure of the perpendicular distance of the line of action of the force from the axis about which its effect is required. This product is referred to as the measure of the 'moment of the force' about the axis, or simply as the 'torque'.

Accepting this definition, we may re-state equation (56) in words as follows: the algebraic sum of the moments of two co-planar forces about an axis at right angles to their plane is zero if that axis intersects the line of action of their resultant determined according to the parallelogram law. Now, the moment of this resultant about such an axis is obviously zero, thus the sum of the moments of the two forces is equal to the moment of their resultant, in this special case. We shall proceed to show that this statement of equality is equally true when the axis about which the moments are taken is any axis at right angles to the plane of the forces. Let AB, AC (fig. 37) represent as to magnitude and line of action two forces, F_1, F_2, applied to a rigid body. Let D complete the parallelogram ABDC. Then AD represents the resultant of the forces concerned. We have AB:AC:AD $= F_1:F_2:F$, where F is the

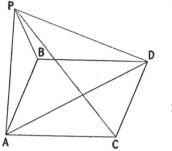

FIGURE 37

magnitude of the resultant. Let P be any point in the plane of the figure. Join PA, PB, PC, PD. Then

$$\triangle PAD = \triangle PAB + \triangle PBD + \triangle ABD.$$

But BD = AC, thus

$$\triangle PBD + \triangle ABD = \triangle PAC,$$

for the bases of all three triangles are of the same length, and the sum of the heights of the first two is equal to the height of the third.

Therefore $\qquad \triangle PAD = \triangle PAB + \triangle PAC.$

Now suppose that d_1, d_2, d represent the perpendicular distances of P from AB, AC, AD, respectively. Then this result may be re-written

$$AD.d = AB.d_1 + AC.d_2,$$

the common multiplier $\frac{1}{2}$ having been omitted throughout. It may equally be written

$$Fd = F_1 d_1 + F_2 d_2 \qquad (57)$$

because the forces are represented to scale in the diagram. Obviously, on the scale of the diagram, also, equation (57) expresses the equality of moments which we set out to prove: the sum of the moments of the co-planar forces F_1, F_2 about an axis at right angles to their plane, through any point P in that plane, is equal to the moment about the same axis of the resultant of the forces as determined by the parallelogram law. This demonstration completes the proof that our introduction of this new concept, the moment of a force, in no way violates previously established principles: the new concept is, in fact, entirely consonant with our earlier notions regarding the composition of forces. Our physical interpretation of equation (56) has to this extent been justified.

9.3. COUPLES

There is one aspect of the problem of parallel forces which we have so far avoided and must now consider. When the forces are oppositely directed and equal in magnitude, the construction of fig. 36 fails, in that it does not give a finite resultant in terms of which the joint turning effort of the forces can be estimated. It in-

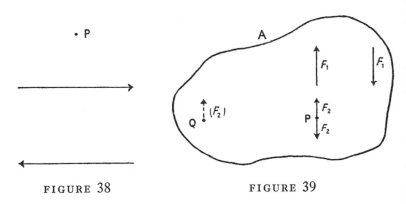

FIGURE 38   FIGURE 39

dicates a resultant of magnitude zero, acting at infinity. We have, therefore, to estimate the turning effort of the forces directly. In fig. 38 we represent two equal forces acting in opposite directions along parallel lines separated by a distance d. Let P be any point in the plane of the forces, at distances d_1 and d_2 from their lines of action ($d_2 > d_1$). If F is the magnitude of either force, G, the sum of the clockwise moments of the forces about an axis through P at right angles to their plane, is given by

$$G = F(d_2 - d_1) = Fd.$$

Thus the magnitude of G is independent of the position of P. Because of this unique result, which does not hold for parallel forces which are unequal, the system of two equal and parallel forces acting in opposite directions is given a distinctive name. Such a system is called a 'couple' (L. Poinsot, 1803), and the quantity G is referred to as the moment of the couple.

A couple is fully specified by its magnitude and the direction (not the position) of the axis about which it acts. If this statement is taken literally, as it is intended to be, it implies that it is not necessary to specify the magnitudes of the two forces constituting a couple, or their lines of action; only the plane parallel to which the forces act, and the product $Fd\,(=G)$, need be known. Consideration of fig. 39 will clarify this assertion. A represents the section of a rigid body by a plane in which forces F_1 act as shown, along parallel lines separated by a distance d_1, constituting a couple of moment $F_1 d_1$. Let P be a point in the line of action of one of these forces. Obviously the situation is not changed by the introduction of equal and opposite forces F_2 acting at P in this line of action. Let us now group the four forces under consideration as follows: (i) a force F_2 acting at P, 'downwards' according to the diagram, (ii) a force $F_1 + F_2$ acting 'upwards' in the line through P, (iii) a parallel force F_1 acting 'downwards' at a distance d_1 from this last force. Now combine forces (ii) and (iii). According to the construction of fig. 36, the resultant is a force F_2 acting 'upwards' along a line through Q, d_2, the perpendicular distance of P from this line, being given by

$$(F_1 + F_2)d_2 = F_1(d_2 + d_1),$$

or
$$F_2 d_2 = F_1 d_1 \qquad\qquad (58)$$

We are left with two equal forces F_2, acting in opposite directions along parallel lines separated by a distance d_2, that is with a couple differently constituted from that with which we started. But equation (58) shows that the moment of the new couple is the same as that of the old, and it is obvious from the figure that its turning effect is in the same direction as that of the couple with which we started. The assertion that only the magnitude of a couple and the direction of its axis of application are significant for its full specification is to this extent justified.

If, now, we assume fig. 39 to represent a rigid body having an axis (through Q and at right angles to the diagram) fixed in space, then the argument which we have just given shows that a couple of moment G about the axis of rotation of the body, by whatever

L

external forces it is in fact applied, may be considered as arising from the action of a single force F parallel to the plane of the couple, the line of action of F being at a perpendicular distance G/F from the axis of rotation.

9.4. HISTORY OF THE LAW OF MOMENTS

By the law of moments we mean the statement that a rigid body, having one axis fixed in space, is in equilibrium under the action of external forces, if, and only if, the sum of the moments of the forces about that axis is zero. This result was well known in essence long before the concept of force was clarified in its kinetic aspects by Newton, and it is instructive to refer briefly to its history.

Consideration of the problem of rotational equilibrium arose first out of familiarity with the use of the lever. As regards this primitive, but very useful, 'machine' itself, man's conscious adoption of it developed gradually, no doubt, through his intuitive reaction to the challenge of his surroundings, through his taking what lay to hand as 'tools' for his immediate tasks. Archimedes considered the theory of the lever, effectively in respect of parallel forces, in the third century BC. He realised that the turning effort of a load is proportional to the magnitude of the load and that it increases with the distance of the load from the fulcrum. He finally convinced himself that the turning effort is directly proportional to this distance (as the modern law of moments assumes), but the theoretical argument by which he reached that conclusion must be carefully framed if it is not to be held fallacious, as we shall show. Let AB (fig. 40) represent a perfectly rigid, weightless beam pivoted at its mid-point, P, on a fulcrum. Let equal loads W be applied to the beam, originally horizontal, at equal distances d on opposite sides of P. Then, because of the symmetry of the arrangement, there is no sufficient reason why the beam should tilt one way or the other (we have used this argument already in relation to the balance—see p. 140), and it may be assumed that it remains at rest. Now, said Archimedes, let the right-hand load be divided into two equal portions $\dfrac{W}{2}$, and let these move from their original point of application, the one towards the fulcrum and the other away from it, at equal rates. At each stage in the process these half-loads are symmetrically placed with respect to their original posi-

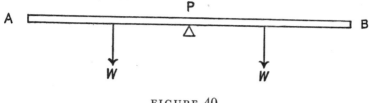

FIGURE 40

tion: in this case, Archimedes maintained, they may still be thought of as acting there together, and the equilibrium is unaffected. Finally, let the process be arrested when the inwards-moving half-load is over the fulcrum. In this position it can have no effect on the equilibrium of the beam. The left-hand load W must then be exactly balanced by the right-hand half-load $\dfrac{W}{2}$ at twice the distance of W from the fulcrum on the other side. The argument may be continued: $\dfrac{W}{2}$ may be halved again, and so on, indefinitely. Thus a load W at distance d is balanced by $\dfrac{W}{2}$ at $2d$, or by $\dfrac{W}{4}$ at $4d$, or $\dfrac{W}{8}$ at $8d$, or in general by $\dfrac{W}{2^n}$ at distance $2^n d$. It is a short step to the conclusion that loads W_1 and W_2 balance when their distances d_1 and d_2 satisfy the relation $W_1 d_1 = W_2 d_2$—and this is the expression for the law of moments for parallel forces.

Archimedes's argument is obviously highly suspect as it stands. Indeed we may refute it directly by a simple demonstration. In order to derive the law of moments Archimedes assumed that equilibrium is undisturbed by the division and separation of the two halves of one load in the way which we have described. But this is the case only if the law of moments is valid, for if d is the original distance of the undivided load, and if the turning effort is proportional to the rth power of the distance, the turning effort when the half-loads are at distances $d-x$ and $d+x$ from the fulcrum, respectively, is $\dfrac{W}{2}(d-x)^r + \dfrac{W}{2}(d+x)^r$, and this is equal to Wd^r only when $r=1$. The validity of the law has been assumed in the course of its derivation, and the proof therefore fails.

There is, however, more intuitive wisdom in Archimedes's argument than at first sight appears: suitably developed it has all the possibilities of the argument which we have given at length in an earlier section (§ 9.2). Once it has been established that the point of actual application of an external force to a rigid body is of no unique importance, any point in the line of action of the force serving equally well as a point of virtual application (p. 155), it is entirely reasonable to assume that the parallelogram law may validly be employed to obtain the resultant of two non-parallel co-planar forces applied to such a body. We could not use the law lightly in this way without some such justification, for, in relation to forces, the parallelogram construction derives its validity directly from the corresponding construction giving the resultant acceleration of a particle in terms of its component accelerations—and ultimately from the parallelogram of displacements of a geometrical point (p. 74). But once the scope of the law has been extended to include the case of co-planar forces acting on a rigid body—and this is the crux of the matter—the rest of the argument follows. By proceeding to the limit, we obtain the construction for the resultant of parallel forces so acting (p. 156), and in respect of Archimedes's argument we have a valid reason for his assertion that the symmetrical separation of the half-loads leaves the magnitude and the line of action of their resultant unchanged. Admittedly, the truth of the law of moments is already implicit at this stage in the argument, indeed equation (56) shows that it is implicit in the parallelogram law as applied to rigid bodies itself: it is only peculiar that in Archimedes's presentation it is not made explicit until the end. Archimedes did not, in fact, in his day produce an adequate proof of the law of the lever, but there was much intuitive wisdom in his thoughts on the problem which has remained for a later age to assimilate and apply.

In the treatment of § 9.2, briefly recapitulated in the last paragraph, the particular case of parallel forces was approached through the more general case of forces which are co-planar but inclined. Historically, the reverse sequence obtained. Archimedes considered parallel loads; not until near the end of the fifteenth century have we any clear statement extending the law of the lever to the case in which its axis of rotation is horizontal but the lever itself is not. It was Leonardo da Vinci who enunciated the principle that in that case the turning effort of any gravitational load, or of any force

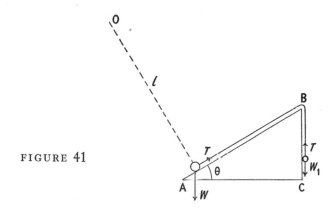

FIGURE 41

applied to the lever in a plane at right angles to the axis, is given
by the product of the force and the perpendicular distance of its
line of action from the axis concerned. Once again, this was a
generalisation based on the intuition of genius— and a more intimate acquaintance with the problems of applied mechanics, in
their relation to the arts of peace and war, than was possessed by
any other thinker of his age.

Almost exactly a century after Leonardo enunciated the law of
moments for inclined forces, Galileo applied the generalised law to
the problem of equilibrium on an inclined plane. We have already
referred to this application (p. 126), described here for its historical
interest—and as providing another example of the use of the principle that it is the actual constraints imposed upon a system, not
the mode of their imposition, which is dynamically important (see
p. 137). Let ABC (fig. 41) represent, in principal section, a triangular
prism having one horizontal and one vertical face, and providing
in the face AB a perfectly smooth plane surface of inclination θ,
as shown. Let a body of weight W rest on this surface, being
attached by a perfectly flexible weightless string to a counterpoise
of weight W_1 hanging vertically, parallel to the face BC. It is
required to find T, the tension in the string, if the system is an
equilibrium. Galileo imagined the triangular prism to be removed
(except for the support provided for the string at B) and, instead,
a perfectly rigid weightless rod to be introduced, attached to the
body of weight W, at one end, and to a pivot at O. He assumed the

rod to be at right angles to the original position of the plane surface AB, and to be capable of rotating about a horizontal axis through O perpendicular to its length. More nearly, as l, the length of the rod, is increased, are the geometrical constraints imposed by the new arrangement the same as those imposed by the old. For the consideration of equilibrium conditions, infinitesimal motions only are in question, and any value of l is acceptable. Taking moments about the axis through O, we have

$$Tl = Wl \sin \theta,$$

or $$\qquad T(=W_1) = W \sin \theta.$$

This result, in the form $W_1 = W \sin \theta$, is seen to be precisely equivalent to that of equation (53), obtained by Stevinus in 1586. It was in that connection that we referred to it previously.

9.5. CENTRE OF GRAVITY

Each particle of a rigid body situated near the surface of the earth is subject to a gravitational force, the weight of the particle, directed vertically downwards and proportional to its mass. The weight of the whole body is the resultant of these forces: it is obviously equal to the sum of the weights of the innumerable particles constituting the body, and the procedure of § 9.2 allows us to determine its line of action in any circumstances. In this section we shall show that, however the body is orientated in space, there is one point, fixed with respect to the body, which always lies in the line of action of its total weight. This point is referred to as the centre of gravity of the body: in all circumstances of local terrestrial motion the weight of a body may be considered as acting vertically downwards through its centre of gravity.

We shall consider the matter first in relation to a lamina of arbitrary shape. Let L (fig. 42) represent the lamina, assumed to be made up of an indefinitely large number of particles the relative positions of which remain fixed. Let the lamina be free to rotate about a horizontal axis through A, at right angles to the plane of the lamina and fixed in space. Take rectangular axes OX, OY, fixed in the plane of the lamina, and let the co-ordinates of A with respect to these axes be x_0, y_0. When the lamina is in equilibrium under gravity, let OX be inclined at θ to the vertical as shown. In this position the algebraic sum of the moments of the weights

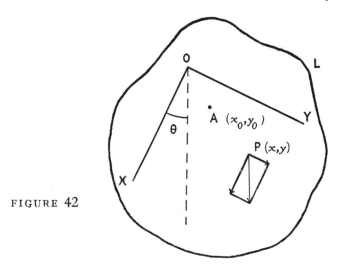

FIGURE 42

of the constituent particles of the lamina, about the axis through A perpendicular to its plane, is zero. Thus, if we consider the case of a typical particle, of mass m, situated at P(x, y), we have, resolving its weight, mg, into components $mg \cos \theta$ parallel to OX and $mg \sin \theta$ parallel to OY, for this particle,

clockwise moment of weight of particle about axis of suspension

$$= mg \cos \theta.(y - y_0) - mg \sin \theta.(x - x_0).$$

For the whole lamina, therefore, dividing through by g, the common acceleration due to gravity, we obtain

$$\cos \theta . \Sigma m(y - y_0) - \sin \theta . \Sigma m(x - x_0) = 0 \qquad (59)$$

Equation (59), in which $\sin \theta$, $\cos \theta$ appear in front of the signs of summation, since θ is constant for the lamina as a whole, has two solutions.

Either

$$\cot \theta = \frac{\Sigma m(x - x_0)}{\Sigma m(y - y_0)} \qquad (60)$$

or

$$\left.\begin{array}{l} \Sigma m(x - x_0) = 0 \\ \Sigma m(y - y_0) = 0 \end{array}\right\} ,$$

giving

$$x_0 = \frac{\Sigma mx}{\Sigma m}, \; y_0 = \frac{\Sigma my}{\Sigma m} \qquad (61)$$

It will be noted that the second solution is independent of θ: we discuss it before turning to the other. Evidently, equations (61) specify uniquely the co-ordinates of a point in the lamina, in terms of the masses and positions of the constituent particles, such that the lamina is in equilibrium under gravity about a fixed horizontal axis passing through that point at right angles to the plane of the lamina, whatever the orientation of the lamina about this axis. In other words, the equations specify the co-ordinates of a point in the lamina through which its weight always acts whatever its orientation (in a vertical plane). Equations (61), in fact, give the co-ordinates of the centre of gravity of the lamina. It is conventional to write these co-ordinates as $\bar{x}$, $\bar{y}$.

Turning now to equation (60), we see that it specifies two orientations of the lamina, 180° apart in the complete rotation of 360° about an axis of suspension through an arbitrary point A (not the centre of gravity), in which the lamina is in equilibrium. For, if we substitute $\Sigma mx = \bar{x}\Sigma m$, $\Sigma my = \bar{y}\Sigma m$, in this equation, dividing through by Σm, we have

$$\cot \theta = \frac{\bar{x} - x_0}{\bar{y} - y_0} \qquad (62)$$

In this case, if G is the position of the centre of gravity (fig. 43), and if AN, NG are parallel to OX, OY, respectively, equation (62) implies either

$$\theta = \angle NAG,$$

or $$\theta = \angle NAG + 180°.$$

The first solution imposes the condition that G shall be vertically below A, the second the alternative condition that G shall be vertically above A, if the lamina is to be in equilibrium.

We may now review the overall result of our analysis. We have located the centre of gravity in the case of a two-dimensional rigid body, and we have obtained the general result that such a body will be in equilibrium about a fixed horizontal axis at right angles to its plane if the centre of gravity of the body lies anywhere in a vertical line intersecting that axis. Equation (60) represents the two cases in which the centre of gravity is (a) below, (b) above, the axis; equations (61) the case in which the centre of gravity lies in the axis. These are, respectively, configurations of stable, unstable and neutral equilibrium.

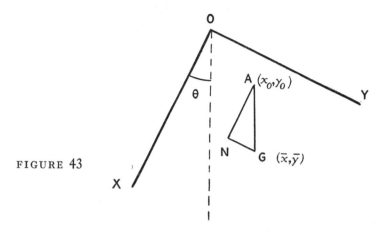

FIGURE 43

In order to locate the position of the centre of gravity of a three-dimensional rigid body analytically, we proceed exactly as we have just done, concentrating attention on the orientation-independent solutions of three equations, of the form of equation (59), having reference to equilibrium about three mutually perpendicular axes through an arbitrary point in the body, and we obtain, as we should now expect, the general result

$$\bar{x} = \frac{\Sigma mx}{\Sigma m}, \bar{y} = \frac{\Sigma my}{\Sigma m}, \bar{z} = \frac{\Sigma mz}{\Sigma m} \tag{63}$$

(We obtain this result, in fact, from any two of the three equations of equilibrium.)

Although we have been led to equations (63) from a realisation that there is a single point in a body through which its weight always acts, so that the term 'centre of gravity' provides an appropriate designation for this unique point, yet it will be observed that only masses and distances enter into the equations in question. This leads us to suppose that the centre of gravity of a body—or indeed of a system of discrete particles, if equations (63) can be applied to such a system—has further properties of a more general nature which merit investigation. We shall find that this is, in fact, the case.   In relation to these more general properties the term 'centre of mass' is to be preferred to 'centre of gravity' for reasons that will be obvious.

Consider a single external force F applied to a rigid body of mass

M along a line passing through the centre of mass of the body. We may reverse our previous argument and say that the force F may be resolved into an innumerable number of components, all parallel to its direction of application, so that each particle of which the rigid body is constituted is acted on by a component of F proportional to its mass. In that case it is clear that the effect of the applied force is to produce, for each particle of the body, a common acceleration of magnitude F/M, and so for the body as a whole. Any external force of constant magnitude and direction applied to a rigid body, initially at rest, along a line passing through the centre of mass of the body produces, therefore, uniformly accelerated rectilinear motion, without rotation, just as the force of gravity does near the surface of the earth.

Suppose, now, that an external force F is applied to a rigid body, initially at rest, along a line which does not pass through the centre of mass. Fig. 44 represents the situation in the plane containing the line of action of the force and the centre of mass, G. The situation is unaltered by the introduction of equal forces F acting through G in opposite directions along the line parallel to the line of action of the external force actually applied to the body. One of these forces, taken together with the external force, constitutes a couple, the other, of the same magnitude and direction as the external force, acts through the centre of mass. We have 'decomposed' the externally applied force into an equal and parallel force acting through the centre of mass of the body, and a couple acting in the plane containing the line of action of the applied force and the centre of mass.

Imagine, now, the applied force to act for a very short time. The body will suffer an infinitesimal displacement parallel to the plane just specified (the plane represented in fig. 44). We have already concluded (p. 154) that, from the point of view of kinematics, such a displacement has a unique component of pure rotation, but that the component of pure translation is indeterminate until we have specified the position in the body of the axis about which the component of rotation is reckoned. As a result of our present discussion, on the other hand, we have just seen that, from the point of view of kinetics, there is in this case a unique component of pure translational displacement, also. It is the pure translation resulting from the action through the centre of mass, for the short time in question, of a force equal and parallel to the external force applied.

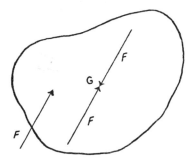

FIGURE 44

That force may be decomposed in any number of ways into a single force and a couple, but if we are to associate the single force with a component displacement of pure translation, and the couple with a component displacement of pure rotation, as we should naturally wish to do in the present case, only one of these decompositions is relevant—it is the one in which the single force acts through the centre of mass, and which we have already described. It is important to note that in this way a unique torque is also determined. Clearly, if the moment of the couple resulting from the relevant decomposition of the applied force were other than unique, its association with a uniquely specified component displacement of pure rotation would be wholly incongruous.

We have just referred to the 'association' of a single force acting through the centre of mass of a rigid body with a pure translational displacement, and of a couple with a pure rotation. We already know the character of the association in the first instance— a force F acting through the centre of mass of a body of mass M for a short time t produces a pure translational displacement of magnitude $\frac{1}{2}(F/M)t^2$—in the next section we shall have to discuss the character of the association in the second instance, also. Meanwhile we may state the general conclusion: so far as the translational motion of a rigid body is concerned, whatever external forces act on it may be considered as acting through the centre of mass, whereby they may be replaced by a single resultant force determining the translational motion completely.

9.6. MOMENTS OF INERTIA

9.6.1. *Kinetic energy of pure rotation.* We have decided already (p. 149) that kinetic energy is a scalar quantity. The total kinetic energy of a rigid body may therefore be obtained simply by arithmetical addition of the kinetic energies of its constituent particles. When the motion of the rigid body is pure rotation, with angular velocity ω, about an axis fixed in the body, the instantaneous speed of any particle situated at a perpendicular distance r from the axis of rotation is $r\omega$, and the kinetic energy of the particle is $\frac{1}{2}mr^2\omega^2$, m being the mass of the particle. In this case the total kinetic energy of the rigid body is $\frac{1}{2}(\Sigma mr^2)\omega^2$. The quantity Σmr^2 depends upon the distribution of mass in the body, but its value also depends upon the axis with respect to which rotation is considered, and r is measured. It is referred to as the 'moment of inertia' of the body about the axis in question, and its measure is generally denoted by I. Adopting that notation, we may write, for the kinetic energy in the case of pure rotation considered, $E=\frac{1}{2}I\omega^2$. Comparing this expression with that for the kinetic energy of a particle in translational motion, $E=\frac{1}{2}mv^2$, we note that moment of inertia appears as the analogue of mass. This fact, and the occurrence of the axial distance, r, in the expression for I, explains the origin of the term 'moment of inertia'. But the analogy with mass should not be allowed to obscure the fact that, whereas the mass of a body is a single-valued quantity, the moment of inertia of a body is a many-valued quantity—as many-valued as there are possible axes of rotation in the body. More correctly, there is no such quantity as the moment of inertia of a body; there are only moments of inertia, each having reference to a specified axis.

Obviously, moment of inertia is a scalar quantity (neither mass nor the square of a length has directional attributes). Equally obviously, if I is the moment of inertia, about a specified axis, of a body of total mass M, a related length k may be defined by the dimensionally homogeneous equations

$$I = \Sigma mr^2 = Mk^2.$$

This length is commonly spoken of as the 'radius of gyration' of the body about the axis concerned.

9.6.2. *Accelerated rotational motion.* When the purely rotational motion of a rigid body is accelerated, the instantaneous acceleration of any particle of the body situated at a perpendicular distance r from the axis of rotation has components $r\alpha$ along the direction of

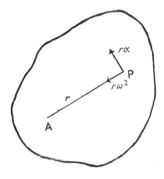

FIGURE 45

instantaneous velocity and $r\omega^2$ at right angles to that direction, towards the axis, α being the angular acceleration and ω the instantaneous angular velocity of the body. If P (fig. 45) represents the position of a particle in a plane at right angles to the axis of rotation, and A the point of intersection of this plane by the axis, the directions of these component accelerations of the particle are as shown by the arrows. If m is the mass of the particle, F and F', the component forces acting on the particle are $mr\alpha$ and $mr\omega^2$, respectively, also in the directions of the arrows. Now force is a vector quantity, and consideration of the diagram makes it clear that the resultant forces on the individual particles constituting the body have all directions parallel to the plane of rotation considered. Thus simply to add these forces arithmetically is meaningless, yet we obviously wish to add their contributions to the rotational effect. The analysis of § 9.2 suggests that we should consider adding the moments of the forces about the fixed axis. For the single particle at P, we have, for the sum of the moments of F and F' about the axis,

$$Fr = mr^2\alpha.$$

The quantity of which mr^2 is the measure is a scalar quantity, as we have just concluded (§ 9.6.1), thus the torque of which Fr is the measure has the same vectorial character as an angular acceleration, here represented by its measure α. In § 5.6 we considered the vectorial character of angular velocity explicitly, and what we decided there is equally true of angular acceleration. Adopting the right-handed screw convention, this quantity can be completely specified by a line drawn in the appropriate direction along the axis about which the acceleration is effective, and of length proportional to its magnitude. Angular acceleration is therefore a vector quantity—to be precise, an axial vector—and torque is therefore a quantity of the same character. In relation to our present problem, in particular, the torques of the resultant forces, acting on the individual particles of the rigid body concerned, all have the same axis, and the same direction along that axis, and may therefore be added arithmetically. We then have

$$\Sigma Fr = (\Sigma mr^2)\alpha = I\alpha \qquad (64)$$

where I is the moment of inertia of the body about the fixed axis through A.

At this stage in our argument the quantities F and F' have been specified only in terms of Newton's second law. It is now necessary to relate them to the external forces applied to the body in any actual situation. In general, the solution of this problem would be extremely complicated; fortunately for our present purposes, however, a very simple result emerges without detailed calculation. To the resultant force on any particle of the body there must contribute (*a*) internal forces arising from the mutual actions of the individual particles of the body, (*b*) components of the external forces applied to the body. According to Newton's third law, the forces under (*a*) may be grouped into equal and oppositely acting pairs, when the whole body is concerned. Therefore these forces contribute nothing to the quantity ΣFr. Concerning the forces under (*b*), they have been described as the components of the externally applied forces. Now it is axiomatic (p. 158) that the sum of the moments of component forces about any axis should equal the moment of their resultant about the same axis. Thus the quantity ΣFr in equation (64) reduces to 'the sum of the moments of the externally applied forces about the fixed axis'—and the equation shows that this quantity, which we shall denote by G (already used for the moment of a couple, p. 160), determines the angular acceleration of the body about that axis, in terms of the associated moment of inertia, in a manner exactly analogous to that in which a force determines the linear acceleration of a particle in terms of its mass. In this connection we compare the equation

$$G = I\alpha$$

with the earlier equation

$$F = ma.$$

The comparison gives added weight to our previous remarks (p. 172) concerning moment of inertia as the rotational analogue of mass.

Equation (64) has been deduced in respect of the motion of a rigid body having an axis fixed in space. In § 9.5 we considered the initial displacement of a rigid body free to move under the action of an arbitrarily applied force. We decomposed that force into an equal and parallel force acting through the centre of mass and a couple acting in the plane containing the line of action of the applied force and the centre of mass. We gave an expression for the component displacement of pure translation arising from the action of the single force through the centre of mass. We are now in a position to complete the solution of the problem, using equation (64) to calculate the angular acceleration of the body about the axis through the centre of mass and at right angles to the plane of the couple, and equation (22) to deduce from this acceleration the component displacement of pure rotation about this axis. For convenience of reference we give the full solution below, repeating the expression for the translational displacement quoted earlier. As before, we denote the measure of the applied force by F, the mass of the body by M, and the short time by t. I is the measure of the moment of inertia of the body about the axis through the centre of mass at right angles to the plane containing the line of action of the applied force and the centre of mass, and d the measure of the perpendicular distance of the centre of mass from this line. Then

component displacement of pure translation $= \frac{1}{2}(F/M)t^2$,

component displacement of pure rotation $\quad = \frac{1}{2}(Fd/I)t^2$.

Of necessity, the first component displacement is in the direction of the applied force, the second is in the appropriate direction about the axis specified.

9.6.3. *Conservation of angular momentum.* When a rigid body is completely isolated, so that no external forces act on it, clearly any velocity of translation, which the centre of mass may have initially, is maintained indefinitely. This result is consonant with the principle of conservation of linear momentum which we have already discussed (§ 8.5). Also, the sum of the moments of the external forces about any axis through the centre of mass of the body is obviously zero. In that case the angular acceleration of the body about such an axis is zero and, therefore, the corresponding angular velocity is constant. If the body is initially rotating with angular velocity ω about an axis through the centre of mass, and if I is the moment of inertia of the body about this axis, in the conditions specified the product $I\omega$ remains constant with the passage of time. By analogy with the corresponding quantity in particle kinetics, the quantity of which $I\omega$ is the measure is referred to as the angular momentum of the body about the axis in question. Denoting this measure by H, we have, in the previous notation,

$$H = \Sigma mr^2\omega = \Sigma m(r\omega)r = \Sigma mvr,$$

v being the instantaneous component of velocity of the particle of mass m situated at a distance r from the axis of rotation, due solely to the rotation of the body about the given axis.

If we consider a system of particles, rather than a rigid body, we may still usefully define the total angular momentum of the system about an axis fixed in space. In this case we adopt the notation

$$H = \Sigma mv'p \qquad (65)$$

in order to emphasise the fact that the velocities of individual particles are no longer tangential to circles centred in the axis concerned and at right angles to it. Instead, these velocities are arbitrarily directed, and for each particle, therefore, we first resolve its velocity into components v'' parallel to the axis and v' at right angles to it, and we determine p the perpendicular distance from the axis to the direction of the latter component. The total angular momentum of the system about the fixed axis is then given in terms of the masses of the particles, and the measures of v' and p for each, according to the equation. Suppose, now, that the system of particles is isolated, so that no external forces act on it. The internal forces occur as equal and oppositely directed pairs acting between pairs of particles. Consider one such pair of forces. The line along which the forces act (in opposite directions) is arbitrarily located with respect to the axis of reference. If the forces are resolved in directions parallel and at right angles to this axis, the latter components will themselves be equal and will act in opposite directions along parallel lines in a plane parallel to the axis of reference. The components of momentum at right angles to the axis which the forces generate in any short interval of time in the particles concerned will therefore be equal and oppositely directed —and a common value of p will apply to them, namely the distance of the axis from the plane parallel to it which we have just identified. In the short interval of time considered, the action of this pair of forces will in consequence add nothing to the value of H specified in terms of equation (65). And similarly, for all pairs of internal forces: these mutual actions leave unchanged the total angular momentum of the system about any axis fixed in space. This is the principle of conservation of angular momentum in its full generality.

For particles whose initial positions and velocities are co-planar there is clearly no need to distinguish between v and v': in that case, if H is the total angular momentum of the system about any axis at right angles to the plane of motion, we have

$$H = \Sigma m v p,$$

or $$H = 2\Sigma m S \tag{66}$$

S being the measure of the instantaneous areal velocity (see § 4.6) of the particle of mass m about the axis in question.

9.6.4. *Vector products.*

In § 8.9 we concluded that work is a scalar quantity; in § 9.6.2 that torque is a vector quantity. Now, the measure of each of these quantities is given by the product of the measures of a force and a distance. The amount of work performed by any force is determined by the distance which the point of application of the force moves in the direction of the force; the moment of a force about an axis (torque) by the distance perpendicular to the direction of the force between its line of action and this axis. Force and distance are, both of them, vector quantities; the difference in the two situations is in the relative directions of the vectors the product of the measures of which determines the measure of the physical quantity which arises from their association. When two vectors are collinear the product of their measures, if it is physically significant, is the measure of a scalar quantity; if the directions of two vectors are mutually perpendicular, subject to the same proviso, the product of their measures is the measure of a vector quantity the direction of which is at right angles to the

M

plane of these vectors. The physical quantities torque and areal velocity belong to this latter class, and, on the basis of equation (66), so does angular momentum. Angular velocity and angular acceleration, though they do not arise explicitly as vector products, have the same vectorial character.

In order to emphasise the difference in vectorial character between work and torque it is preferable to use different designations for the units in which they are measured. Thus, in the c.g.s. metric system, the unit of work is the erg, the unit of torque the dyne centimetre. On the other hand, the dimensions of the two quantities are clearly the same, namely, ML^2T^{-2}: this is an obvious case in which the principle of dimensional homogeneity (§ 4.4) is not sufficient criterion of the admissibility of a mathematical equation as physically significant. It would not, in any situation, be significant physically to add together the measures of a quantity of work and a torque.

9.6.5. *Moments of inertia*: *special cases and general theorems.* For most practical purposes the idea of a structureless solid body is more useful than that of a rigid body constituted of individual particles on which we have so far based our discussions. We give here, therefore, expressions for the moments of inertia of certain symmetrical and homogeneous solid bodies about their axes of symmetry. The results which we quote may be derived by straightforward application of the calculus; as quoted, rather than derived, they constitute Routh's rule (E. J. Routh, *Rigid Dynamics*, 1860). Three representative solid bodies are in question: they are the rectangular parallelepiped, the elliptical lamina and the ellipsoid. We are concerned with the moments of inertia about axes through the centre of gravity in each case.

In the case of the rectangular parallelepiped there are three axes of symmetry, parallel, respectively, to the three sets of mutually perpendicular edges of the figure. If these edges have lengths $2a$, $2b$, $2c$, the moments of inertia about the corresponding 'principal' axes are $M\dfrac{b^2+c^2}{3}$, $M\dfrac{c^2+a^2}{3}$, $M\dfrac{a^2+b^2}{3}$, M being the total mass of the body.

In the case of the elliptical lamina we consider first the axis through its centre at right angles to its plane. If $2a$, $2b$ are the lengths of the major and minor axes of the ellipse, the moment of inertia about the perpendicular axis of symmetry is $M\dfrac{a^2+b^2}{4}$, if the mass of the lamina is M. The moment of inertia about the major axis of the ellipse is $Mb^2/4$, and that about the minor axis $Ma^2/4$.

For the ellipsoid, the axes of symmetry are the longest and shortest diameters and the diameter at right angles to these two. If $2a$, $2b$, $2c$ are the lengths of these diameters, the moments of inertia about them are, respectively, $M\dfrac{b^2+c^2}{5}$, $M\dfrac{c^2+a^2}{5}$, $M\dfrac{a^2+b^2}{5}$, M being the mass of the ellipsoid.

Routh's rule provides the 'special cases' referred to at the head of this sub-section. The 'general theorems' with which we shall be concerned are two in number, and, although they, also, are most frequently applied in respect of structureless solid bodies, they do not depend for their validity on the assumption of uniform density, so we shall consider them accordingly. The two theorems in question are usually referred to as the 'lamina theorem' and the 'theorem of parallel axes'.

The lamina theorem states that, if, through any point in a lamina, rectangular axes OX, OY are taken in the plane of the lamina, and if OZ is perpendicular to this plane through the same point, then I_X, I_Y, I_Z, the moments of inertia of the lamina about the three axes concerned, satisfy the equation

$$I_Z = I_X + I_Y \tag{67}$$

This result is obvious once the quantities I_X, I_Y are expressed, in terms of the masses of the individual particles and their two-dimensional co-ordinates, according to the definition of § 9.6.1. We have, in this way, $I_X = \Sigma m y^2$, $I_Y = \Sigma m x^2$, thus $I_X + I_Y = \Sigma m(x^2+y^2) = \Sigma m r^2 = I_Z$, r being the distance of any particle from O, and in consequence its perpendicular distance from OZ.

The theorem of parallel axes is a little less obvious, as formally expressed. It states that if I is the moment of inertia of a rigid body about any axis, and if the moment of inertia of the body about the parallel axis through the centre of mass is I_G, then

$$I = I_G + Md^2 \tag{68}$$

M being the total mass of the body and d the separation of the two axes concerned.

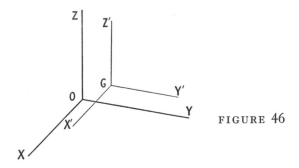

FIGURE 46

Let G (fig. 46) represent the centre of mass of the rigid body and OZ, GZ′ the parallel axes about which the moments of inertia of the body are I and I_G, respectively. Let OX, OY be rectangular axes perpendicular to OZ, and GX′, GY′ be parallel to these axes. Let the co-ordinates of a typical particle of the body be (x, y, z) referred to the axes OX, OY, OZ, and $(x′, y′, z′)$ referred to the axes GX′, GY′, GZ′. Then, if the co-ordinates of G referred to the former axes are $(\bar{x}, \bar{y}, \bar{z})$, we have

$$x = x′ + \bar{x}, \quad y = y′ + \bar{y}, \quad z = z′ + \bar{z}.$$

Also

$$I = \Sigma m(x^2 + y^2),$$

thus, substituting for x and y,

$$I = \Sigma m(x′ + \bar{x})^2 + \Sigma m(y′ + \bar{y})^2$$
$$= \Sigma m(x′^2 + y′^2) + (\bar{x}^2 + \bar{y}^2)\Sigma m + 2\bar{x}\Sigma mx′ + 2\bar{y}\Sigma my′.$$

Now, the co-ordinates of the centre of mass referred to the axes GX′, GY′, GZ′ are $(0, 0, 0)$, thus $\Sigma mx′ = 0$, $\Sigma my′ = 0$, and we have

$$I = \Sigma m(x′^2 + y′^2) + M(\bar{x}^2 + \bar{y}^2)$$
$$= I_G + Md^2$$

in the former notation, establishing the required result.

9.7. TORSIONAL OSCILLATIONS

It is an experimental fact, which we shall consider in greater detail in Chapter 16, that the torque necessary to twist a cylindrical rod or filament about its cylindrical axis is, in very many cases, directly proportional to the angle of twist over a considerable range. If a cylindrical metal wire, firmly held at its upper end in a rigid support, hangs vertically, carrying at its lower end a cylindrical drum or pulley, coaxial with the wire, to which a couple may be applied in the form of equal and oppositely directed horizontal forces, it will generally be found that the system reaches equilibrium when the angle turned through by the lower end of the wire is directly proportional to the moment of the couple applied. In such a situation the wire itself is in equilibrium under the joint action of the couple acting through the drum or pulley at its lower end and an equal and oppositely directed couple brought into play in the material of the support, and the drum or pulley is in equilibrium under the joint action of the applied couple and an equal and oppositely directed 'restoring' couple generated in the wire due to its deformation. We conclude that, in such a case, whenever the wire is deformed in this particular way, that is, twisted about its cylindrical axis, a restoring couple is brought into play which is directly proportional to the total angle of twist over a considerable range.

Let us assume, therefore, that a metal wire, supported as just described, and having the properties indicated, carries at its lower end a rigid body, firmly attached to the wire, the position of the centre of gravity of the body being such that the wire hangs vertically. Let us consider the free motion of rotation of the body about the axis of the wire. Let θ be the measure of the instantaneous angular displacement of the body about this axis, reckoned from the equilibrium position in which the restoring couple, G, is zero. If I is the moment of inertia of the body about the axis of rotation and α is the instantaneous angular acceleration, we have (see equation (64))

$$G = \mu\theta = -I\alpha,$$

μ being the constant relating the twist to the restoring couple for the wire in question. The minus sign implies that the direction of the restoring couple is that of decreasing displacement. Thus

$$\alpha = -(\mu/I)\theta \tag{69}$$

Equation (69), specifying an angular acceleration directed towards a position of equilibrium and directly proportional to the angular displacement, is characteristic of simple harmonic motion in angle (compare equation (38)) with periodic time T given by

$$T = 2\pi\sqrt{\frac{I}{\mu}} \tag{70}$$

This, then, is the motion which the suspended body would execute, in the case considered, if it were initially displaced through an arbitrary angle about the axis of the wire, and subsequently released. For obvious reasons, such motion is referred to as 'torsional oscillation'.

The method of torsional oscillation provides a direct means of determining the moment of inertia, about an axis through the centre of gravity, of a body of arbitrary shape. For, if T_1 is the period of torsional oscillation of such a body, when rigidly attached to the end of a vertical 'torsion wire' so that the axis in question is also the axis of the wire, and T_2 is the period of oscillation of a rectangular 'inertia bar' of mass M about a principal axis, when similarly attached to the same torsion wire, we have, in terms of equation (70) and Routh's rule,

$$I = M\frac{a^2 + b^2}{3} \cdot \frac{T_1{}^2}{T_2{}^2},$$

I being the required moment of inertia of the experimental body, and a and b the half-lengths of the other two principal axes of the bar (see p. 178). Clearly, the moment of inertia of the body about any axis whatsoever can be deduced by use of equation (68), if the moment of inertia about a parallel axis through the centre of gravity has first been determined by the method of torsional oscillation as just described.

9.8. PENDULUM OSCILLATIONS

A rigid body, which is capable of free motion under gravity about a fixed horizontal axis, is referred to as a 'pendulum'. An ideal 'simple pendulum' is constituted of a massive 'bob' of infinitesimally small size attached by a massless, inextensible, 'string' to a perfectly rigid support. Physical systems which may be realised in practice in some cases approximate fairly closely to this ideal, but, quite obviously, the precise specifications here given can never be fully satisfied. It is preferable, therefore, to consider first a pendulum of arbitrary shape, and later to derive the properties of a practical simple pendulum from the more general results valid for all rigid bodies in pendulum motion. A (fig. 47) represents a plane section of a rigid body, capable of free rotation about a horizontal axis through O, the plane of section being at

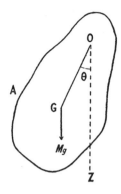

FIGURE 47

right angles to this axis and passing through G, the centre of gravity of the body. In the position shown, OG makes an angle θ with the vertical OZ. If M is the mass of the body, its weight Mg acts vertically downwards through G, and this is the only force producing torque about the axis. In terms of equation (64), therefore,

$$a = -\frac{Mgh}{I} \sin \theta,$$

I being the moment of inertia of the body about the axis of suspension, a the angular acceleration about this axis, and h the measure of the distance OG. For sufficiently small values of θ, $\frac{\sin \theta}{\theta}$ does not differ significantly from unity, thus, for small values of θ, to a good approximation,

$$a = -\frac{Mgh}{I}\theta,$$

and we conclude, as in § 9.7, that the pendulum motion of the system is simple harmonic in angle, provided the angular amplitude is small. In that case, the periodic time, T, is given by

$$T = 2\pi\sqrt{\frac{I}{Mgh}} \tag{71}$$

If the angular amplitude is in fact Θ, more detailed treatment of the problem, first carried out by D. Bernoulli in 1747, shows that the periodic time is longer than is given by equation (71) in the ratio $(1+\dfrac{\Theta^2}{16}+\cdots):1$. If $\Theta = 0\cdot1$ radian (approximately $5\cdot7°$), for example, equation (71) underestimates the periodic time by 1 part in 1600. This is, for most purposes, a negligible error: it is completely negligible in relation to the celebrated observations which the young Galileo made in the cathedral at Pisa in 1581. Shortly after he had matriculated at the university there, at the age of seventeen, Galileo was watching a lamp swinging in the cathedral, and he noticed, with some amazement, that as the amplitude of the oscillations died down the periodic time remained constant. On that occasion he had only his own pulse against which to time the oscillations, but later he verified his conclusions in the laboratory and in so doing established empirically for the first time that there can occur in the world periodic motions of which the observed period is independent of the amplitude. We have already seen (§ 6.2) that this independence is an essential characteristic of simple harmonic motion in general: it is an interesting reflection to note that it was first recognised in relation to motion which is now known to be not strictly simple harmonic.

We need make only one further comment on the general situation. Galileo's pendulum motion died down because of air resistance. In our treatment of the problem we have paid no attention to the effect of the surrounding air. The expression for the angular acceleration on which our conclusions are based describes motion which once started goes on for ever: it exemplifies the physicist's habitual procedure of idealising his problems. In practice the motion of a pendulum oscillating in air is determined by factors other than those we have described. The weight of the pendulum is opposed by the buoyancy of the surrounding air, the motion of the pendulum is resisted because of the viscosity of the air (see Chapter 13)—and it is characteristic of such action that the air in the immediate neighbourhood of the pendulum participates in greater or less degree in the motion of the pendulum. All these effects are capable of detailed study and their nature is now well known. A theory which takes account of all of them can be formulated. We have neglected them here for two main reasons. First, the reason at which we have already hinted—the desire to elicit the fundamentals of a physical situation through the process of idealising it; secondly, because in practice the neglect of these

effects is justified by the smallness of the error which
it occasions. We may approach the truth more closely
if we say that our concern throughout this section is
with pendulum oscillations in vacuum. Then, at least,
effects due to the surrounding air are eliminated 'by
definition'.

Let us consider now a practical simple pendulum,
of which our only remaining idealisation is the
assumption that the 'string' is entirely massless,
rigid and inextensible. If the bob is spherical, and
of radius r, and if l is the distance from the point of
support to the centre of the bob, we have, in terms
of equation (71), equation (68), and Routh's rule,
$I = \frac{2}{5}Mr^2 + Ml^2$, $h = l$, therefore

FIGURE 48

$$T = 2\pi\sqrt{\frac{l}{g}\left(1 + \frac{1}{5}\frac{r^2}{l^2} - \cdots\right)}.$$

For an ideal simple pendulum, $r/l \rightarrow 0$, and in this case we obtain

$$T = 2\pi\sqrt{\frac{l}{g}} \tag{72}$$

Strictly, equation (72) is valid for oscillations of the smallest
angular amplitude only, as is equation (71), and the form of the
correction term is the same in the two cases. There is this difference, however, that with a simple pendulum, having a flexible
string, compensation can be made automatic so that ultimately no
correction is necessary. A little consideration of equation (72) will
show that the increase of period with amplitude could be counter-
acted if the effective length of the pendulum could be made to
decrease as its angular displacement increased. Figure 48 indicates
in principle, how this result may be achieved. It is supposed that
the plane of the figure represents the plane of oscillation of the
simple pendulum OG, and that symmetrically shaped 'jaws', A,
A', are rigidly fixed, one on each side of O, so that, as the pendulum
swings, the string wraps itself first on to one curved jaw and then
on to the other. At any stage in the motion the effective length of
the pendulum is clearly the free length of string (measured, of
course, to the centre of the spherical bob). This certainly decreases
as the displacement increases, thus the remaining problem is

merely to calculate the geometrical form of the jaws. We shall not attempt the calculation here: the result is that the form is cycloidal, the portion AOA′ being that part of a cycloid, the generating circle of which has radius $l/4$, lying on either side of a cusp. A simple pendulum oscillating between compensating jaws of this specification is referred to as a cycloidal pendulum: not only are the the jaws cycloidal, but the centre of the bob describes an arc of an equal cycloid as the pendulum swings.

The prescription which we have just given for the compensating jaws was originally given by Huygens. It is one of the many great achievements described for the first time in *Horologium oscillatorium* in 1673 (see also pp. 114, 188). For an ordinary clock pendulum, constituted of a rigid metal rod carrying a large flat 'bob' at one end, approximate compensation can be achieved by suspending the pendulum by a short piece of flat watch spring as indicated in fig. 49. Flexure of the spring, as the pendulum swings, has the same general effect of reducing the length, to an extent which increases with increasing displacement.

We return now to the further consideration of a pendulum of arbitrary shape. If I_G is the moment of inertia of such a pendulum about an axis through the centre of gravity parallel to the axis of suspension, and if $I_G = Mk_G{}^2$, equation (71) may be written

$$T = 2\pi\sqrt{\frac{k_G{}^2 + h^2}{hg}}.$$

Also, if we define a quantity l, the length of the ideal simple pendulum having the same periodic time T, by the equation

$$T = 2\pi\sqrt{\frac{l}{g}},$$

we have

$$h^2 - lh + k_G{}^2 = 0 \tag{73}$$

Considering k_G as given, that is, restricting our consideration to oscillations of a particular pendulum about all possible axes which are parallel to a specified axis through the centre of gravity, equation (73) can be interpreted from two points of view. In the first place, taking h as the independent variable, and l (or T) as the dependent variable, equation (73) shows how the periodic time

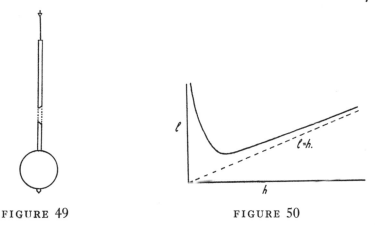

FIGURE 49   FIGURE 50

varies with the distance of the axis from the centre of gravity. Figure 50 indicates the general nature of this variation. For values of h very small compared with k_G, to a first approximation $l = k_G^2/h$, thus $l \to \infty$ as $h \to 0$; for values of h very large compared with k_G (such values may not, of course, correspond to possible positions of the axis of suspension), $l \to h$.

From the second general viewpoint, l may be regarded as the independent variable in equation (73), and h as the dependent variable. Then the equation shows, and fig. 50 demonstrates the same result graphically, that, for any value of l—that is, for any specified periodic time—there are in general two possible values of h, the distance of the axis of suspension from the centre of gravity of the pendulum. If we denote these two values by h_1, h_2, we have

$$h_1 h_2 = k_G^2,$$
$$h_1 + h_2 = l \qquad\qquad (74)$$

When k_G is given, reference to fig. 50 indicates that the value of $h_1 + h_2$ cannot be less than $2k_G$ (when $h_1 = h_2 = k_G$), so that the periodic time of pendulum oscillation cannot be less than $2\pi\sqrt{2k_G/g}$ in this case.

9.9. KATER'S PENDULUM

We have just shown that, for a 'compound' pendulum (this is the name generally given to a rigid body of arbitrary shape capable of pendulum oscillations) of which the period of oscillation about a particular axis is T, it is generally possible to find other axes parallel to the first, but at a different distance from the centre of gravity of the pendulum, about which the period of oscillation is also T. Moreover, equation (74) shows that in general one of these axes will be so located that its distance from the first axis is equal to l, the length of the ideal simple pendulum of which the period is likewise T. In that case the distance between the first and second axes is related to the common periodic time T in terms of equation (72). Figure 51 indicates the conditions which must be satisfied in order that this simple relation may become applicable. As in fig. 47, A represents a plane section of a compound pendulum through G, its centre of gravity, and we are concerned with axes of suspension at right angles to this plane of section. In respect of such axes, that is, in relation to the corresponding value of k_G, C_1 and C_2 are the portions, within the plane section A, of circles of radii h_1, h_2, calculated on the basis of equation (73) with $l = T^2 g / 4 \pi^2$. This construction ensures that the period of oscillation of the pendulum, about any axis through C_1 or C_2 and perpendicular to the plane of section, has the same value, T. Let one such axis cut the section in O_1. We identify this with the 'first' axis of our former statement. The 'other' axes parallel to this, and at a different distance from G, about which the period is also T, are those which cut the section in points lying in C_2. Only one of these axes, that which cuts C_2 in O_2, is distant l from the first axis. In relation to fig. 51 the obvious final condition is that O_2 lies in O_1G produced. The prior condition, $O_1 G \neq O_2 G$, has already been imposed in terms of the definition of C_1 and C_2.

The property of the compound pendulum which we have just discussed was originally described by Huygens in 1673. It was first put to practical use by Captain Henry Kater (1777-1835) in 1818, in a classical determination of the acceleration due to gravity in London. Using a bar pendulum with fixed knife-edges, Kater adjusted the position of the centre of gravity of the pendulum by altering the distribution of mass along its length, until the periods of oscillation about the two knife edges were the same to about 1 part in 10^5. An accurate measurement of the separation of the knife edges and of the common periodic time allowed the acceleration to be calculated from equation (72), correction being made for the effects of the buoyancy of the air and of the finite amplitude of the oscillations.

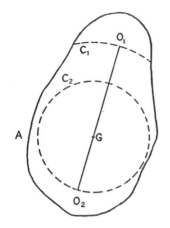

FIGURE 51

The theory of Kater's pendulum was examined in great detail by the German astronomer Friedrich Wilhelm Bessel (1784-1846) in 1826, and as a result two suggestions were made which were later adopted in practice with considerable advantage. In the first place, Bessel pointed out that it was unnecessary to follow through the extremely tedious procedure of equalisation of periods to the length which Kater had done. He showed that, if the periods of oscillation about the two knife edges were adjusted to near equality, a sufficiently accurate value of the acceleration could be calculated, provided the position of the centre of gravity of the pendulum could be determined, as a subsidiary datum, with only moderate precision. This could obviously be done by balancing the pendulum on a fixed horizontal fulcrum, and measuring the distance of each of the knife edges from this fulcrum when the directions of all three were parallel. We may justify this modification of procedure as follows. Let T_1, T_2 be the nearly equal periods of oscillation about the knife edges, the distances of which from the centre of gravity of the pendulum are h_1, h_2. Then we have

$$\frac{T_1{}^2 g}{4\pi^2} = h_1 + \frac{k_G{}^2}{h_1}, \quad \frac{T_2{}^2 g}{4\pi^2} = h_2 + \frac{k_G{}^2}{h_2},$$

or

$$\frac{g}{4\pi^2}(h_1 T_1{}^2 - h_2 T_2{}^2) = h_1{}^2 - h_2{}^2 \tag{75}$$

Writing $h_1 = \dfrac{h_1+h_2}{2}+\dfrac{h_1-h_2}{2},\quad h_2 = \dfrac{h_1+h_2}{2}-\dfrac{h_1-h_2}{2},$

we obtain

$$\frac{g}{4\pi^2}\left\{(h_1-h_2)\frac{T_1{}^2+T_2{}^2}{2}+(h_1+h_2)\frac{T_1{}^2-T_2{}^2}{2}\right\} = h_1{}^2-h_2{}^2,$$

or $$\frac{g}{4\pi^2}\left\{\frac{T_1{}^2+T_2{}^2}{2}+\frac{h_1+h_2}{h_1-h_2}\frac{T_1{}^2-T_2{}^2}{2}\right\} = h_1+h_2 \qquad (76)$$

Comparison of equation (76) with the simple-pendulum equation which Kater employed, namely,

$$\frac{g}{4\pi^2}T^2 = l \qquad (77)$$

shows the very small change in actual experimental procedure which is involved. Because T_1 and T_2 are nearly equal, the second term on the left-hand side of equation (76) is a correcting term only; h_1+h_2 on the right-hand side of this equation represents the same physical measurement—the distance between the knife edges—as does l in equation (77); even more obviously, the same procedure of accurately timing the oscillations about each knife edge in turn is required for the determination of $(T_1{}^2+T_2{}^2)/2$ in the one case as for the determination of T^2 in the other. The one difference is in respect of the correcting term itself. In this connection suppose that the periods are adjusted to equality to within 1 part in 10^3, rather than 1 part in 10^5 as Kater laboriously achieved, and that $h_1\sim 2h_2$. Then a little consideration will show that a knowledge of h_2 correct only to 1 part in 10^2 will ensure that the overall uncertainty, which adoption of the less rigorous procedure has introduced into the final value of g, is less than 2 parts in 10^5, the accuracy of the basic measurements of time and of distance between the knife edges being assumed unaffected by the change. In order to attain an accuracy of 1 part in 10^2 in h_2, in the circumstances which we have postulated, it is necessary to know the position of the centre of gravity of the pendulum to 1 part in 300 of the distance between the knife edges. This is evidently a very modest requirement for a pendulum of normal length, for which $h_1+h_2\sim 100$ cm. We see, therefore, that the modified procedure

of incomplete equalisation of periods is fully justified
according to our analysis.

Bessel's second suggestion was equally practical,
and equally well-founded—though we shall not
attempt to justify it in detail here. He showed that
if the pendulum were made symmetrical in geometric
form about its centre of figure, though of necessity
it must be unsymmetrical in respect of distribution
of mass, then the two most important effects of the
surrounding air, those due to buoyancy and air
motion (see p. 184), are automatically corrected for
without further refinement. Under these conditions,
when the effect of the air is allowed for in the calcula-

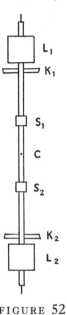

tion, each of the quantities $\dfrac{g}{4\pi^2}h_1T_1{}^2$ and $\dfrac{g}{4\pi^2}h_2T_2{}^2$

of equation (75) is increased by essentially the same
amount—by a small correction due to buoyancy,
and another due to air motion—and, because the
corresponding correction terms are the same in the
two cases, they disappear in the subtraction, and the

FIGURE 52

value of g deduced from experiments in air on the basis of equation
(76) is the same as would be obtained from similar experiments in
vacuum.

The first 'reversible' pendulum made according to Bessel's
specification was designed by the Hanoverian instrument makers
Repsold in 1860 (the business was started by Johann Georg
Repsold (1771-1830), who was at one time chief of the fire brigade
at Hamburg, and was carried on in succession by his sons and his
grandsons). A laboratory-type instrument designed on the same
principle is illustrated in fig. 52. A uniform solid cylindrical
metal rod carries an index pointer at each end, two fixed knife
edges, K_1, K_2, and two large and two small cylindrical masses,
L_1, L_2, S_1, S_2, respectively. In outward form L_1 and L_2 are
exactly similar, and so are S_1 and S_2, but L_1 is made of wood
and L_2 of metal, S_2 of wood and S_1 of metal. K_1, K_2, L_1 and L_2
are fixed rigidly to the rod, symmetrically disposed with respect
to C, the centre of figure. S_1 and S_2 can be clamped in any position between K_1 and K_2. Obviously, the centre of gravity of the
system cannot be made to coincide with C. In the construction of
the pendulum, once the masses L_1, L_2, S_1, S_2 have been chosen,

and L_1 and L_2 have been fixed, there is clearly only a small range of symmetrical positions for K_1, K_2 such that the times of oscillation about these knife edges can be brought into equality by the adjustment of S_1 and S_2, but when K_1 and K_2 have finally been fixed symmetrically within this range the pendulum may be used indefinitely for laboratory experiments following the procedure which Bessel devised. In the ultimate adjustment, of course, the masses S_1 and S_2 must both be moved, so that the symmetry of the arrangement shall be maintained.

The final requirement, in any pendulum experiment, is the accurate determination of the periodic time. If the standard of comparison is a pendulum clock (or any system which provides a visible or audible counterpart to the beating of a clock pendulum), then this determination can most conveniently be made when the periodic times of the experimental pendulum and the clock pendulum are nearly the same (or when one is nearly an integral multiple of the other). Then we may employ the 'method of coincidences', first used by Pierre Bouguer (1698-1758) in 1737 and perfected by J. C. Borda and J. D. Cassini in 1792. Jacques Dominiques Cassini was the last in line of four notable astronomers, father, son, grandson and great-grandson, each of whom in turn was in charge of the observatory in Paris, who were remarkable not only for their contributions to astronomy but also for their longevity, for their average age at death was eighty-three years. In 1792, at the request of the Commission set up by the National Assembly, Borda and Cassini were investigating the alternative possibilities of defining the metre in terms of the length of the seconds pendulum or the quadrant of the meridian (see § 2.10). They had, therefore, the definite task of determining the periodic times of pendulums so adjusted as to gain or lose ever so slightly on the pendulum of a standard clock. (Based upon the practice of clockmakers, the term 'seconds pendulum' is generally used for a pendulum having a periodic time of two seconds, the escapement of a pendulum clock being operated at each end of the swing, that is once every second.) Thus it was entirely natural that they should use the method of coincidences. As we shall see, the method has certain affinities to the method of the vernier in relation to the measurement of length (p. 21).

As its name suggests, the method of coincidences depends upon the observation of the successive occasions on which the oscillations of two pendulums have the same phase (§ 6.1). Either the two pendulums are set up with their planes of oscillation parallel to one another and at right angles to the vertical plane in which their undeflected positions lie, when the coincidences may be observed directly, or an optical system is employed whereby the two pendulums may be observed indirectly, in the same field of view. Suppose that T is the period of oscillation of the experimental pendulum, and T_0 the period of oscillation of the clock pendulum, and assume, for the sake of definiteness, that the former loses slightly in relation to the latter. Then T_c, the time between successive coincidences, is given by

$$T_c = NT = (N+1)T_0 \qquad (78)$$

In this expression N is in general not integral, and any particular coincidence occurs at an arbitrary phase in the oscillations. But, when the periods are nearly equal, the two pendulums pass through their undeflected positions very nearly in phase during several successive transits, and it is indeed difficult to determine which of these transits is the nearest in time to the true coincidence. In practice, therefore, attention is concentrated upon the difference in phase at zero displacement, since discrimination is most effective under these conditions, when the angular velocities are greatest. Equation (78) is interpreted in terms of an integral value of N, and observations over a number of coincidence intervals, s, show that this integer can be specified with a possible uncertainty of n. In such a case the period of oscillation of the experimental pendulum has been determined with an accuracy given by

$$T = \left(1 + \frac{1}{N \pm n}\right)T_0 ,$$

or

$$T = \left(1 + \frac{1}{N} \mp \frac{n}{N^2} + \cdots\right)T_0 \qquad (79)$$

It will readily be agreed that, so long as s is constant, the ratio n/N is unlikely to vary greatly with N: it is determined chiefly by the smallest difference in phase which can just be detected with certainty as the pendulums pass through their mid-positions, but it will certainly decrease as s increases, being proportional to $1/s$. If this is conceded, then equation (79) shows that the fractional uncertainty in the determination of T is proportional to $\frac{1}{sN}$. Now

N

sN represents the total time of observation, in terms of the number of oscillations of the experimental pendulum, thus, whatever the coincidence period, so long as our assumptions are not invalidated, the accuracy of the determination of T is dependent only on the total time over which the oscillations of the experimental pendulum can be compared with the standard. In an experiment of Borda and Cassini, when 5 coincidence intervals had been observed, n was 6, and N about 1500. In that case the term $\dfrac{n}{N^2}$ in equation (79) is about $2 \cdot 7 \times 10^{-6}$. In an experiment lasting not more than a few hours, therefore, in favourable circumstances, it is possible to compare the periods of oscillation of two pendulums with a residual uncertainty of only a few parts in a million.

9.10 THE COMMON BEAM BALANCE

We are now in a position to complete our consideration of the common beam balance which was introduced in § 8.7. For this purpose it is necessary first of all to be a little more realistic than we have previously been concerning the method of use of a balance of high sensitivity. Qualitatively, the sensitivity of a balance is said to be the greater, the smaller is the least difference in mass which can be detected with its aid. We shall give a quantitative definition of sensitivity when we have discussed the practical question in more detail.

On p. 141 we stated 'The criterion of equality of loading of the pans . . . is, therefore, that the beam shall be in equilibrium when it is horizontal.' There are two points in relation to this over-idealised statement which are all-important in practice. In the first place it will be clear that in any practical balance the equilibrium position must be a position of stable equilibrium. If the beam did not tend to return to a perfectly definite position when displaced, the balance would have little interest for the experimental physicist. The centre of gravity of the whole rigid portion of the pivoted system of beam and scale pans must therefore be below the central knife edge, if the balance is to be of general utility (see p. 168). The second point is that, in practice, it is well-nigh impossible— and, indeed, it is basically undesirable—to judge equality of loading in terms of the direct observation of static equilibrium. The natural oscillations of the pivoted and loaded system are observed,

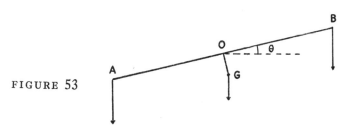

FIGURE 53

with the aid of a long pointer attached symmetrically to the beam, or by reflection of light from a mirror so attached, and when in these oscillations the beam moves symmetrically about a mean position which is horizontal the loading of the pans is adjudged equal. Obviously, for a balance to be of general utility, the periodic time of its natural oscillations must not be too long. We have, therefore, to consider sensitivity in relation to time of swing. We shall find that we cannot, as is obviously desirable, increase the value of the former 'constant', without in general increasing the value of the latter also—which is normally undesirable. In fig. 53, let AB represent the beam and O the central knife edge. Let the centre of gravity of the rigid portion of the pivoted system be at G, OG being perpendicular to AB. Then the weight of this portion of the system acts vertically downwards through G, and it is assumed that the weights of the scale pans and their respective loads act vertically downwards through A and B, whatever the inclination of the beam. In the figure the beam is shown inclined at an angle θ to the horizontal. If it is assumed that this represents the equilibrium position of the pivoted system when the scale pans carry masses $M+m$ and M, respectively, if $AB=2l$, $OG=h$, if the mass of each scale pan is P and that of the rigid portion of the pivoted system is B, and if g is the acceleration due to gravity, taking moments about the central knife edge, we have

$$(P+M)gl \cos \theta + Bgh \sin \theta - (P+M+m)gl \cos \theta = 0,$$

or $$Bh \sin \theta - ml \cos \theta = 0,$$

whence $$\tan \theta = ml/Bh.$$

In practice we are concerned with small values of θ exclusively, and if we define S, the measure of the sensitivity of the balance, by the equation $S = \theta/m$, we have

$$S = l/Bh \qquad (80)$$

Here the quantities B, l and h refer to the rigid portion of the pivoted system only, so that provided fig. 53 represents the actual case—the central knife edge and the knife edges supporting the scale pans lying in one plane—the sensitivity is independent of the load (or of the weight of the scale pans).

Clearly, in calculating the time of oscillation of the pivoted system we cannot expect this, also, to be independent of the load, and determined by the constants of the rigid portion only. We require, however, a definite standard of comparison, so we calculate the time of oscillation for the unloaded balance, and we make the simplifying assumption that the entire pivoted system, of total mass $B+2P$, moves as a rigid body, of moment of inertia I about the central knife edge, correcting this fiction only by noting that the restoring torque is provided by the weight Bg of the strictly rigid portion of the system acting through G, not by the total weight $(B+2P)g$ acting through the centre of gravity of the system as a whole. On this assumption the oscillations of the pivoted system are pendulum oscillations (see § 9.8), and the periodic time T is given by

$$T = 2\pi\sqrt{\frac{I}{Bgh}}.$$

More detailed consideration shows that, in this case, $I=(fB+2P)l^2$ f being a proper fraction depending upon the distribution of mass in the beam, thus

$$\frac{T^2 g}{4\pi^2} = \frac{fB+2P}{B}\frac{l^2}{h} \tag{81}$$

We have now calculated both the sensitivity, S, and the time of swing, T, making certain simplifying assumptions. In terms of equation (80) we see that the sensitivity may be increased by increasing l, the length of the beam, by decreasing B, the mass of the beam and its rigid attachments, or by decreasing h, the distance of the centre of gravity of this system below the central knife edge, the other two 'variables' being kept constant in each case. But consideration of equation (81) shows that any one of these procedures results in an increase in the time of swing, and that it is therefore of strictly limited utility: in the first case T increases in proportion as S, in the last case T increases in proportion as $S^{\frac{1}{2}}$, and the same is true in the second case, at least under normal conditions when the mass of the beam is not large compared with the mass of the scale pans. Obviously, there are considerations of rigidity and strength which introduce additional limitations: in any well-designed balance, the beam will not be over-rigid or over-strong for its purpose, thus the practicability of any suggestion to increase the length of the beam without increasing its mass—or to decrease the mass of the beam without at the same time decreasing its length—must depend on the utilisation of a new material for its construction, on the use of a new alloy, lighter for the same strength or the same rigidity than the alloy previously used. Apart from this possibility, the attainment of maximum sensitivity is in general circumscribed by considerations of the longest time of oscillation which can be tolerated in practice.

It has been pointed out already that our formal results apply only to the case in which the three knife edges on the beam lie in a single plane (in practice advantage can sometimes be derived from other arrangements); for such a case we may combine equations (80) and (81) in the form

$$S = \frac{cT^2}{(fB+2P)l},$$

where c is constant. This last result implies that, for geometrically similar systems, and for the same limiting oscillation time T, the limiting sensitivity is inversely proportional to the fourth power of the beam length (the mass term, $fB+2P$, is proportional to the third power of the beam length for similar balances). Here the term 'geometrically similar' refers to the overall form of each pivoted system, but not to the precise positions of the knife edges with respect to its centre of gravity: obviously these must be regarded as freely variable in order that oscillation times may be the same, as postulated in the comparison.

CHAPTER 10

UNIVERSAL GRAVITATION

10.1. TERRESTRIAL GRAVITY AND UNIVERSAL GRAVITATION

During a brief period of thirty years, from 1590 to 1620, the natural motions of bodies near the surface of the earth, and of the planets about the sun, were for the first time revealed in their quantitative simplicity. About 1591 Galileo proved to his own satisfaction that, but for the resistance of the air, all bodies near the surface of the earth would have the same acceleration of free fall: in 1619 Kepler completed his analysis of the observations of Brahe and published his third law of planetary motion. We have already described these important discoveries (§§ 8.1, 7.2). In the year in which Kepler's third law was published, Jeremiah Horrocks was born. He entered Emmanuel College, Cambridge, at the age of thirteen and died at twenty-one. When he was nineteen, and curate of Hoole in Lancashire, he had shown that Kepler's first law applied, not only to the motions of the planets around the sun, but also to the relative motion of the moon around the earth, except that the major axis of the moon's ellipse slowly rotates and its eccentricity varies periodically. Horrocks had in this way established the first link in the chain of relation between 'celestial' and 'terrestrial' motions, but after his early death there was no one to follow the genius of his intuition, until twenty-five years later the young Newton carried the matter almost to its conclusion, then put his papers aside for twenty years longer before he was satisfied with his own demonstrations.

Before the time of Newton the word 'gravity', in its physical sense, was used to denote the property of heaviness, natural to terrestrial bodies, in virtue of which, it was assumed, they tend to fall towards the impassive earth. This usage was strictly Aristotelian (see p. 120). It is true that there had been earlier attempts to explain terrestrial gravity in terms of an 'attraction'. The general notion of attraction, or mutual action between bodies, can be traced back at least to the first half of the thirteenth century in

Europe. Peter of Maricourt (Peregrinus) had studied and elucidated the action of one lodestone on another, and had attempted to explain the setting of a freely suspended stone by the assumption that 'the heavens have poles'. From then on, though Peregrinus's detailed knowledge of magnetic phenomena was lost for more than three hundred years, from time to time the notion of magnetic attraction entered into discussions of gravity. A suggestion that magnetic action from the moon was responsible for the tides originated in the fourteenth century, and, in the first decade of the seventeenth, Kepler maintained a point of view which was essentially the same. By that time, however, William Gilbert (1544-1603), President of the College of Physicians in London, had published (1600) *De magnete, magneticisque corporibus, et de magno magnete tellure*, Peregrinus's knowledge had been regained and greatly extended, and the subject magnetism had become the first branch of the science of physics to be placed on the sure foundation of fact, elicited by controlled experiment in the modern manner. Proceeding beyond his experiments, Gilbert, too, had speculated on the larger possibilities of magnetic attraction as a cause of gravity. He had suggested that the moon always shows the same face to the earth because it is bound to the earth by such attraction. *De mundo nostro sublunari philosophia nova* (1651), published after his death, contains many speculations on these matters.

But, for Gilbert, the Aristotelian dichotomy remained: it was still a 'sublunar' philosophy which he had to offer. There was no theory of universal gravitation. Nor was there a coherent theory in the later writings of Kepler. Not until 1643 did anyone, discarding completely the distinction between earthly and heavenly bodies in the context of physics, venture the suggestion that every particle of matter in the universe in fact attracts every other particle of matter. This purely qualitative assertion of the principle of universal gravitation was first made by Giles Personne (Roberval), who held the chair of mathematics at the Royal College of France from 1633 until his death at the age of seventy-three in 1675. Another eminent French mathematician, Bernard Frenicle de Bessy (1605-1675), an almost exact contemporary of Roberval, entertained a very similar notion, but neither of these savants gave quantitative shape to this otherwise powerful and original idea.

On 22 December 1666 the Académie des Sciences held its first meeting in the Royal Library in Paris, with Frenicle as one of its founder members. A few days later Isaac Newton celebrated his twenty-fourth birthday at Woolsthorpe in Lincolnshire. It was the second year of the plague, and, as in the previous year, Trinity College had been dismissed in the summer: on this occasion Newton did not return to Cambridge until the following spring. By that time, isolated from libraries and from contact with his fellows, he had forged and almost perfected the tool of the calculus, he had adumbrated a theory of the composition of sunlight, and in all its essentials he had formulated and already submitted to rough numerical test a quantitative account of a gravitational force which was universal in its operation. Here we are concerned only with the last and most original of these momentous achievements. As it is fair to say that Newton's first ideas in this field owed little, if anything, to any inspired guess of an older philosopher, so it will become clear that in their later systematisation in the *Principia* they far transcended any earlier synthesis in subtlety and depth. In very many places already in this book other advances due entirely, or at least largely, to Newton's genius have been recorded without reference to the circumstances of his life, or to his total impact on our subject: here it is appropriate that we should pause to consider these matters, for the history of the Newtonian law of universal gravitation spans the greater part of its author's active life as scientist, and its whole concept is his greatest single contribution to scientific thought.

10.2. ISAAC NEWTON

Isaac Newton was born on 25 December 1642, in the manor-house at Woolsthorpe (Colsterworth), the first child of his parents. His father, 'a wild, extravagant and weak man', had died before he was born, and his mother, marrying again three years later, was widowed a second time when he was thirteen. During the period of his mother's second marriage the boy remained with his maternal grandmother at Woolsthorpe, his mother and his step-father, the Rev. Barnabas Smith, lived at North Witham, two miles away, and his mother's brother, the Rev. William Ayscough, was rector of Burton Coggles, not more than five miles through country lanes to the east. His uncle saw to the boy's early education. In 1654 he sent him to the King's School at Grantham, but when the Rev. Smith died in 1656 the widow returned to Woolsthorpe, and before long she had taken her son away from school hoping to make a yeoman farmer of him. The attempt did not succeed. His formal education had been interrupted, but the young Newton was not thereby separated from his books, nor was his markedly mechanical bent diverted, from the making of water-clocks and sundials, to the upkeep of the ploughs and harrows on his mother's estate.

In the autumn of 1660, Isaac Newton returned to the King's School, his fees having been remitted by the headmaster as an encouragement towards this course, and in June 1661, sufficiently prepared for the university, but considerably older than most men of his year, he went up to Cambridge as an undergraduate. On 29 October 1669—little more than eight years later—he was elected Lucasian professor of mathematics in the university in circumstances which are sufficiently unusual to be worthy of record. Isaac Barrow, one of the first elected fellows of the Royal Society, and first occupant of the Lucasian chair, had just resigned his professorship. Newton had been his pupil, and most writers say that Barrow resigned 'in favour of Newton'. The episode has tended to become romanticised: the eminent professor, recognising his own unworthiness in the presence of his brilliant protégé, modestly making way for him. It needs no such gloss. It is true that Barrow recommended the appointment of Newton as his successor, and actively supported his cause, but he was himself in holy orders, he had previously held and resigned the professorship of Greek at Cambridge, and in 1669 he wished to devote his full energies (he was only thirty-nine at the time) to the study of divinity. Moreover, the change was not without its material rewards: in less than three years Isaac Barrow had been installed as master of his college. From that eminence he could accept Newton as an equal, with magisterial condescension.

It is surprising enough that a young man of twenty-six should have been elected professor of mathematics at Cambridge, even in the seventeenth century, when eight years previously he had had little from his teachers beyond the elements of arithmetic, but in those eight years—in the fifth and sixth of them, to be precise— Newton had devised the calculus, and had thought his way into the theories of light and gravitation as no one had done before him. That is the altogether amazing and incontrovertible fact from which we started. Let us return to it now. We can see it only in retrospect, for Newton published nothing of his work at the time.

When he was an old man Newton wrote, 'In the same year

[1666] I began to think of gravity extending to the orb of the moon
. . . from Kepler's rule of the periodical times of the planets. . . . I
deduced that the forces which keep the planets in their orbs must
be reciprocally as the squares of their distances from the centres
about which they revolve: and thereby compared the force requisite
to keep the moon in her orb with the force of gravity at the surface
of the earth, and found them answer pretty nearly . . . in those days
I was in the prime of my age for invention, and minded mathematics and philosophy more than at any time since.' It is fairly
certain that in 1666 Newton had deduced the inverse-square law
of acceleration (or force—though at that time 'force' had not been
defined dynamically with the clarity later achieved in the *Principia*)
on the approximation of circular planetary orbits uniformly described (see p. 114), but he must have become convinced that it
could be deduced for elliptical orbits also. What is more to the
point is that he then began 'to think of (terrestrial) gravity extending to the orb of the moon', exhibiting the same inverse-square
variation with distance. He found this hypothesis to 'answer pretty
nearly'—but only if in the calculation he allowed himself a far
greater jump of approximation than before. If he assumed that the
gravitational force on a small body at the surface of the earth is the
same as it would be if the whole mass of the earth were concentrated at its centre, then his hypothesis answered nearly enough.
In that case the 'acceleration due to gravity' and the acceleration
of the moon in its orbit would be in the inverse ratio of the squares
of the radii of the earth on the one hand and the moon's orbit
on the other. If the measure of the former radius were to be
denoted by r and that of the latter radius by R, we should have
(see p. 80)

$$g \left/ \left(\frac{2\pi}{T}\right)^2 R = R^2/r^2, \right.$$

or
$$g = \frac{4\pi^2}{T^2} \frac{R^3}{r^2} \tag{82}$$

T representing the measure of the period of revolution of the moon
in orbit about the earth. With the numerical data available to him
at Woolsthorpe in 1666, Newton calculated T in terms of r, R and
g, and found the discrepancy to be about 16 per cent. The hypothesis 'answered pretty nearly', but the major approximation remained unresolved and he put his calculations aside. Also, the

danger of the plague receded and he returned to Cambridge: then, on 1 October 1667, he was elected a minor fellow of his college.

When Newton began to think seriously about gravitation again —in 1680, or thereabouts—a new determination of the earth's radius had been made (by Jean Picard, in 1669), and with the new value for r equation (82) revealed a discrepancy of less than 1·6 per cent, rather than 16 per cent in T. This was a great encouragement, but the stimulus to re-thinking came almost certainly from the unresolved approximations rather than from the improved numerical agreement. Amongst the fellows of the Royal Society the whole matter had become one of great interest. Wren (1632-1723), Hooke (1635-1703) and Halley (1656-1742) had discussed it at length, and eventually Hooke claimed to have a full solution. This was in January 1684. But, by August of that year, Hooke having 'not been so good as his word', Halley sought out Newton in Cambridge. Newton was emphatic that he himself had proved, some seven or eight years previously, that any closed orbit, described by a particle under an inverse-square law force directed to a fixed point, was an ellipse, and in November he sent Halley a formal demonstration. (Later he proved what is essentially the converse of this theorem, namely that Kepler's first and second laws imply an inverse-square law force directed towards the centre of the sun—and we have, in fact, already indicated (p. 115) the character of this later proof.)

Halley visited Newton a second time early in December 1684, and he found then that Newton had indeed proceeded very much farther than to reproduce his earlier proof of the elliptical orbit. He had already compiled 'a curious treatise', *De Motu Corporum*. This treatise contained four theorems and seven problems, and obviously was intended to foreshadow a much larger and more systematic account of the whole subject. Halley's reaction was twofold: he obtained a promise from Newton that *De Motu* should be entered upon the register of the Royal Society to establish his priority in the matter, and he urged him to begin at once on the more systematic work which its writing had foreshadowed.

It is unlikely that Newton in fact required external stimulus towards the writing of *Principia*, though he needed repeated persuasion to allow it to be published. He set to work on it in earnest in April 1685, and he devoted himself to it with little remission for more than a year. On 28 April 1686 the manuscript of the first book was presented to the Royal Society, and less than eight weeks later (on 20 June) its author was writing to Halley 'I designed the whole to consist of three books: the second was finished last summer, being short, and only wants transcribing, and drawing the cuts fairly. Some new propositions I have since thought on, which I can as well let alone. The third wants the theory of comets.' At that time, however, he was in mind to suppress the third book entirely, though he realised clearly enough that 'The first two books, without the third, will not so well bear the title of *Philosophiae Naturalis Principia Mathematica.*' A recurring sensitiveness to criticism (and there had been some ill-informed criticism of the first book, and a frivolous accusation of plagiarism from Hooke) had taken command of him for a spell, and only Halley's mediation restored him to the natural excitement of his task. In spite of other interruptions, by March 1687 the second book had been transcribed and prepared for the printers, and in the following month the third book also was ready for the press. In all, the writing and transcribing of this great work had been spread over two years, precisely: not the least of its marvels is that it was accomplished in so short a time. Newton was capable of sustained concentration beyond the endurance of ordinary men: 'His peculiar gift', a recent Newton-scholar has said, 'was the power of holding continuously in his mind a purely mental problem until he had seen straight through it' (J. M. Keynes, 1942).

On 5 July 1687 Halley wrote, 'I have at length brought your book to an end, and hope it will please you. . . . I intend the price of them, bound in calves' leather, and lettered, to be 9 shillings here.' For this price, in a quarto volume of 500 pages, the men of science of the day were able to acquire, in its original magnificence, the most remarkable and profound contribution which a single man has ever made to the learning of his generation. Edmond Halley was only just thirty years old when Newton's *Principia* was published. It had been written at his instigation, it had been sponsored by the Royal Society as a result of his recommendation, it had been printed at his personal expense, he had even written a Latin poem in honour of its author to commend it to his readers. Both before 1687 and for long afterwards Halley contributed much of his own to the science of his age, but his unequalled contribution was that through his devotion and tact he secured for future ages, and for all men, Newton's *Principia*, 'bound in calves' leather, and lettered', at nine shillings a copy.

We have turned aside from our immediate interest in universal gravitation to recount the history of the writing of the *Principia*: we must now return to the major 'approximation' which Newton made when in 1666 he first compared the acceleration of the moon in its orbit with the acceleration due to gravity at the surface of the earth—the assumption that the earth attracts a small exterior body as it would if its whole mass were concentrated at its centre. During the summer of 1685 Newton justified this assumption to the limit: his elegant demonstration of the conditions under which it is valid falls into place naturally as proposition 71 of book 1 of *Principia*. Here, elaborating somewhat in order to provide the necessary background of definition and explanation, we give Newton's proof in modern form, for sake of the sheer power and beauty of its construction, and as an example of the geometrical method which he used throughout his work with such amazing economy and success.

Let A (fig. 54) represent a uniform spherical shell of material, of mass σ per unit surface area, and negligible thickness. Let O be the centre of the sphere, ρ be the measure of its radius, and let there be a particle of mass m situated at P an external point distant R from O. If m' is the mass of any particle in the shell—say a particle situated at Q, distant r from P—we assume that this particle attracts the particle at P with a force of magnitude Gmm'/r^2 directed along PQ. Here G is a constant. Our immediate problem is to determine the resultant attraction due to all the constituent particles of the shell. Obviously, by symmetry, the direction of this resultant force is along PO, and, if $\angle OPQ = \theta$, we note that the attraction of the representative particle at Q contributes an amount $Gmm' \cos \theta / r^2$ to this resultant.

Now, instead of a representative particle at Q, let us consider a small portion of the spherical shell of area A surrounding Q. Obviously, in the limit, when this portion is sufficiently small, it contributes to the resultant force of attraction along PO an amount $Gm\sigma A \cos \theta / r^2$. The essence of Newton's analysis of the problem was that he devised a geometrical construction by which he was able to specify the mass which placed at O, the centre of the sphere, would exert the same attraction along PO as that exerted in the same direction by the small portion of the shell of area A around

Q—and the geometrical construction itself made it clear that, when the effect of the whole shell was obtained by addition, the mass which had to be placed at O to give the same effect as the shell was precisely the mass of the shell itself. Let us now follow Newton's construction.

In OP (fig. 54) let the point P' be chosen such that $OP \cdot OP' = \rho^2$ (P' is referred to as the 'inverse point' of P). Then, in $\triangle$s QOP', POQ, which have $\angle P'OQ$ in common,

$$\frac{OP'}{OQ} = \frac{OQ}{OP},$$

so that the triangles are similar triangles, and in particular

$$\angle OQP' = \angle OPQ = \theta \tag{83}$$

and

$$\frac{P'Q}{OQ} = \frac{QP}{OP},$$

or

$$\frac{r'}{\rho} = \frac{r}{R} \tag{84}$$

if we write r' for P'Q. Now, let OQ' be drawn parallel to P'Q cutting the spherical shell in Q', and let there be a small area A' around Q' related to the area A around Q as follows: let A be regarded as the intersection with the spherical shell of an elementary cone, drawn from P' as vertex and with P'Q as axis, and let an exactly similar cone be drawn from O as vertex with OQ' as axis to define A' by its intersection with the shell. We note first of all that if the whole surface of the shell be regarded as made up of small areas such as A, the corresponding areas A', as above defined, must likewise together make up the whole surface of the shell, for in each case the small areas are determined by the intersections with the shell of a bundle of elementary cones filling the whole space surrounding the appropriate vertex—P' for the one bundle and O for the other. Since the small area A' around Q' is normal to OQ', and the small area A around Q is normal to OQ, taking count of equation (83), we have

$$\frac{A \cos \theta}{A'} = \left(\frac{r'}{\rho}\right)^2,$$

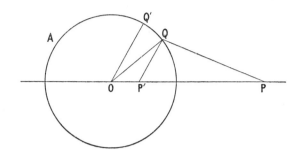

FIGURE 54

or, substituting from equation (84),

$$\frac{A \cos \theta}{A'} = \left(\frac{r}{R}\right)^2.$$

Thus $\qquad A \cos \theta / r^2 = A'/R^2$

and $\qquad Gm\sigma A \cos \theta / r^2 = Gm\sigma A'/R^2 \qquad\qquad (85)$

Now, the left-hand term of equation (85) is the expression which we have already obtained for the contribution, due to the small portion of the shell of area A around Q, to the attraction of the whole shell on the external particle at P. Also, the right-hand term of this equation represents the attraction of a mass $\sigma A'$ situated at O on the same particle. The equation itself asserts that the magnitudes of these two attractions are equal, indeed it establishes the fact that our geometrical construction has done what was claimed for it originally: it has enabled us to specify the mass $\sigma A'$ which placed at the centre of spherical shell would exert the same gravitational force towards that centre as is exerted in the same direction by any arbitrarily chosen small mass-element σA of the shell itself. Moreover, we have already adduced the argument by which the construction may be naturally extended to obtain the attraction of the whole shell. We have seen, in effect, that in that case there must be concentrated at the centre a mass $\sigma(4\pi\rho^2)$, that is a mass equal to the entire mass of the shell. To be precise, we have established the result that a uniform spherical shell attracts an external particle as if the whole mass of the shell were concentrated at its centre.

With this proposition of 1685 finally established, Newton's inspired guess of 1666 was at last fully justified; the only 'approxima⁻

tions' that remained were the assumptions that in external shape the earth is a sphere, and that, if it is not of uniform density throughout, then at least the distribution of its mass is spherically symmetrical. Newton had much of significance to say concerning these two assumptions in other places, but for his immediate purpose, that of the numerical test of the law of universal gravitation, he did not doubt that they were entirely acceptable. With proposition 71 of book 1 of *Principia* finally established, he was no longer worried over a discrepancy of a per cent or two (see p. 203) amongst astronomical magnitudes admittedly difficult of accurate measurement—and having, in the earlier section of that work, been himself responsible for the first precise definitions of 'mass' and 'force', he was content to base the whole of the third book on the confident assertion 'Between each pair of particles in the universe there exists a force of gravitational attraction, in magnitude directly proportional to the product of the masses of the particles and inversely proportional to the square of their distance of separation'. As is the case with every fundamental law of nature, this law of universal gravitation was an assertion of such scope that it could never be submitted to crucial test: only the cumulative effect of its successful application in one instance after another earned for it the unquestioning acceptance of men of science for some two centuries after Newton's death (see p. 132). For our purposes we accept it today.

Newton's law of universal gravitation contains two factors. The inverse-square law of distance we have seen to be deducible from Kepler's first and second laws of planetary motion, on the assumption that the planets can be regarded as point-masses (and the logically distinct assumption that the mass of the sun is very much greater than that of any of the planets, which assumption we shall leave for further consideration in succeeding sections). The second factor, that which involves the product of the masses of the attracting particles, we introduced without further explanation (p. 205) as axiomatic for the proof of Newton's proposition 71. It might be assumed, therefore, that the comparison of the moon's acceleration with the acceleration due to gravity at the earth's surface, for which proposition 71 was basic, provided the first evidence for this factor in the universal law. On the other hand a good case can be made for it on the basis of Kepler's laws alone.

We have already shown (p. 118) that once it has been deduced, from the first and second laws together, that the acceleration of each planet in its orbit is directed towards the sun and that its magnitude is instantaneously proportional to the inverse square of the planet's distance from the sun, then consideration of the third law shows that the constant of proportionality is the same for all planets. For any planet, therefore, indeed for any small body, at distance r from the sun, the acceleration is μ/r^2 where μ is a constant. On the basis of Newton's second law of motion, the fact that there is such an acceleration implies that there is a force of magnitude $\mu m/r^2$ directed towards the sun, m being the mass of the planet. But this attractive force must be mutual as between sun and planet (Newton's third law of motion): if, therefore, the expression for its magnitude involves the mass of the planet, it must involve the mass of the sun symmetrically. The quantity μ, therefore, which is constant for all bodies in revolution around the sun, must be of the form GM, M being the mass of the sun and G being a universal constant. Only in this way will the expression for the force between sun and planet have the necessary symmetry: $F = GMm/r^2$. The universal constant G, here—and previously—introduced, is referred to as the Newtonian constant of gravitation, or more simply as the gravitational constant.

10.3. CELESTIAL MECHANICS

We have just seen how the law of universal gravitation may be deduced—if we accept Newton's definitions of mass and force, and his assertion that in the actual world forces occur only in equal and oppositely directed pairs—from Kepler's empirical laws of planetary motion. Our interpretation of these laws implicitly assumes that the acceleration of each planet is determined by a single force only, the force of attraction between the planet and the sun. Moreover, though it assumes of necessity that the sun is acted on by forces from all the planets, it proceeds on the assumption that the sun may be regarded as permanently at rest. On this basis we finally conclude that every particle in the universe attracts every other particle, the magnitude of the force in each case being proportional to the product of the masses of the two particles concerned. That there is a logical flaw in the argument is obvious: we appear to start from the assumption that the planets do not attract one another, and we finally conclude that they do. We

o

assume that the sun remains at rest, though the resultant force on it is not zero, at the same time as we accept Newton's second law of motion. Logically, there is glaring inconsistency; in fact, we have a perfect example of the way in which the step-by-step method of science, with intuition operating in fortunate circumstances, may extract a universal law from limited experience.

We have to admit that the circumstances were (and remain) fortunate: the planets are small enough in comparison with their distances from the sun to be treated as point-masses in revolution around it, they are small enough in comparison with the sun itself for their mutual attractions to be many orders of magnitude smaller than the attractions which the sun exerts on them individually, and small enough too, in the same comparison, for the sun's local motion to be negligible to a good approximation. But, in making these admissions, we must also claim that the law of gravitation is indeed a universal law, in the Newtonian sense. The motions of the planets are not, in fact, in the last refinement, precisely as Kepler's empirical 'laws' describe them: the crowning success of Newton's law of gravitation was not that it provided a physico-mathematical 'explanation' of those laws, but rather that it has proved capable of providing an equally satisfactory explanation of the major discrepancies which have arisen between later observation and prediction based upon them.

Newton himself laid the foundations of the further elaboration of the matter in book 3 of *Principia*. When he was engaged in the writing of this book he was in frequent correspondence with Flamsteed, the astronomer-royal. 'Your information about the errors of Kepler's tables for Jupiter and Saturn has eased me of several scruples,' he wrote in acknowledgment of one particular piece of information. This interplay of observation and reconciling calculation continued, carried forward by a succession of theoretical astronomers, to culminate in the work of Pierre Simon, Marquis de Laplace (1749-1827), whose *Mécanique céleste*, published in five volumes between 1799 and 1825, earned for him the title of 'the Newton of France'. Laplace died an old man; he lived long enough to see the early development of the last great problem of planetary theory, and to appreciate its significance, but he did not live to see its final triumphal solution.

The planet Uranus had been discovered in 1781 (see p. 100). By 1820 it had been observed over less than half of one circuit of the zodiac. Already, however, it was clear that its motion failed to conform to the close predictions which application of Laplace's mathematics made possible. Over the next ten years the discrepancy became more obvious and more exactly defined. The conviction grew that the 'perturbations' arose from the action of a yet-undiscovered planet still more distant from the sun. In 1843 a prize was offered by the Royal Society of Sciences of Göttingen for a solution of the problem, and in the same year John Couch Adams (1819-1892), having just taken his degree at Cambridge, set to work on the subject. In September 1845 he sent his conclusions to the professor of astronomy, and on 21 October 1845 he deposited a further copy with Sir George Airy (1801-1892), the astronomer-royal at Greenwich. He had shown to his own satisfaction that the motion of Uranus could be completely explained if there existed 'a new planet' of specified mass, moving in an orbit about twice as large as the orbit of Uranus, and at the time of writing occupying a specified position in the sky. Surprisingly, his communications excited little interest in the observatories at Cambridge and Greenwich. Meanwhile, without knowing of Adams's work, U. J. J. Leverrier (1811-1877), a more experienced mathematician, had taken up the problem, and subsequently, in successive communications to the French Academy on 10 November 1845, 1 June and 31 August 1846, he described the results of his detailed analysis. Already the second of these communications, brought to the notice of the astronomer-royal, aroused his strong suspicions that the work of Adams had deserved greater attention than he had originally given it. At his suggestion a search for the new planet which Adams had postulated was instituted at Cambridge, but the prosecution of the search lacked both conviction and vigour, and nothing was found. When his own calculations were completed at the end of August, Leverrier, still in ignorance of what was afoot at Cambridge, wrote to J. G. Galle (1812-1910) at Berlin suggesting that he should look for the planet. The search was begun immediately, and, through the fortunate circumstance that a new star-chart had recently been made at the observatory covering the region of the heavens concerned, Galle was able to identify an object seen during his first night's observing as one not previously charted. On the following night (24 September 1846) this object was found to have moved against the background of the stars. The planet Neptune—'the new planet' of Adams and

Leverrier—had thus been discovered, on no other basis than that of Newton's laws of motion and universal gravitation.

We have referred to the problem of the perturbation of the motion of Uranus as the last great problem of planetary theory. It was not, of course, the last problem. As observations of greater refinement were made, the suspicion came to be entertained, in the present century, that the motion of Neptune itself was not entirely 'regular'. Thoughts of a trans-Neptunian planet could not be avoided. Eventually, in 1930, Pluto was discovered at the Lowell observatory, Flagstaff, Arizona. But history had not repeated itself dramatically, as before: there had been no unique solution, or unequivocal prediction, therefore no new spectacular demonstration of the truth of the law. In spite of that, all that we know concerning the mass of this ninth major planet we know only on the basis of the assumption that Newton's law of gravitation is true beyond shadow of doubt.

10.4. DOUBLE STARS AND COMETS

In the last section we have exposed the logical fallacy in the supposition that the sun remains permanently at rest (or in uniform rectilinear motion) whilst the planets revolve in orbits around it—a fallacy which cannot be removed by any attempt at greater precision in the specification of the orbits. We are bound to admit that the sun experiences a resultant force which varies in magnitude and direction, and we cannot properly avoid taking count of the acceleration produced. Only the fact that the mass of the sun is so much greater than that of any of the planets makes the logically false supposition a tolerably good approximation to the truth. Let us consider the position more closely.

Let there be an isolated system of particles of masses $m_1, m_2, \ldots,$ either individual particles, or particles bound together in rigid bodies of finite size. Let their positions at time t be represented by co-ordinates $(x_1, y_1, z_1), (x_2, y_2, z_2), \ldots,$ and, similarly, after a short time interval, at t', by co-ordinates $(x_1', y_1', z_1'), (x_2', y_2', z_2'), \ldots$ Let the co-ordinates of the centre of mass of the system at time t be $(\bar{x}, \bar{y}, \bar{z})$, and, at time t', $(\bar{x}', \bar{y}', \bar{z}')$. Then the components of average velocity of the centre of mass between t and t' are

$$\frac{\bar{x}' - \bar{x}}{t' - t}, \quad \frac{\bar{y}' - \bar{y}}{t' - t}, \quad \frac{\bar{z}' - \bar{z}}{t' - t},$$

or, substituting from equations (63),

$$\frac{\Sigma m_r(x_r' - x_r)}{(t' - t)\Sigma m_r}, \quad \frac{\Sigma m_r(y_r' - y_r)}{(t' - t)\Sigma m_r}, \quad \frac{\Sigma m_r(z_r' - z_r)}{(t' - t)\Sigma m_r} \quad (86)$$

the subscript r taking all the values 1, 2, . . . corresponding to the particles in the system. In expressions (86), obviously,

$$(x_r' - x_r)/(t' - t)$$

is the x-component of the average velocity of the rth particle between t and t', and correspondingly for similar quantities in the stated sums. Thus the components of the average velocity of the centre of mass of the system between t and t' may be written

$$\frac{P_x}{\Sigma m_r}, \quad \frac{P_y}{\Sigma m_r}, \quad \frac{P_z}{\Sigma m_r} \quad (87)$$

P_x, P_y, P_z being the components of resultant linear momentum of the system as a whole—averaged, if that is necessary, over the time interval from t to t'. We know, however, that no averaging is necessary: the system is an isolated system, thus its resultant linear momentum remains constant with time (§ 8.5). The components of instantaneous velocity of the centre of mass of the system, therefore, remain constant, not only over the time interval from t to t', but in general. The motion of the centre of mass of the system is, in fact, entirely undisturbed by the mutual forces between the particles.

Let us return now to the consideration of the relative motions of a planet and the sun. If these two bodies constituted a truly isolated system, the correct approach would be to refer the motions of each to the centre of mass of the system, assumed to be at rest, not to refer the motion of the planet to the centre of the sun, as we have done hitherto, assuming the sun itself to be at rest. The difference between the two procedures is greatest in respect of Jupiter: in that case the correct reference point is just outside the sun, roughly 1·07 times the sun's radius distant from its centre. In every other case the correct reference point lies well within the sun's volume: in the case of the earth it is distant no more than 1/1500 of the radius from the centre of the sun. We appreciate more clearly now the fortunate circumstances in which Kepler's laws came to be formulated: if the constitution of the solar system had been otherwise, no such simple formulation would have described the motions of its members, even as a first approximation to the truth.

Although the distinction between the centre of mass and the centre of the sun is luckily unimportant in relation to the main features of relative motion within the solar system, the situation is quite otherwise in respect of the relative motions of 'double stars'. When, about 1780, Sir (Frederick) William Herschel (1738-1822), the discoverer of Uranus (p. 100), first began his systematic survey of the heavens, he was greatly exercised by the discovery that many stars which appeared single to the unaided eye, or as seen through a small telescope, appeared double when a more powerful instrument was employed. Over a period of some three years he made careful observations of the aspects of a large number of these double stars, and in 1793 he repeated his observations. He found that in many cases the relative positions of the components had changed. Herschel was not the first astronomer to pay particular attention to the occurrence of apparently double stars—Christian Mayer, quite independently, produced a catalogue of 89 such systems in 1784—nor was he the first to suggest that these systems were indeed close pairs of suns, the members of each pair revolving about their common centre of mass—John Michell (1724-1793) probably preceded him in this—but he was certainly the first to establish the latter conclusion as the result of accurate measurement. In 1802 he reported in full his observations on a double star in the Great Bear, showing that, as Newton's laws would predict, the orbits of the two components are similar ellipses, described in the same period, a single point, dividing the line of centres of the component stars in a constant ratio, being a common focus of the two ellipses. Now, when several thousand double stars are known, with revolution periods ranging from a few hours to some thousands of years, this assumption is taken for granted universally.

It has been stated (p. 203) that in the year 1677, or thereabouts, Newton satisfied himself that if a particle moves in a closed orbit under an inverse-square law force directed towards a fixed point then the orbit is an ellipse having the centre of force as one focus. When he came to consider the matter more fully, when writing the *Principia*, he realised that there were circumstances in which a particle acted on by such a force would not move in a closed orbit at all: in such circumstances the orbit would be an hyperbola, or, less generally, a parabola. He quickly perceived that this result had particular relevance to the problem of comets. By observations on the bright comet of 1577, Tycho Brahe had been the first to show conclusively that these bodies travel in outer space, not in the sublunar regions as had been popularly supposed. In 1665, Giovanni Alfonso Borelli (1608-1679) having analysed the observations made on the great comet of the previous year, suggested that their orbits were parabolas about the sun as focus. Newton perceived that this result is precisely what would be expected if a comet started 'from rest' at an effectively infinite distance, moving solely under the gravitational attraction of the sun. Edmond Halley took up the matter systematically in 1695. Ten years later he published an analysis of all the trustworthy observations that had been made on the bright comets which had appeared between the years 1337 and 1698.

He dealt first with the observations which had been made at Greenwich on the comet of 1683. On 7 September 1695 he wrote to Newton, 'I have exceeded my expectation, finding that a parabolic orb limited according to your theory will most exactly answer all the observations . . . even within the compass of one minute.' Three weeks later, however, concerning the comet of 1680, he wrote, 'I find certain indication of an elliptic orb . . . and am satisfied that it will be very difficult to hit it exactly by a parabolic.' Concerning the comet of 1682 he had come to a similar conclusion, adding 'I am more and more confirmed that we have seen that comet now three times, since the year 1531.' Ten years later, when all his material was assembled, he wrote, 'Hitherto I have considered the orbits of comets as exactly parabolic; upon which supposition it would follow, that comets being impelled towards the sun by a centripetal force, . . . by their falls acquire such a velocity, as that they may run off again into the remotest parts of the universe, . . . never to return again to the sun. But since they appear frequently enough, . . . 'tis highly probable that they rather move in very eccentric orbits, and make their returns after long periods of time: for so their number will be determinate, and, perhaps, not so very great . . . indeed there are many things which make me believe that the comet which Apian observed in the year 1531 was the same with that which Kepler and Longomontanus took notice of and described in the year 1607 and which I myself have seen return, and observed in the year 1682. . . . Hence I dare venture to foretell, that it will return again in the year 1758.' In 1758 'Halley's' comet returned according to prediction, and in 1835 and 1910 it was seen again about the appointed time. Historical research and further calculation has proved beyond reasonable doubt that it had been observed in 1456 and in 1066—the comet of the Bayeux tapestry—that it was one with the comet of 87 BC and very probably with the comet of 240 BC also.

In this way the motions of the least obviously regular of the heavenly bodies have been shown in fact to be subject to rule, as those of the planets are: the force of gravitation, the mode of operation of which Isaac Newton first described in intelligible terms, not 'the death of princes', occasions the appearance of comets in their due times and foreordained places in the evening or morning sky.

10.5. THE CONSTANT OF GRAVITATION

Newton's law of universal gravitation is expressed mathematically by the formula $F = Gm_1m_2/r^2$ (p. 205). Here G represents the measure of a physical quantity, the constant of gravitation, which is a fundamental constant of nature. In this section we are concerned with experiments designed to determine the magnitude of this constant. In principle the problem is a simple one: we have to determine, in terms of our chosen unit, the force of gravitational attraction between two bodies, and, similarly, to determine their masses and geometrical disposition in terms of measured lengths, and we have then to calculate G by substitution in the formula. In practice the problem is difficult just because the force of gravitation is so small in comparison with other forces to which experimental bodies are normally subject. In spite of the implicit assertion of Newton's law, it is entirely foreign to common experience to find that two bodies, placed close together on a highly polished plane horizontal surface, move slowly towards one another until contact is achieved. The force of friction (§ 13.2), even in the most favourable circumstances, is sufficient to prevent this otherwise inevitable result.

In view of what has just been said, it is not surprising that most of the early attempts to determine the gravitational constant experimentally made use of a large natural feature as one of the bodies between which the attraction was determined. Also, in order to minimise the effect of friction, it was an obvious expedient to suspend the smaller experimental body, as the bob of a pendulum is suspended. Thus there were experiments in the eighteenth and nineteenth centuries in which real pendulums were used to determine the local variations in the acceleration due to gravity over and around mountains or plateaux, and other experiments in which the horizontal attraction due to a mountain mass was estimated from the deflection of a plumb-line suspended in its neighbourhood. In any such experiment—of the one type or the other—the essential comparison is between the force F' due to the local feature and the gravitational force F due to the earth as a whole. If the local feature can be represented as a mass m at a distance r from the bob of the pendulum (or plumb-line), and if M is the mass of the whole earth of radius R, we have, generally,

$$F'/F = mR^2/Mr^2.$$

But g, the acceleration due to gravity, is given by

$$g = GM/R^2 \qquad (88)$$

Thus $$G = (r^2g/m)(F'/F).$$

The main difficulty of such experiments is the complexity of the survey necessary to determine m/r^2 for the natural feature with even moderate accuracy.

The first experimental determination of the gravitational constant in which two 'artificial' masses were employed was made by Henry Cavendish (1731-1810) in 1798. The Rev. John Michell, rector of Thornhill in Yorkshire and previously professor of geology at Cambridge, whose views on double stars we noted in the last section, had suggested the method and built the original apparatus, but he died before he was able to put it to use. His apparatus passed to Cavendish, and, modified somewhat by him, served for his pioneer investigation. Although more powerful experimental methods have since been devised, more particularly methods involving the resonance of oscillating systems, the history of the Michell-Cavendish method extends over a century or more and exemplifies such important aspects of the design of experiment in general that we shall confine attention here to its discussion. In principle the method is extremely simple: the forces of gravitational attraction between two exactly similar pairs of experimental bodies are applied as a couple to produce a static twist in a long torsion wire, the torsional constant of which is determined by timing the oscillations of a suspended system of known moment of inertia (see § 9.7). From the static twist and the torsional constant, the deflecting couple, and so the magnitude of the gravitational forces, is deduced.

Let AB (fig. 55) represent a light rigid beam of length $2l$ suspended horizontally by a vertical torsion wire attached at its mid-point C. Let the torsional constant (restoring couple per unit twist) of the wire be μ, and let similar bodies of the same mass m be suspended symmetrically from the two ends of the beam. If the moment of inertia of the suspended system about the axis of suspension is denoted by I, T, the time of torsional oscillation of the system is given (equation (70)) by

$$T = 2\pi\sqrt{\frac{I}{\mu}}.$$

Suppose now that similar 'deflecting' bodies, each of mass M, are brought into symmetrical positions D as shown, close to the 'suspended' bodies, so that the line of centres in each case is perpendicular to the length of the beam (the bodies being spherical). If, in equilibrium, the beam is deflected through a small angle θ, the magnitude of the gravitational couple must be $\mu\theta$, and we may write

$$\mu\theta = G\frac{mM}{d^2} . 2l,$$

where d is the distance between the centres of suspended and deflecting bodies when equilibrium is reached. Eliminating μ from these two equations, we have

$$\theta = G\frac{mM}{d^2} . \frac{T^2 l}{2\pi^2 I} \tag{89}$$

Ideally, in equation (89), every quantity except G may be derived by measurement and calculation: thus the magnitude of the gravitational constant may be deduced. We are interested here to consider the precision and sensitivity of the determination.

Obviously, for a given arrangement of suspended and deflecting bodies, the deflection, θ, is greater, the greater the period of oscillation, T, of the suspended system (equation (89)). For a

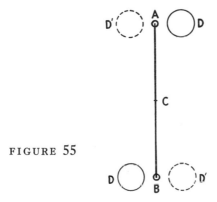

FIGURE 55

given suspended system, that is for a specified value of I, T may be increased by decreasing μ, the torsional constant of the wire. In principle this is always possible: the wire must have a certain minimum diameter if it is to support the beam and its attachments without breaking, but the torsional constant may always be decreased by increasing the length of the wire. The limitations of the method are therefore essentially limitations relative to T. These may arise in either of two ways: either the attempt to increase the sensitivity of the arrangement reaches a natural limit when the length of the wire suspension becomes too great for practical convenience, or, before this happens, the period of oscillation itself becomes too long. The fact is (compare our previous discussion of the sensitivity of the beam balance, § 9.10) that static equilibrium is never attained in the deflection experiment: the angle θ is measured by observing the oscillations of the system about the equilibrium position, and if these oscillations are of too long a period the method fails. We shall assume, to begin with, that the second situation is the more probable—the real limitation arises directly in relation to the magnitude of T, as here described.

Suppose, then, that we have two complete sets of apparatus for the Cavendish experiment, which, apart from the wire suspensions, are such that the linear dimensions of each component of the second set are f times as large as the linear dimensions of the corresponding component of the first set. Let the same materials be used for the attracting bodies in each case, and let the wire suspensions be such that the oscillation periods of the two suspended systems are the same. Then, if θ_1 and θ_2 are the deflections to be expected, in terms of equation (89), we have

$$\frac{\theta_2}{\theta_1} = \frac{f^3 f^3}{f^2} \cdot \frac{f}{f^5} = 1.$$

This is, at first sight, a surprising result: the angular sensitivity does not depend upon the linear size of the apparatus, once its geometrical design has been fixed and the constructional materials have been decided upon, so long as the sensitivity is limited by the period of oscillation of the suspended system. Michell's apparatus, which Cavendish took over, had a braced wooden beam about 6 feet long, suspended by a silvered-copper wire more than 3 feet in length. The attracting masses were of lead, the smaller about 2 inches in diameter, the larger about 12 inches in diameter. The period of oscillation of the suspended system was of the order of 7 minutes. The result which we have just obtained implies that the same angular sensitivity could have been obtained with a much smaller version of the same arrangement, provided that the suspension could be so modified that the oscillation period remained the same. That there is no essential difficulty in meeting this requirement may be seen as follows. The torsional constant, μ, of a wire of length L and radius of cross-section r is proportional to r^4/L (see § 16.2). If the material of the wire is not changed, therefore, the requirement is that IL/r^4 shall be kept constant when the linear dimensions of the apparatus (apart from the suspension) are decreased. As before, we denote by f the factor by which the dimensions are modified, and we use the subscripts 1 and 2 to refer to the original (larger) apparatus and the modified (smaller) one ($f < 1$). Then we must have, for wires of the same material,

$$\frac{L_2}{L_1} = \frac{I_1}{I_2}\left(\frac{r_2}{r_1}\right)^4.$$

Naturally we suppose that the original wire was no stronger than it need have been to support the beam and its attachments, and we assume that in the smaller apparatus the same relative margin of safety is allowed. Then, since the weights to be supported are in the ratio $1 : f^3$, we obtain

$$\left(\frac{r_1}{r_2}\right)^2 = \frac{1}{f^3}$$

as the condition that the load per unit cross-sectional area is the same for each wire. Since $I_1/I_2 = 1/f^5$, as before, we have

$$\frac{L_2}{L_1} = \frac{1}{f^5} \cdot f^6 = f.$$

We conclude that the requirement can be met, and the length of the suspension decreased into the bargain.

During the period 1870-1883 a long series of experiments was carried out in Paris by M. A. Cornu (1841-1902) and J. B. A. Baille using an apparatus only about one-quarter the size of the original Cavendish apparatus, but no one at that time fully understood the advantage to be gained from a reduction in size, and the suspension which these workers used was about four times as long as that which Cavendish himself had employed. The discussion which we have just given is of later date, being based on the work of C. V. Boys (1855-1944), published in 1895. Boys, in fact, carried the scaling-down process one stage farther than we have hitherto described—and the possibility of his second stage is, at first sight, even more surprising than the possibility of his first.

Let us suppose that we have a small-scale Cavendish apparatus obtained by an overall reduction in dimensions, the oscillation period remaining constant, as previously specified. Let us now further reduce the length of the beam, keeping all other essential dimensions constant, and adjusting the suspension so that the oscillation time remains constant, also. If the new beam is f' times as long as the previous one ($f' < 1$), and if subscripts 2 and 3 now refer to the second and final versions of the apparatus, respectively, we have, from equation (89),

$$\frac{\theta_3}{\theta_2} = \frac{f'}{f'^2} = \frac{1}{f'}$$

—at least to the approximation in which the mass of the suspended system is assumed concentrated equally at the centres of the suspended bodies. To this approximation, therefore, $l_3\theta_3 = l_2\theta_2$: the shorter the beam is made, the greater (in inverse ratio) is the final deflection.

Clearly, the modification which this result suggests cannot usefully be carried beyond a certain stage: when the length of the beam becomes comparable with the diameter of the deflecting bodies (see fig. 55), the attraction of each such body on the suspended body at the other end of the beam has to be taken into account in the calculations—and reduces the sensitivity of the arrangement. Boys overcame this difficulty to a large extent by arranging the suspended bodies to be at different distances below the beam, and positioning the deflecting bodies accordingly. In his final arrangement the beam consisted of a small rectangular mirror only 2·4 cm. long (serving itself to reflect the light by which the deflections were measured), supporting gold balls about 5 mm. in diameter, and with lead spheres of about 10 cm. diameter as deflecting bodies. As in the original Cavendish experiment, and in all its repetitions in the intervening century, so in Boys's experiment, the deflecting masses were not removed in order that the 'undeflected' position of the beam might be determined, but instead they were rotated as a rigid system, about the suspension as axis, so that the suspended system was deflected in the opposite sense, and the angle actually measured was the sum of the individual deflections to the right and the left of the undetermined 'zero'. In the Cavendish arrangement the second positions of the deflecting bodies are the positions D′ of fig. 55.

Boys's achievement will already be seen to have been a remarkable one, but it involved the overcoming of a serious difficulty to which reference has still to be made. The problem of maintaining maximum sensitivity—that is, of keeping the time of oscillation constant—admitted of no easy solution when the final reduction of beam length was carried out. Referring back to our previous discussion (p. 220), and using an obvious extension of the notation there used, we have

$$\frac{L_3}{L_2} = \frac{I_2}{I_3}\left(\frac{r_3}{r_2}\right)^4,$$

if it is assumed that the oscillation time may in fact be kept constant by changing the dimensions of the suspension without changing the material of which it is made. Since the modification which we are considering is one in which the load on the suspension is unaltered, we must have $r_3 = r_2$. Making the same approximation concerning the moment of inertia as before, $I_3 = f'^2 I_2$, and we have, finally,

$$\frac{L_3}{L_2} = \frac{1}{f'^2}.$$

This result exposes the difficulty. The same load has to be supported, reduction in the length of the beam reduces the deflecting
couple; using the same material for the suspension, one must
increase its length even to achieve the same deflection as before—
to achieve the increased deflection of which the arrangement
should be capable, one must increase the length of the suspension
still further. This is not the recipe for success: the whole object of
a reduction of size of the Cavendish apparatus is to make it less
susceptible to extraneous disturbance—to air currents and mechanical shock. Even under the most carefully controlled conditions
it would be well-nigh impossible to observe the small angular
deflection of a short bar at the end of a long vertical wire against
the inevitable random 'pendulum' motion of the system. Boys,
therefore, had to look for another material for the suspension, one
exhibiting a much greater strength under tension, for the same
resistance to torsional deformation, than the metals which had
been used, and equally capable of fabrication in long filaments of
uniform circular section. He found such a material in fused quartz,
and himself devised the method of producing long fibres of this
highly refractory material. In that way he gained a factor of 5 over
those workers who for preference used platinum for their suspensions, or a factor of nearly 4 over those who used copper. It would
have been difficult to have drawn steel piano-wire to the fineness
which was necessary for his purposes; even so, his quartz-fibre
suspensions would have had an advantage of some 50 per cent over
any steel wires which might have been produced. It was an outstanding technical achievement, and it is hardly necessary to add
that it has revolutionised standard practice in whatever field of
physics the 'torsion balance' of Michell has come to be applied.

The value which Boys finally deduced for the gravitational con-
stant was 6.658×10^{-8} cm.^{3} g.$^{-1}$ sec.$^{-2}$. The value at present
accepted (with an uncertainty of one part in a thousand) is
6.670×10^{-8} cm.^{3} g.$^{-1}$ sec.$^{-2}$. It will be seen that these values agree
to within twice the uncertainty currently admitted: indeed, the
past sixty years have seen little by way of improvement on the
precision which Boys achieved in his classical researches.

During the last decades of the nineteenth century it was customary to refer, popularly at least, to experiments such as those of
Cavendish and Boys as experiments designed for the weighing of
the earth. They do, in fact, provide one of three data from which

the mass, M, or the mean density, $\varDelta$, of the earth may be calculated, if its shape is assumed to be spherical. Re-writing equation (88), we have

$$M = gR^2/G,$$

and, in consequence,

$$\varDelta = 3g/4\pi GR.$$

According to our present knowledge of G, $\varDelta = 5\cdot517$ g. cm.$^{-3}$ Here there is only one further comment to be made. It may well be made in the words of Thomas Young (1773-1829), physician and egyptologist, himself in the front rank of natural philosophers: 'Newton had long ago advanced it as a probable supposition that the mean density of the earth might be about five or six times as great as that of water, and the perfect agreement of the result of many modern experiments with this conjecture affords us a new proof, in addition to many others, of the accuracy and penetration of that illustrious philosopher.' Newton's 'conjecture' is to be found in *Principia*, book 3, proposition 10.

CHAPTER 11

POTENTIAL ENERGY

11.1. CONSERVATION OF ENERGY IN PERFECTLY ELASTIC COLLISIONS

We have already (§ 8.2) discussed, in one aspect, the experiments of Wallis and Wren on the direct impact of hard spherical bodies, and the deductions which Newton made from them. In view of the all-embracing success of Newtonian dynamics in the two centuries which followed, no doubt can remain that the empirical result which we have discussed, namely, that for any pair of bodies the changes of velocity which occur in any direct impact bear a constant ratio, is universally true—at least for gross bodies which retain their identity after collision. Generalised in Newton's third law of motion, this result underlies the principle of conservation of momentum which admits of no exception in phenomena with which we are presently concerned.

But there is a second aspect of the experiments, which we must now discuss, which is of a different character. It is represented by a generalisation which Newton recognised to refer to ideal conditions only, that is, to a quantitative 'law' to which actual systems never precisely conform. Newton wrote 'bodies absolutely hard return one from another with the same velocity with which they meet'. In modern phraseology we should rather say 'in the ideal case of the direct collision of perfectly elastic bodies, the relative velocity after collision is equal in magnitude and opposite in direction to the relative velocity before collision'. If we represent the initial velocities of the colliding bodies by v_1, v_2, $(v_1 > v_2)$, and the final velocities by v_1', v_2', this result may be written

$$v_2' - v_1' = v_1 - v_2.$$

If the masses of the bodies are m_1, m_2, the law of conservation of momentum requires

$$m_1 v_1' + m_2 v_2' = m_1 v_1 + m_2 v_2.$$

P

We may re-arrange these equations as follows:

$$v_2' + v_2 = v_1' + v_1,$$

$$m_2(v_2' - v_2) = m_1(v_1 - v_1').$$

Combining them, in the new form, by multiplication, we have

$$m_2(v_2'^2 - v_2^2) = m_1(v_1^2 - v_1'^2),$$

or $$\tfrac{1}{2}m_1v_1'^2 + \tfrac{1}{2}m_2v_2'^2 = \tfrac{1}{2}m_1v_1^2 + \tfrac{1}{2}m_2v_2^2 \qquad (90)$$

Equation (90) shows that in the ideal case of the direct collision of two perfectly elastic bodies the sum of the kinetic energies (§ 8.9) of the bodies after collision is equal to the sum of the kinetic energies before collision. In the ideal case, therefore, we have the appearance of a conservation law in respect of kinetic energy—at least as long as we overlook the period during which the bodies are in actual contact. During that brief period the relative velocity of the bodies is rapidly reduced to zero, and restored again to its former magnitude in the opposite direction: certainly during that period the total kinetic energy of the two bodies does not remain constant.

But, laying aside these considerations for the moment, we note, first of all, that the apparent conservation law applies equally to oblique collisions, in the ideal case. If A′A, B′B (fig. 56) represent the directions of the initial velocities of two perfectly elastic spherical bodies which come into collision as shown in the figure, then we may resolve these initial velocities along and at right angles to AB, the instantaneous position of the line of centres of the bodies, and in the ideal case we may assume that the components of velocity at right angles to AB are unaltered in the collision. (We have illustrated a collision in which the directions A′A, B′B are co-planar, but the argument is essentially the same if they are not.) The situation is, therefore, that equation (90) refers to the components of velocity along AB, and that a similar equation, in fact an identity, refers to the components of velocity at right angles to AB which are unaltered. Adding these equations together, and remembering (see equation (26)) that if x, y, z are

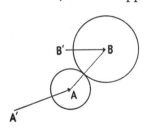

FIGURE 56

the magnitudes of the components, along rectangular axes, of a vector of magnitude R, then $R^2 = x^2 + y^2 + z^2$, we obtain the result already quoted: the sum of the kinetic energies of the colliding bodies is the same after the collision as before.

With this conclusion established, it is worth while to consider the situation during the collision in greater detail. For it is possible that the energy-concept might be generalised in such a way that we could properly speak of energy being conserved throughout the collision process, in the ideal case, as momentum is always conserved. We should have to say—indeed the results of experiment make it natural to say—that kinetic energy is 'transformed' during the initial phases of a collision into energy of another kind, being 'stored' in the colliding bodies, until, during the later phases of the collision, it is released and re-converted into energy of motion. Consideration of equation (54) of § 8.9 gives added cogency to this idea. In any actual collision between real bodies it is easy to show that deformation takes place around the initial point of contact, and that in a large class of cases no permanent deformation persists after the collision is complete. It is natural to correlate the forces which must be brought into play, if equation (54) is valid for each of the colliding bodies throughout the entire collision process, with this deformation, and in the ideal case to suppose that the instantaneous magnitude of the latter determines the magnitude of the force from instant to instant during contact. If this view is taken, the total kinetic energy of the colliding bodies first decreases as work is done against the forces so developed, and, these forces acting in the same direction as before as long as any deformation persists, the kinetic energy increases again to its original value as work is done by the forces acting. Furthermore, on this view, the region of deformation of the colliding bodies provides a natural location for the energy temporarily 'stored'—and subsequently restored as energy of motion. As we shall see, this whole point of view is a very useful one and capable of further generalisation: as we extend it we shall use the term 'potential energy' to refer to energy stored in the way that we have just described—or in any analogous way.

Following Leibnitz (p. 38), Newton, writing in Latin, used the term 'vis viva' for the quantity represented, in our conventional notation, by the product mv^2. Huygens had independently recognised the importance of this quantity in particle dynamics (p. 114), and Jean Bernoulli (1667-1748) and his son Daniel (1700-1782) made great use of the 'principle of conservation of vis viva' in many investigations. The idea of potential energy is implicit in the *Mécanique analytique* (1788) of Joseph Louis Lagrange (1736-1813), but two generations were to pass before the distinction between energy of motion and stored energy (energy of position) was set out 'in plain English', unadorned—and unobscured—by the elegant mathematics of the continental academicians. Thomas Young (p. 224) had suggested the use of 'energy' as a convenient English equivalent of vis viva in 1807, but the suggestion proved unacceptable to many, and it was not until mid-century that the new nomenclature became standardised. Several writers, including Hamilton (p. 77), preferred to translate the Latin literally as 'living force', then for a time 'actual energy' was the fashionable form. Our present term 'kinetic energy' (with its reference to $\frac{1}{2}mv^2$ rather than mv^2) was introduced by Thomson and Tait in an article in *Good Words* in 1862. W. J. M. Rankine (1820-1872) had been the first to use 'potential energy' (to replace 'virtual living force', a translation from a French usage) in a paper published in Glasgow in 1853. It is indicative of the confusion of the times—and the character of the individual—that Hamilton should have written to Tait in 1862, 'Energy and Work in the old English meaning, are things not unfamiliar to me. But I have only the dimmest views of the modern meanings attached to those terms.' However, in 1867, Thomson and Tait adopted potential energy and kinetic energy as standard terms in their monumental *Treatise on Natural Philosophy* (see, also, p. 78): thereafter there was no back-sliding.

11.2. GRAVITATIONAL POTENTIAL ENERGY

We have introduced the idea of 'potential' energy, and have recognised its usefulness, in relation to the ideal case—never fully realised in practice—of the collision of 'perfectly elastic' bodies. We have concluded that the condition that two bodies shall be perfectly elastic, in this connection, is that the force of mutual repulsion brought into play on impact shall, throughout any collision, be uniquely determined by the instantaneous magnitude of the deformation of the bodies. This is the justification for our reference to potential energy as energy of position. It might better be termed energy of configuration.

We have an example of a situation of the same kind, but on a much larger scale of distance, in the gravitational energy of a body near the surface of the earth, or, indeed, on an even larger scale, in the configurational energy of mutually gravitating bodies wherever situated. For a body of mass m and weight W in the local gravitational field of the earth, the work done against gravitational attraction when the height of the body above the earth's surface is increased from h_1 to h_2 is given by $W(h_2 - h_1)$ —W being assumed constant when heights much smaller than the radius of the earth are in question. In conformity with our previous ideas, we define this quantity as the increase of potential energy of the body (or, more strictly, of the mutual potential energy of the body and the earth) corresponding to the change in position. Applying equation (54) to the vertical motion of the body, and remembering that its horizontal motion is unaffected by the force of gravity (compare p. 136), if v_1 is the magnitude of its velocity at height h_1 (the direction of motion being unimportant), and v_2 the magnitude of its velocity at height h_2, neglecting air resistance, we have

$$\tfrac{1}{2}mv_2{}^2 - \tfrac{1}{2}mv_1{}^2 = -W(h_2 - h_1).$$

The terms on the left-hand side of this equation represent the increase of kinetic energy of the body (in the conditions specified any kinetic energy of rotation (§ 9.6.1) remains constant during the motion (§ 9.5)), and the terms on the right-hand side represent the decrease of potential energy. Formally, then, if we represent the kinetic energy by E and the potential energy by V, at any stage in the motion, we have

$$E + V = \text{constant} \tag{91}$$

It should be noted that in equation (91) the value of the constant is not specified. Indeed we are at liberty to choose, with convenience as our only criterion in a particular case, any configuration as the standard configuration of zero potential energy. In respect of local motion near the earth's surface, it is natural to choose the configuration in which the experimental body is at ground level as that in which the potential energy is zero. In that case the potential energy of a body of weight W at height h above the ground is conventionally given by $V = Wh$. In collision problems we more generally choose the initial configuration of 'infinite' separation as the standard configuration, and we do this naturally in all problems of gravitational attraction on the astronomical scale.

It is of the essential character of potential or configurational energy that for a given system its magnitude shall be specified in terms of the relative separations of all the constituent bodies of the system, and of quantities representative of the forces operative, but that it shall not depend upon the velocities of the bodies. The phenomena of collision are physically complex, and we have done no more than indicate the configurational dependence of the stored energy by postulating that it is specified uniquely by the deformation in the ideal case, but in local motion near the earth's surface, when air resistance is neglected, the force on a body is independent of height and its potential energy is found to be directly proportional to this positional co-ordinate. We are led to expect that whenever the force on a body is specified in a simple mathematical way in terms of its position there will be a correspondingly simple expression for the potential energy of the body.

As an example of the fulfilment of this last expectation we may take the case of a small body of mass m situated at a distance $r(>R)$ from the centre of a much larger spherically symmetrical body of mass M and radius R. The gravitational attraction at this distance is given by GmM/r^2. It is easy to verify that the gravitational potential energy (assumed zero at infinite separation) at the same distance is given by $-GmM/r$. For, on this basis, the increase of potential energy when the body moves from a distance r_1 to a distance r_2 is $GmM\left(\dfrac{1}{r_1}-\dfrac{1}{r_2}\right)$, or $GmM(r_2-r_1)/r_1r_2$, an amount which would in fact be involved if there were a uniform attractive force of magnitude GmM/r_1r_2 acting over the whole distance r_2-r_1. However, we know that the actual force is not uniform over any finite distance, but the result which we have obtained is valid for each infinitesimal step belonging to any finite displacement, and for such a step there is no significant difference between GmM/r_1r_2 and $GmM/r_1{}^2$ or $GmM/r_2{}^2$. This being proved for each step in a finite displacement, the expression $GmM\left(\dfrac{1}{r_1}-\dfrac{1}{r_2}\right)$ must in fact represent the work done against a centripetal force given by $F=GmM/r^2$ when the point of application of the force moves from

r_1 to r_2. We have verified, therefore, that the potential energy in this case is given by $-GmM/r$.

A gravitational field such as we have just considered (for example, the external gravitational field of the earth) may be specified in three ways in terms which we have already defined: in terms of the force F on a small body of mass m situated in the field ($F = GmM/r^2$), in terms of the acceleration a of any small body of whatever mass situated in the field ($a = GM/r^2$), or in terms of the gravitational potential energy of a small body of mass m ($V = -GmM/r$). The last of these specifications leads to a fourth, having the same relation to it as the specification in terms of the acceleration has to the specification in terms of the force, in that the mass of the 'test' body does not enter. We define a gravitational potential ϕ, in this case, by the equation $\phi = -GM/r$, so that, for a small body of mass m, the gravitational potential energy is given by $V = m\phi$. Obviously we can use any of these methods of specification for the description of more complicated gravitational fields equally well: the advantage of a specification in terms of gravitational potential (or potential energy) over the corresponding specification in terms of acceleration (or gravitational force) in every case is that the former employs a scalar, the latter a vector, quantity for the description. For the former specification magnitudes only, for the latter both magnitudes and directions, are required.

We may summarise—and, without proof, generalise—the conclusions of the present chapter, at this stage, as follows: if in any isolated system of small bodies the mutual forces between the bodies do not depend upon the velocities of the bodies, but only on their positions, then it is possible to define the mutual potential energy of the system in such a way that the sum of this quantity and the total kinetic energy of the individual bodies remains constant with time.

Two things should be noted in respect of this statement. In the first place we have used the term 'bodies', rather than 'particles', to emphasise the fact that we are stating a principle of conservation of mechanical energy for macroscopic phenomena: as yet we have not considered its validity at the molecular level. In the second place we have stated an ideal principle which has no immediate relevance to everyday experience: in the collision of real bodies kinetic energy is incompletely restored, in local motion under gravity air resistance depends upon velocity not upon position macroscopically considered. In respect of immediate relevance to terrestrial motions, the principle of conservation of mechanical energy is altogether less important than the principle of conservation of linear momentum, at the macroscopic level. In spite of this, those who seized upon the new principle were following a sure instinct: when our considerations are extended to the molecular level we shall find that the principle assumes greater significance, not less.

11.3. ENERGY IN SIMPLE HARMONIC MOTION

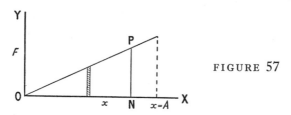

FIGURE 57

In § 6.2 linear simple harmonic motion has been defined kinematically as the rectilinear motion of a point the acceleration of which is, at each instant, proportional to the distance of the moving point from a fixed origin in its line of motion, and directed towards that origin. If a particle of mass m executes such motion, we have, from equations (36) and (37) of § 6.1,

$$\tfrac{1}{2}mv^2 = \tfrac{1}{2}m\omega^2 A^2 \sin^2 \omega t \qquad (92)$$

$$ma = -m\omega^2 A \cos \omega t = -m\omega^2 x \qquad (93)$$

A being the amplitude and $2\pi/\omega$ the periodic time of the motion. It will be seen that equation (92) gives E, the kinetic energy of the moving particle, directly as a function of the time. In order to calculate V, the potential energy of the particle, as a function of the time (or the displacement), we have to obtain a value for the work done against the restoring force $F = -ma$ (given by equation (93)) when the particle moves from the standard reference point (which we shall take as the origin) through the displacement in question. According to equation (93)—that is according to the kinetic definition of linear simple harmonic motion—the restoring force is directly proportional to the displacement, a situation represented graphically in fig. 57.

There should be no need to repeat in detail here the argument set out fully in § 4.4 in what is essentially a similar case. In the present case, as in the former one, the shaded area on the figure represents to the scale of the diagram, the contribution, corresponding to the small change of the independent variable involved (in this case a small change in displacement), to the quantity the measure of the change of which is represented by the product of the instantaneous measure of the dependent variable (in this case the restoring force) and the measure of the small change of the independent variable itself. In the present case the quantity so represented is the work done, or the increase of potential energy. If we follow the argument, step by step, as before, we conclude that the increase of potential energy, as between zero displacement and displacement x (represented by ON in the figure), is represented by the triangular area OPN, on the appropriate scale. We have, therefore,

$$V = \tfrac{1}{2}x \, . \, m\omega^2 x.$$

Since (equation (93))

$$x = A \cos \omega t,$$

$$V = \tfrac{1}{2}m\omega^2 A^2 \cos^2 \omega t \qquad\qquad (94)$$

Combining equations (92) and (94), we now have

$$E + V = \tfrac{1}{2}m\omega^2 A^2,$$

or

$$E + V = 2\pi^2 m A^2 / T^2 \qquad\qquad (95)$$

T being the periodic time.

Equation (95) establishes a result which we should have anticipated. We have been discussing a situation in which a force is specified in terms of position only; it is not surprising that the principle of the conservation of mechanical energy should apply, that is that the sum of the kinetic and potential energies should be constant with time. Beyond this general comment, we note that equation (95) shows that the total energy in simple harmonic motion is directly proportional to the square of the amplitude and inversely proportional to the square of the periodic time (or directly proportional to the square of the frequency). This result enables us to calculate the periodic time, if the mass of the particle, its total energy, and the amplitude of its motion are given.

As an example of this use, we may apply equation (95) to the case of an ideal simple pendulum (§ 9.8). We approximate to reality by assuming that the motion of the bob of the pendulum in its circular arc is linear motion of amplitude determined by the corresponding chord (see fig. 27, § 8.6). This approximation is the more exact as the angular amplitude is smaller. Next, we calculate the total energy as the value of the potential energy at maximum displacement. Referring to fig. 27, with OA=l, NP=A, and $A \ll l$, we have

$$AN = A^2/2l,$$

therefore
$$E + V = mgA^2/2l \tag{96}$$

Finally, combining equations (95) and (96), we obtain the familiar result (see equation (72))

$$T = 2\pi\sqrt{\frac{l}{g}}.$$

CHAPTER 12

COLLISIONS

12.1. COLLISIONS BETWEEN REAL BODIES

We introduced the subject of potential energy in the last chapter by considering the ideal case of the collision of perfectly elastic bodies. It was there stated (§11.1) that it was recognised in the time of Newton that the collisions between real bodies never entirely conform to this ideal. Regarding such collisions, Newton wrote 'In bodies imperfectly elastic . . . the elastic force . . . makes the bodies to return one from the other with a relative velocity, which is in a given ratio to that relative velocity with which they met.' This empirical result, which Newton derived largely from his own experiments, is generally accepted today as giving a reasonably correct description of collision phenomena at low speeds over a wide range of conditions. Indeed, the 'given ratio' is, to a first approximation, a constant for a given pair of materials rather than for a given pair of bodies, so that, for example, the same 'coefficient of restitution' (of relative velocity) applies with reasonable accuracy over a considerable range of speeds to the collisions between one sphere of brass and one of steel whatever the radii of the spheres— or, in the limit, to the rebound of a brass sphere of whatever radius from the flat surface of a large steel anvil. That this empirically defined 'constant' has this degree of generality makes it a worth while object of experimental determination and tabulation, although it refers to a phenomenon of some complexity which cannot be discussed simply in its more fundamental aspects. We may, however, understand the implications of Newton's empirical result, at the macroscopic level, by considering in some detail the dynamics of the direct collision of two spherical bodies for which the coefficient of restitution is e.

In this case, as in the ideal case of perfectly elastic collision when $e = 1$, conservation of momentum applies exactly. Thus, if we take over the formalism of § 11.1, we obtain the dynamical equations for the completed collision in the form

$$v_2{}' - v_1{}' = e(v_1 - v_2) \tag{97}$$

$$m_1 v_1{}' + m_2 v_2{}' = m_1 v_1 + m_2 v_2 \tag{98}$$

Solving these equations for $v_1{}'$, $v_2{}'$, we have

$$\left.\begin{aligned} v_1{}' &= v_1 \frac{m_1 - em_2}{m_1 + m_2} + v_2 \frac{m_2(1+e)}{m_1 + m_2} \\ v_2{}' &= v_1 \frac{m_1(1+e)}{m_1 + m_2} + v_2 \frac{m_2 - em_1}{m_1 + m_2} \end{aligned}\right\} \tag{99}$$

We may now denote by L the loss of kinetic energy of macroscopic motion of the bodies, and since, be definition,

$$L = \tfrac{1}{2} m_1(v_1 + v_1{}')(v_1 - v_1{}') + \tfrac{1}{2} m_2(v_2 + v_2{}')(v_2 - v_2{}'),$$

substituting from equations (99), after some re-arrangement, we obtain

$$L = \tfrac{1}{2} \frac{m_1 m_2}{m_1 + m_2} (v_1 - v_2)^2 (1 - e^2) \tag{100}$$

Except to note that when $e = 1$, $L = 0$, as we have already shown (p. 226), we defer comment on this result until we have approached the matter from another point of view.

From this alternative, and more detailed, point of view, we assume that I is the magnitude of the impulse generated in the collision (see § 8.9). Then, instead of equation (98), we may write

$$\left.\begin{aligned} m_1 v_1{}' &= m_1 v_1 - I \\ m_2 v_2{}' &= m_2 v_2 + I \end{aligned}\right\} \tag{101}$$

and we may now regard equations (97) and (101) rather than (97) and (98) as the dynamical equations for the completed collision. Solving these new dynamical equations for I, we obtain

$$I = \frac{m_1 m_2}{m_1 + m_2} (v_1 - v_2)(1 + e) \tag{102}$$

In more detail still, if I_1 is the magnitude of the impulse generated in the first phase of the collision, during which the relative velocity of the bodies is completely destroyed, and I_2 is the magnitude of the impulse generated in the second phase, during which the bodies separate again, so that $I_1 + I_2 = I$, then from the form of equation (102) we must have

$$I_1 = \frac{m_1 m_2}{m_1 + m_2}(v_1 - v_2)$$
$$I_2 = \frac{m_1 m_2}{m_1 + m_2}(v_1 - v_2)e$$

$$(103)$$

To justify this conclusion we note that when $e = 0$ the bodies stick together permanently, their relative velocity being permanently destroyed, and that, in any case, we cannot in principle know whether the bodies are going to separate again after collision, that is whether e is in fact greater than zero, until the first phase of the collision is complete. We are now in a position to comment on our results.

First, in respect of their more formal aspects, we note that the apparent loss of energy in the collision is never greater than

$$\tfrac{1}{2}\frac{m_1 m_2}{m_1 + m_2}(v_1 - v_2)^2,$$

its value when $e = 0$. Thus the kinetic energy of macroscopic motion remaining after collision is never less than

$$\tfrac{1}{2}m_1 v_1{}^2 + \tfrac{1}{2}m_2 v_2{}^2 - \tfrac{1}{2}\frac{m_1 m_2}{m_1 + m_2}(v_1 - v_2)^2,$$

or

$$\tfrac{1}{2}(m_1 + m_2)\left(\frac{m_1 v_1 + m_2 v_2}{m_1 + m_2}\right)^2.$$

This residual kinetic energy, which no mutual action of the colliding bodies can destroy, is the energy which a mass equal to the sum of the masses of the two bodies would possess if it were moving with the velocity which the centre of mass of the bodies was moving before the collision. We have already concluded (§ 10.4) that for an isolated system in general the velocity of the centre of mass of the system remains constant. Our present result, therefore, should cause no surprise, for after a collision for which $e = 0$ the total mass of the system is indeed moving with the velocity of the centre of mass.

We next note that, in each of the equations (100), (102) and (103), the mass-term has the form $m_1 m_2 / (m_1 + m_2)$. This quantity, which is of frequent relevance when the dynamics of two bodies is in question, is referred to as the 'reduced mass' of the binary system. In the extreme case, when $e = 0$, the whole impulse generated in the collision may be said, in colloquial terms, to be equal to the momentum of the reduced mass travelling with the initial relative velocity of the bodies (equation (102)), and the apparent loss of energy to be equal to the energy of the same mass travelling with the same velocity (equation (100)).

From a more physical point of view, we note the result given by equations (103), namely, $e = I_2 / I_1$. The coefficient of restitution, originally defined in terms of the ratio of relative velocities, after the collision and before, is here seen as the ratio of the impulses generated in the two phases of the collision, the phase following the instant of zero relative velocity and the phase preceding it. In these two phases the changes of momentum, for either body separately, bear this ratio the one to the other.

Our only other comment at this stage is not strictly a comment on the results which we have derived in this section: it is that in the case of the oblique collisions of imperfectly elastic, but perfectly smooth, spherical bodies, as in the ideal case of oblique collisions considered in § 11.1, we may assume that the components of velocity at right angles to the instantaneous line of centres of the bodies are unaltered in the collision. In such a case equations (97) to (103) remain valid, but the velocities represented in them are the components of velocity along the instantaneous line of centres of the bodies, not their actual velocities in three-dimensional space. With this reservation, equation (100) correctly represents the apparent loss of kinetic energy, and equation (102) the whole impulse generated as a result of the collision.

12.2. COLLISIONS BETWEEN ATOMIC NUCLEI

At various times in our recent discussions we have laboured the point that our immediate concern has been exclusively with macroscopic phenomena. By implication we have foreshadowed the discussion of the conservation of mechanical energy at the molecular level (§ 11.2), but that must be postponed for Chapter 14. Meanwhile we digress briefly to consider certain aspects of collisions at the sub-atomic level. We can properly do so at this stage for the subject is one in its own right, having no relevance to the unsolved problems which our recent discussions have raised.

In modern times evidence concerning the reality—and the general structural pattern—of atoms has in large measure come from experiments with radioactive substances. It has been concluded that although atoms are minute in the extreme, by ordinary standards, possessing volumes of the order of 10^{-23} cm.^{3}, almost the whole of the mass of any atom is concentrated in a single central nucleus the volume of which is no more than about 10^{-36} cm.^{3}, even for the heaviest atom. It has been concluded that the phenomena of radioactivity originate in the break-up of atomic nuclei in various ways. With the radioactive elements found in the earth's crust—uranium, radium and others—one common type of disintegration is that in which the radioactive nucleus emits a 'heavy' fragment identical with the nucleus of the helium atom. These fragments are called α-particles, as they were designated by Rutherford (1871-1937), who first recognised their presence (1898) before their true nature was known. α-particles may be detected in several ways, by the very faint flashes of light which individually they produce when they impinge on a phosphorescent screen coated with specially prepared crystals of zinc sulphide or other suitable material, by the electrical discharges which may be 'triggered' by their passage through the gas in a Geiger counter, or by the trail of minute drops which condense along the paths which they traverse through a gas made supersaturated with water vapour or alcohol. The last-mentioned method, that of the Wilson expansion chamber, is the one with which we shall be here concerned. Obviously, of the methods referred to, it is the one most directly suited to the study of such collisions as may occur, for if other sub-atomic particles are projected in these collisions, with kinetic energies comparable with the energies of the α-particles themselves, then it may be anticipated that the paths of these particles also will be marked by condensation-trails of drops.

α-particles are emitted from radioactive nuclei with initial velocities of the order of 10^9 cm. sec.$^{-1}$. It is because these velocities are so great, by ordinary standards, that individual α-particles may be detected at all; it is by the same token that our previous assertion is justified—our assertion that the general subject of α-particle collisions has no relevance to that of the collisions of 'real bodies' moving with velocities no greater than 10^3 cm. sec.$^{-1}$, or there-abouts. As revealed in the Wilson expansion chamber, the paths of individual α-particles are of finite length—a few centimetres in air of normal density—and usually straight, except towards their extremities. The fact that the paths are terminated indicates that the α-particles rapidly dissipate their original energy as they pass through the gas: we need not here consider by what mechanism this occurs.

Occasionally an α-particle cloud-track is seen forked, as repre-sented by the full lines in fig. 58. From what has already been said, the obvious interpretation of such an appearance is that, having travelled normally along OA, the α-particle has 'collided' at A with another particle, and that after this collision the two particles have moved off, one along AB, the other along AC. Our interest in such events derives from the fact that detailed investigation has shown that in the majority of them kinetic energy is conserved with an accuracy which is not approached in any class of collisions of real bodies of which we have immediate experience. We are justified, therefore, in applying to these events the dynamical equations of § 11.1. We shall do this in what follows, considering what deductions may be made, from the simplest observational material, on the basis of the two conservation laws alone.

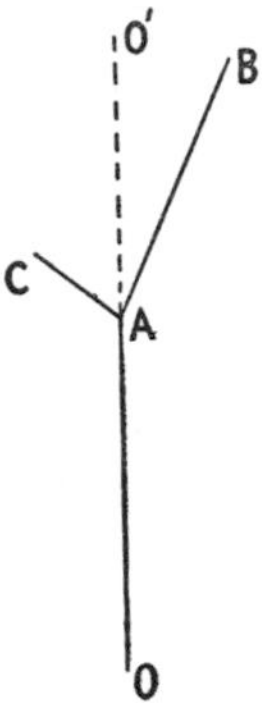

FIGURE 58

In fig. 58 we assume that the path of the α-particle is represented by OAB, and that AC represents the path of the particle set in motion in the collision (the 'struck' particle). OA being produced to O', $\angle O'AB = \phi$ is the deflection of the α-particle in the collision, and $\angle O'AC = \theta$ is the angle of projection of the struck particle. Suppose that the mass of the α-particle is m and that of the struck particle is M. Let the velocity of the α-particle before collision be v_1 and after collision v_2. Let V be the velocity of the struck particle after the collision. It is a reasonable approximation to suppose that the struck particle was at rest before the collision (under ordinary conditions its velocity would be of the order of 10^4 cm. sec.$^{-1}$ (p. 302), compared with some 10^9 cm. sec.$^{-1}$ for the α-particle). Then the law of conservation of momentum gives: along OA

$$mv_2 \cos \phi + MV \cos \theta = mv_1 \qquad (104)$$

at right angles to OA

$$mv_2 \sin \phi - MV \sin \theta = 0 \qquad (105)$$

And, if kinetic energy is also conserved, we have

$$\tfrac{1}{2}mv_2{}^2 + \tfrac{1}{2}MV^2 = \tfrac{1}{2}mv_1{}^2 \qquad (106)$$

Of the quantities involved in equations (104), (105) and (106), only the angles are measureable when a collision event has been recorded on an expansion-chamber photograph. It is our object to see what conclusions can be drawn regarding masses and velocities from this limited information.

Solving equations (104), (105), for v_2, V, we have

$$v_2 = v_1 \frac{\sin \theta}{\sin (\theta + \phi)} \qquad (107)$$

$$V = v_1 \frac{m}{M} \frac{\sin \phi}{\sin (\theta + \phi)} \qquad (108)$$

Equation (107) shows that we may deduce, directly from the measured angles, the ratio in which the velocity of the a-particle is reduced as a result of the collision (the velocity must decrease, otherwise kinetic energy could not be conserved). In a similar way we may calculate the ratio V/v_1, using equation (108), if the mass-ratio m/M is known.

Let us now substitute from equations (107), (108) in equation (106). After some re-arrangement, we obtain

$$\sin^2 \theta + \frac{m}{M} \sin^2 \phi = \sin^2 (\theta + \phi).$$

Finally, further simplification leads to the explicit result

$$\frac{m}{M} = \frac{\sin (2\theta + \phi)}{\sin \phi} \qquad (109)$$

We see that we can, in fact, deduce the required mass-ratio from the measured angles, directly. Summarising, then, we can deduce the two velocity ratios, v_2/v_1, V/v_1, and the mass-ratio, m/M, from our measurements of θ and ϕ, without any knowledge of the details

Q

of the collision process, assuming only that the conservation laws apply, and that the struck particle is at rest before the collision. Of these possibilities, the possibility of deducing the mass-ratio, m/M, from the measured angles is the most interesting one. Let us, therefore, examine the predictions which we may make on the basis of equation (109).

If the struck particle is less massive than the α-particle ($m > M$), then since the greatest value which $\sin (2\theta+\phi)$ can take is 1, the maximum value of $\sin \phi$ is M/m. When α-particles pass through hydrogen gas, it is found that single deflections of the α-particle paths through more than 15° are most exceptionally rare. We conclude, therefore, that the 'struck particles' in hydrogen are less massive than α-particles, roughly in the ratio sin 15°:1, or about 1:4.

In the special case when the colliding particles are of equal mass ($m = M$), equation (109) reduces to

$$\sin (2\theta+\phi) - \sin \phi = 0,$$

or
$$\cos (\theta+\phi).\sin \theta = 0,$$

whence
$$\theta+\phi = \frac{\pi}{2}.$$

In this case the collision fork-angle, ∠BAC of fig. 58, is precisely one right angle, whatever the value of ϕ (or, alternatively, of θ). It is a fact of experience that when α-particles pass through helium gas the collision fork-angles are always right angles, whether the collisions are symmetrical ($\theta=\phi$) or widely asymmetrical. From this result we conclude that the 'struck particles' in helium are of the same mass as α-particles. We note, however, that the condition $\theta+\phi=\frac{\pi}{2}$ is only one solution of equation (109) when $m=M$, though it is the significant solution. The other solution is $\theta=0$. In this case $v_2=0$ (that is, the α-particle is brought to rest in a head-on collision, the whole of its kinetic energy being transferred to the struck particle), and ϕ is indeterminate. It is strictly true, but physically irrelevant, that we should not be able to detect any difference between the track of an α-particle which had traversed the whole of its 'range' in helium without making any collisions of the general type we are considering and the equally straight track, started by an α-particle of the same energy as before, and carried on to its natural end by a succession of struck particles of equal mass, each transferring to the next the whole of its kinetic energy in a head-on collision. This gloss on the solution $\theta = 0$ is physically irrelevant because we know from other considerations that not more than about one α-particle in ten thousand makes a head-on collision over the whole length of its natural path in helium gas.

The last possibility in relation to equation (109) is that $m < M$. Then the maximum value of $\sin (2\theta + \phi)$ is m/M. This result implies that $2\theta + \phi$, being always less than 180°, does not differ from 180° by more than $\sin^{-1}(m/M)$, whatever the value of ϕ. When the mass of the struck particle is several times greater than that of the α-particle, say 10 times as great, $2\theta + \phi$ cannot differ from 2 right angles by more than a few degrees. In this case the cloud track of the struck particle appears fairly accurately to bisect the external angle between the initial and final portions of the track of the α-particle. Thus, in fig. 58, $\angle O'AC = \theta$ and $\angle BAO = \pi - \phi$. If $2\theta + \phi = \pi$, $\pi - \phi = 2\theta$ as we have indicated. When the photographs of the cloud tracks of α-particles are obtained using an expansion chamber containing argon gas, characteristic collision forks are observed having the character which we have just described: one prong of the fork always much shorter than the other and apparently bisecting the external angle as predicted.

In fig. 59 we plot the relation between the characteristic collision angles ϕ and θ as deduced from equation (109), for $m/M = 4$, 1 and 1/10. The three curves of the figure represent with considerable accuracy the results of measurements on collision forks photographed when α-particles pass through hydrogen, helium and argon, respectively. The atomic weights of these elements are 1, 4 and 40. Obviously, all the observations are consistent with the assumption that an α-particle is a helium atom (or, at least, that it has effectively the same mass as a helium atom) and that the 'struck particle' set in motion in any gas is a whole atom (or, at least, very nearly a whole atom) of the gaseous element concerned. In the introduction to this section we stated categorically that α-particles are the nuclei of helium atoms. We now conclude that, in the 'perfectly elastic' collisions which may be observed with the aid of the Wilson expansion chamber, these high-speed nuclei transfer kinetic energy directly to the nuclei of the atoms through which they pass. Just because the volume occupied by an atom

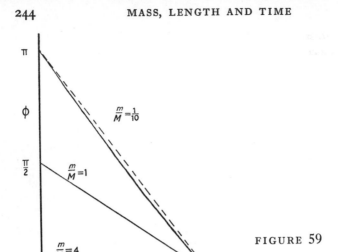

FIGURE 59

nucleus is such a small fraction of the whole volume of the atom, are these inter-nuclear collisions so infrequent.

CHAPTER 13

FRICTION OF SOLIDS, LIQUIDS AND GASES

13.1. GENERAL

Towards the end of the sixteenth century Galileo made experiments with real bodies sliding or rolling along wooden rails, or on polished surfaces inclined to the horizontal. As we have described in § 8.1, from these experiments with real bodies he was led by the instinct of genius to the concept of the ideal perfectly smooth plane surface—and on that abstraction he laid the foundations of dynamics. He had isolated, in thought, a fundamentally significant feature of the real world, dismissing another feature as a complication which could safely be left on one side for later understanding. The feature which he dismissed we now speak of—and attempt to understand—as an effect of friction between solid bodies in contact.

In the seventeenth century Galileo's experiments were followed by the experiments of Wren and Newton on the collisions of real bodies supported as pendulum-bobs. We have referred to these experiments in §§ 8.2, 11.1 and 12.1. and in § 8.6 we compared the two arrangements in detail. Although, in the second arrangement, the complication of solid friction is avoided, we concluded that an effect of the same nature remains, a slowing down of movement which we ascribe to the frictional resistance of the air. Newton was well aware of this effect, and took particular care to make allowance for it empirically. In that way he was able to discover the basic regularities of the phenomena which he was studying. That these regularities still exhibited residual 'imperfections' in the behaviour of real bodies is not now our immediate concern: we have discussed these in the last chapter; they have been regularised in his definition of the coefficient of restitution (§ 12.1).

In the present chapter we deal systematically with the complications which we have previously dismissed as irrelevant, with friction between solid bodies in contact, and with frictional resistance to relative motion in liquids and gases.

13.2. FRICTION OF SOLIDS

The simple facts in relation to friction between solid bodies in contact across dry surfaces in air under ordinary conditions may be described in terms of an ideal experiment. Let us suppose that a number of bodies of different shapes and sizes, and constructed of different materials, are placed upon a large plane surface which is initially horizontal. Suppose that each body possesses a plane face (or co-planar facets) on which it stands, and that its shape is such that the supporting surface may be tilted through a considerable angle without the body falling over. Then, if the inclination of the supporting surface is gradually increased from zero, and particularly if the surface is kept in a state of steady vibration (of very small intensity), a perfectly regular series of happenings ensues. At first none of the bodies moves, then, as the inclination of the surface increases, one by one the bodies begin to slide down the plane. For each body the inclination at which motion begins is perfectly definite, and, if there are several bodies made of the same material, whatever their sizes and shapes, all begin to slide down the plane when the inclination reaches the same value. For motion down a beech-wood plane, for example, bodies made of steel all begin to move when the inclination has a definite value, about 30°; moreover, if the situation is reversed, if the supporting plane is made of steel and the bodies of beech-wood, the critical inclination at which sliding begins is the same. We define, therefore, for a given pair of materials, an 'angle of limiting friction', being the inclination to the horizontal of the plane surface of contact separating bodies made of the materials in question when relative motion begins, under the action of gravity, in circumstances such as we have described. It is worth while emphasising some of our presuppositions, at the risk of repetition: the surfaces in contact must be clean and dry and macroscopically plane, and the bodies must be in air under ordinary conditions.

In § 8.7 we obtained an expression for the force necessary to prevent a body sliding down an ideally smooth inclined plane of arbitrary inclination. For a real body of weight W resting on a plane surface in air, the results which we have just described indicate that, when the inclination of the plane has the critical value ϕ, a restraining force has been developed across the area of contact, parallel to the surface, of magnitude $W \sin \phi$. For smaller values of the inclination, motion having yet to begin, the restraining 'force of friction' must be correspondingly less than this.

In order to discover what is the restraining force for angles of inclination greater than ϕ, it is necessary to supplement our previous results by a series of determinations of acceleration in sliding motion at greater inclinations. It is easy to see that if the force of friction remained constant for angles of inclination, θ, greater than ϕ, the acceleration in sliding motion would be given by g (sin $\theta -$ sin ϕ). In fact, the acceleration increases with increasing inclination more rapidly than this expression predicts.

This last result should occasion no surprise: when the plane surface becomes vertical, the question whether or not the body is still resting on the surface is an academic one, and we should expect the acceleration to be that of free fall, as it is indeed found to be. This, in particular, contradicts our trial expression, which predicts an acceleration of g $(1 -$ sin $\phi)$, rather than g. We conclude, therefore, that, as the inclination of the plane surface is increased beyond ϕ, the restraining force of friction decreases. A more accurate expression might be based on the assumption that the maximum restraining force bears a constant ratio, μ, to W cos θ, the normal reaction across the surface of contact, rather than a constant ratio to W, the total weight of the body, in all ordinary circumstances. On the basis of this assumption (see fig. 29, § 8.7)

$$\mu = \tan \phi \qquad (110)$$

and the acceleration in sliding motion for an inclination $\theta(> \phi)$ is given by

$$a = g \text{ (sin } \theta - \mu \text{ cos } \theta),$$

or $\qquad a = g \sin (\theta - \phi)/\cos \phi \qquad (111)$

Experiment confirms the predictions of equation (111). We conclude, therefore, that our assumption provides a satisfactory empirical rule. The quantity μ, defined as above, and related to the angle of limiting friction by equation (110), is referred to as the coefficient of limiting friction for the two materials concerned. This quantity was first clearly introduced into physics by Charles Augustin Coulomb (1736-1806), in 1779.

The assumption which we have just made, that the restraining force of friction may have any value up to a constant fraction, characteristic of the materials concerned, of the normal reaction across the surface of contact of bodies, over a wide range of conditions in air—and which we have seen to be consistent with experiment—seems at first sight difficult to justify in physical terms. For it is essential to the assumption that the force of friction does not depend upon the area of the surface of contact but only on the force normal to that area, whether due solely to the weight of the supported body or not. But a little reflection will show that the situation is otherwise. Forces of friction are brought into play by interaction between individual atoms or molecules of the one body and those of the other. We are familiar with the three states of matter, solid, liquid and gaseous, and we must necessarily assume, in any assessment of the qualitative differences which matter exhibits in these different states (see Chapters 15 and 16 for a more detailed discussion), that the strong 'cohesive' forces which act between atoms and molecules in the solid state are relatively ineffective in the gaseous state. On the other hand, when a liquid boils, under normal atmospheric pressure, the saturation density of its vapour is in general not much less than one-thousandth of the density of the liquid. Thus the mean distance of separation of the molecules is not much greater, in the vapour, than ten times the mean distance in the liquid (or solid). We conclude, therefore, that the intermolecular forces of attraction become insignificantly small when the separation of the molecules is ten times the separation in the solid state, or that contact between the surfaces of bodies must be closer than some ten atomic diameters before frictional forces can be brought into play. Ten atomic diameters (see p. 28) is not much greater than 10^{-7} cm.

We begin our discussion of the 'laws' of friction, therefore, with the assumption that when two bodies are in contact across surfaces which are macroscopically plane, the area of 'true' or effective contact is very much smaller than the area over which, in ordinary usage, we should say that one body is resting upon the other. It would indeed be sufficient for stability that there should be true contact between the bodies over three small regions of the interfacial plane, only. Let us suppose that, whatever the number of such regions, the total area of true contact increases proportionately to the force acting normal to the surfaces, and that the limiting strength of a region of true contact in resisting 'sideways' motion is proportional to its area. Then it will be seen that we have the necessary ingredients of a plausible description of phenomena in physical terms. We are suggesting that quasi-solid 'welds' are developed across the interfacial plane, and that the overall strength of these against a sideways force is proportional to the normal re-action by which they are established. In order to make our description fully acceptable we have to suppose that once sideways motion has begun, the welds initially established having broken, others are re-established only to be similarly destroyed, and so on, as long as the motion persists. There is good evidence that these speculations are not mere fantasy: it has been possible to demonstrate, under controlled conditions, both the discontinuous nature of sliding motion as such, and also the fact that the electrical resistance across a sliding contact varies in a haphazard way with time, much as we should expect if the main current-bearing paths were through the transient welds that we have postulated.

We have already stressed that we have been dealing, hitherto, with frictional effects as observed between ordinarily clean and dry surfaces 'in contact' in air under standard conditions. Now that we have recognised the importance of effects at very small distances, it is pertinent to ask whether our specification of 'clean' and 'dry' is sufficiently precise—or sufficiently rigorous. That it is reasonably precise (and correspondingly significant for engineering practice) is evident from the fact that determinations of the coefficient of friction can be made with fair accuracy and good reproducibility in widely different arrangements, but, when it is realised that a layer of a foreign substance two or three molecules thick is all that is required almost completely to mask the cohesive forces due to the atoms or molecules of the underlying solid, it appears much more doubtful whether 'clean and dry surfaces in ordinary air' really exhibit frictional effects characteristic of the materials of which the bodies themselves are made. It is perfectly easy, by smearing an almost imperceptible film of oil over metallic surfaces, to reduce experimentally determined values of μ from say 0·2, the 'standard' value, to 0·1 or even less. It is obviously a matter for enquiry whether, when more than ordinarily careful cleaning is undertaken, and air is excluded, values of μ higher than the standard value may be recorded. The answer to this enquiry is very remarkable. If the experiments are done in the absence of air, the ordinarily clean metal surfaces having previously been 'out-gassed' by prolonged heating 'in vacuum', frictional effects are greatly intensified: instead of the standard value of about 0·2,

μ may be as large as 5 or 10. This is not the only line of evidence which leads us to conclude that the surfaces of solid bodies in air, particularly metallic surfaces, rapidly become coated with an extremely thin film of 'adsorbed' gas or other 'dirt' which ordinary washing or polishing is powerless to remove.

The fact of the occurrence of a restraining force of friction between solid bodies in contact, when there is, or is a tendency towards, relative motion, is of great importance in conditions of modern civilisation. Engineering practice, in one large field of application, is perpetually directed towards minimising the effects of this force; in another its success depends entirely on friction being adequate. In all machines in which there are shafts rotating in bearings, or pistons working in cylinders, friction is uneconomic and generally undesirable, and much ingenuity is devoted to its reduction. In the operation of railways, on the other hand, if the limiting friction between driving wheels and track is not great enough, a stopped train is unable to re-start: the wheels slip and rotate at great speed, much to the delight of the attendant school-boy, but nothing useful is achieved. Even with a train in uniform motion along a horizontal track, force is necessary to counteract the resistance of the air (§ 13.4), and this force, also, is transmitted from the engine to the train as a whole through the friction of the track preventing the slipping of the driving wheels. Examples of either situation could be multiplied, but enough has been said to establish the bipolarity of the problem.

13.3. FRICTION OF LIQUIDS: LUBRICATION AND VISCOSITY

If experiments are carried out with shafts rotating in 'flooded' cylindrical bearings, the conclusion may be drawn that the frictional torque, for a shaft of given diameter, is determined primarily by the properties of the liquid lubricant; neither the weight of the shaft nor any intrinsic property of the solid materials 'in contact' in the bearings is important. On the other hand, if the lubricant is not too 'thin' or the speed of the shaft too great, the frictional torque is proportional to the angular velocity—and in that case it is markedly dependent on temperature, decreasing rapidly as the temperature rises.

The basic facts in relation to friction in fully lubricated motion were discovered by Beauchamp Tower, a railway engineer, in 1883.

Less than three years later a complete theory of the effect was published by Osborne Reynolds (1842-1912). Here we are not concerned with details, though they may be all-important for the technologist; suffice to say that, in the conditions which we have described, the rotating shaft is never in contact with its bearing— a film of lubricant thick enough to have the properties of the liquid in bulk separates the moving parts, and in consequence the frictional effects observed are those characteristic of relative motion of layers of liquid rather than the characteristic effects of solid friction which we have already discussed. We pass, therefore, to a consideration of liquid friction in its own right—and under simpler conditions.

Imagine an ideal experiment in which small balls of different diameters, and made of different materials, are released just below the surface of a transparent liquid (say a medium-heavy lubricating oil) contained in a tall cylindrical vessel of large radius. It will be observed that all these balls, which in free fall would have the same uniform acceleration, rapidly acquire in the liquid uniform velocities which are different for the different balls. The following empirical results may be established:

1. For balls made of the same material the terminal velocity is proportional to the square of the radius of the ball, at least up to a limiting value of the radius.

2. For balls of the same radius the terminal velocity is proportional to the difference between the density of the material of the ball and the density of the liquid, at least up to a limiting value of this quantity.

It will be seen that, from these empirical results on resisted fall under gravity, we are able to deduce how the resistance due to fluid friction depends upon the radius of the ball and upon its velocity—over a wide range of circumstances.

For suppose that the effect of fluid friction on a spherical body moving through a liquid with velocity v is to produce a resultant resistive force of magnitude R acting through the centre of the body in the direction opposite to that of its instantaneous velocity. Then, if r is the radius of the moving body, and if ρ, ρ_0 are, respectively, the densities of the material of the body and of the liquid through which it is moving, in the case of fall under gravity, *a*, the measure of the acceleration of the body at any instant, is given by

$$\tfrac{4}{3}\pi r^3(\rho-\rho_0)g - R(r,\, v,\, k) = \tfrac{4}{3}\pi r^3\rho a.$$

Here *g* is the acceleration due to gravity, and the functional notation $R(r,\, v,\, k)$ has been adopted to indicate that we expect the magnitude of the frictional force to depend upon the radius of the body, upon its velocity, and on a quantity *k* characteristic of the liquid in which the force is generated. In the initial stages of such motion the acceleration must be supposed to decrease as the velocity increases, until, when the terminal velocity v_f is reached, $a = 0$. Then

$$R(r,\, v_f,\, k) = \tfrac{4}{3}\pi r^3(\rho-\rho_0)g \qquad (112)$$

But our second empirical result states that, *r*, *k* and ρ_0 being constant, over a considerable range

$$v_f = c_1(\rho-\rho_0),$$

c_1 itself being constant within experimental uncertainty. Obviously, this result is consistent with equation (112) only if

$$R(r,\, v_f,\, k) = v_f R_1(r,\, k) \qquad (113)$$

Referring now to our first empirical result, when $(\rho-\rho_0)$ and *k* are constant, we have

$$v_f = c_2 r^2,$$

to the same accuracy and over a corresponding range. For consistency with equations (112) and (113), we therefore require

$$R_1(r,\, k) = rk \qquad (114)$$

wherein, *k* having been hitherto but vaguely defined, it is no longer necessary to retain a functional notation for this constant alone. Finally, then, we obtain formally

$$R(r,\, v,\, k) = rvk \qquad (115)$$

a result valid for any velocity for which the empirical 'laws' are valid—and we may express this result in words: when a spherical body moves with uniform velocity through a liquid it experiences a resistive force due to fluid friction proportional in magnitude to the radius of the sphere and to its velocity, at least for velocities less than some limiting value.

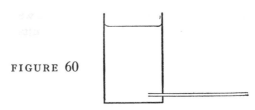

FIGURE 60

We may note in passing that this result is consonant with the observations of Tower on film lubrication: the frictional force is generally independent of the properties of the material of which the moving body is made, and it is proportional to its velocity. We should also note, for future reference, that the quantity k, characterising the properties of the liquid in our formal argument, has dimensions $M^1L^{-1}T^{-1}$. We pass now to consider another ideal experiment which has an important bearing on our general problem.

Suppose that liquid is contained in a vessel of large cross-sectional area, as represented in fig. 60, and that it escapes through a horizontal capillary tube let into the side of the vessel as shown. Let l be the length and a the cylindrical radius of the capillary tube, and let the surface of the liquid in the vessel be at a height h above the axis of the tube. If ρ is the density of the liquid, the pressure at the end of the tube projecting into the vessel is greater than the atmospheric pressure by an amount $g\rho h$, whilst the pressure at the other end of the tube in air is the atmospheric pressure. There is, therefore, a force of magnitude $\pi a^2 g\rho h$ acting on the liquid in the tube, tending to produce an acceleration along the tube. However, direct observation shows that there is no such acceleration of the liquid in the tube itself: if the velocity of the liquid were to increase along the tube, the cross-section of the moving stream of liquid would of necessity decrease with increasing distance along the tube. No such effect is observed: the liquid fills the tube along its whole length, and we are forced to conclude that the force due to the difference of pressure is balanced by a resistive force of which the origin is to be sought in the fact that there is relative motion between the liquid and a solid body. In this case the solid body is the capillary tube through which the liquid is flowing.

Suppose, now, that we measure the rate at which liquid flows through the tube, and that we represent this rate by Q, the volume transported per unit time. If, for a given liquid and a given tube, we relate Q to the pressure difference $p_2-p_1=g\rho h$, we obtain results as shown in fig. 61.

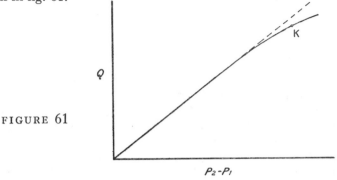

Q

FIGURE 61

$P_2 - P_1$

Over a considerable range of pressures, Q is directly proportional to the pressure difference. We obtain a curve of the same general form if, for a given liquid and a given pressure difference, using different lengths cut from the same capillary tube, we plot measured values of Q against $1/l$. Finally, and in practice more difficult, if, for a given liquid and a given pressure difference, we use tubes of the same length but different radii, we obtain a similar curve if we plot Q against a^4. Confining attention to the conditions represented by the initital portions of these various curves, we may assume that we have established the empirical result

$$Q = k_1 a^4 (p_2 - p_1)/l \qquad (116)$$

the frictional properties of the liquid being represented in this case by the quantity k_1.

Our first comment on equation (116) is that the dimensions of the quantity k_1 are $M^{-1}L^1T^1$, so that the quantity of which $1/k_1$ is the measure has the same dimensions as the quantity which we have represented by k in equation (115). We re-write equation (116), therefore, as

$$Q = a^4 (p_2 - p_1)/k_2 l \qquad (117)$$

thereby rendering it more directly comparable with equation (115). According to that equation, the greater the value of k for the liquid in question, the greater the resistive force arising from frictional effects, the other parameters being unchanged. According to equation (117), correspondingly, the greater the value of k_2 the smaller the rate of flow of liquid, other things being equal. The two results, therefore, are entirely concordant, as we should expect them to be if the common dimensions of the quantities which k and k_2 represent are evidence for the fact that a single physical quantity is involved in the two cases, not a separate quantity in each, significant only for the particular arrangement for which it was defined. We accept this fact, writing $k = n\eta$, $k_2 = n_2\eta$, where n and n_2 are pure numbers, and η represents the unique quantity of dimensions $M^1L^{-1}T^{-1}$ to which the name 'coefficient of viscosity' is given.

The precise definition of the coefficient of viscosity of a liquid was first given by Newton. A large part of book 2 of *Principia* is devoted to a consideration of resisted motion in liquids, and though

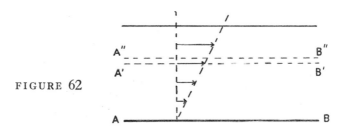

FIGURE 62

most of the discussion deals with the case in which the resistance to motion varies as the square of the velocity (see p. 261), rather than as the velocity simply, which is the situation represented by equation (115), Newton concluded that in special circumstances a linear relation would apply. These special circumstances are illustrated in fig. 62. Here AB represents the plane surface of a solid, and liquid is supposed to be flowing over the surface in the direction of the arrows, which are the velocity vectors. Every particle of the liquid moves parallel to the surface in the same direction, and v, the velocity of any particle, is directly proportional to d, its distance from the surface. Across $A'B'$, any plane in the liquid parallel to AB, the more quickly moving liquid above the plane exerts a tangential force tending to accelerate the more slowly moving liquid below the plane, whilst the liquid below the plane tends to retard that above. The motion of the liquid in any thin stratum bounded by parallel planes, $A'B'$, $A''B''$, will be steady motion if the accelerating force from the liquid above A"B" exactly balances the retarding force from the liquid below A'B'. This will be the case if the magnitude of the tangential force per unit area is everywhere proportional to the normal gradient of velocity (rate of increase of tangential velocity with distance at right angles to the plane), for this quantity we have assumed to be constant and equal to v/d. If F is the measure of the tangential force over an area S parallel to AB in the figure, Newton defined η, the coefficient of viscosity, by the equation

$$F = \eta Sv/d \qquad (118)$$

According to this definition, as we have already implied, the dimensions of η are $M^1L^{-1}T^{-1}$. In the c.g.s. system the unit is the poise.

We have just considered the simplest possible case of 'stream-line' flow of liquid. In general, liquid flow is spoken of as stream-line flow if the pattern of flow is a stable one, such that the velocity of flow at any point in the liquid is constant with time. In such circumstances, if we follow the motion of any particle of the liquid, the particle traces out a 'stream-line', and any other particle of the liquid subsequently found to be on this stream-line remains on it. Stream-line flow is flow without mixing. Experiment shows that when equation (115) is valid for a sphere moving through a liquid, or equation (117) valid for the flow of liquid through a cylindrical tube, the flow is stream-line flow, in either case. A mathematical discussion of the effects of viscosity in stream-line flow in general was first given by Siméon Denis Poisson (1781-1840) in 1831.

Experiments on the stream-line flow of liquids in tubes were carried out by G. H. L. Hagen (1797-1884), a physicist turned engineer, in 1839, and by Jean Louis Marie Poiseuille (1799-1869), a physiologist turned physicist, from 1840 to 1842. On the assumption that the liquid immediately in contact with the walls of the tube remains at rest, application of Poisson's mathematics leads to the result $k_2 = 8\eta/\pi$, so that equation (117) becomes explicitly

$$Q = \pi a^4(p_2 - p_1)/8\eta l \qquad (119)$$

This equation has come to be known as Poiseuille's equation, though being an experimenter he was responsible more for its verification as an empirical result, and for its use in the first

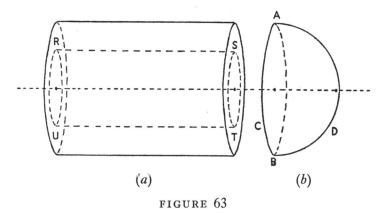

(a)   (b)

FIGURE 63

accurate determinations of coefficients of viscosity, than for its
precise form as deduced by mathematical reasoning.

We can appreciate something of the details of stream-line flow
through tubes from simple considerations. Obviously the velocity
of flow, if zero at the walls, must be a maximum along the axis of
the tube, the whole pattern of flow being cylindrically symmetrical.
In fig. 63, therefore, in which (a) represents a section of the tube,
some such diagram as (b) will represent the velocity distribution.
Here the dome-shaped surface ADB is the envelope of the velocity
vectors drawn from points in the circle ABC corresponding to the
cross-section of the tube. We may appreciate how this velocity
distribution is appropriate to the situation, by considering the
forces acting on the liquid occupying in the tube a cylindrical
volume such as RSTU at any instant. Let the radius of this
cylindrical volume be r. Then the area of each of its plane end-
faces is proportional to r^2, and the area of its curved surface is
proportional to r. The first area multiplied by the difference of
pressure between the ends of the cylinder gives the force acting
down the tube, the second area multiplied by the absolute magnitude of the radial velocity gradient is proportional to the resistive
force due to viscosity. In the steady state these two forces must be
equal. We conclude, therefore, that the radial velocity gradient
must be proportional to r, the distance from the axis. This type
of variation is not inconsistent with the form we have given to
fig. 63 (b): the velocity gradient is obviously zero on the axis,
when $r=0$, and it increases in absolute magnitude as r increases.

R

Starting from the result that the radial velocity gradient is proportional to the radial distance, we could work out the form of the velocity distribution precisely. Experimentally, the problem may be studied by injecting a very fine stream of coloured liquid into the flow tube at the high-pressure end. If this stream of liquid is periodically interrupted, the progress of the 'gaps' in the coloured stream may be followed, and the velocity of flow deduced at different distances from the axis of the tube. Obviously, the method is not one of high precision, but the general form of fig. 63 (*b*) may be shown to be correct.

On the assumption that when a spherical body moves through an 'infinite' liquid there is no abrupt discontinuity of velocity between solid and liquid over the surface of the body ('the liquid in immediate contact with the body moves with the body'), equation (115) was given precise form first by George Gabriel Stokes (1819-1903) in 1845. Stokes found $k = 6\pi\eta$ in this case, thus we have, instead of equation (115),

$$R = 6\pi\eta r v \qquad\qquad (120)$$

a result which is generally referred to as Stokes's law. Equation (120) may be put in the form

$$R = \eta . 4\pi r^2 . (3v/2r)$$

and compared with equation (118). $S = 4\pi r^2$ is the surface area of the sphere over which the resistive forces act, and $3v/2r$ is an average velocity gradient at the surface of the sphere. Actually, we overestimate the effective area, and therefore underestimate the mean radial velocity gradient, since the force is everywhere tangential to the surface in the direction of the stream-lines. But we are concerned with an order of magnitude only. To that accuracy we can certainly say that the velocity gradient at the surface is such that if it were continued over a distance of one-half the radius in the equatorial plane of the sphere it would completely annul the whole relative velocity of sphere and liquid. Obviously, the velocity gradient rapidly decreases with increasing distance, so that the liquid at a distance of a radius and a half from the axis of motion is not entirely unaffected; on the other hand the general conclusion is equally obvious, that, when a spherical body is moving through a liquid and Stokes's law is valid, the main motion of liquid is confined to a cylindrical region around the axis of motion of diameter only a few times the diameter of the sphere. An empirical result, generally referred to as the Ladenburg correction, and useful as a first approximation, is that when a sphere of radius r is moving through liquid along the axis of an infinite cylinder of radius C the resistive force is given by

$$R = 6\pi\eta r v \left(1 + 2 \cdot 4 \frac{r}{C}\right).$$

In our earlier discussion we have stressed the fact that the equations of Poiseuille and Stokes are valid only for relatively small velocities, and for systems having relatively small linear dimensions at right angles to the direction of flow: spheres of small radius, and relatively narrow tubes. We must now consider on what scale these estimates of smallness are to be judged. Some help may be gained by examining more closely the conditions under which the simple laws fail to give a correct account of phenomena. Suppose that the difference of pressure between the two ends of a capillary tube is such that Poiseuille's equation no longer gives the experimentally observed value of the rate of flow. This situation is represented by a point such as K on fig. 61. If a fine stream of coloured liquid is injected into the flow tube under these conditions it will be found to break up into eddies and become thoroughly mixed with the main stream as it flows down the tube. This effect, first demonstrated by Osborne Reynolds (see p. 251), shows clearly that the character of the motion changes as the velocity increases: it is no longer the stream-line motion in terms of which we defined the Newtonian coefficient of viscosity, thus some other property of the liquid must enter into its description. The observation that the motion is 'turbulent', or eddying, motion suggests that the property most likely to be involved is the density. The energy associated with any configuration of eddies, the velocities being given, is proportional to the density of the liquid; this energy must have been derived as work done by the applied forces, however it is dissipated (see § 14.2): not to include the density as a parameter in our discussion would obviously be entirely unrealistic.

Suppose, therefore, that ρ is the measure of the density of the liquid, and η, as before, the measure of the coefficient of viscosity. For our present considerations, r may represent either the radius of the sphere, as in equation (120), or the cylindrical radius of the capillary tube, represented by a in equation (119). In either case the quantity of which $\eta/r\rho$ is the measure has dimensions $M^1L^{-1}T^{-1}/L^1M^1L^{-3}$, or L^1T^{-1}; in other words, the quantity so represented is a velocity. Let us write

$$v_0 = \eta/r\rho,$$

hen we have defined a characteristic velocity which the particular circumstances of the case determine—in terms of the properties of the liquid (its density and coefficient of viscosity) and a length descriptive of the region of disturbance caused by the solid body concerned. The basic assumption of the present argument is that the nature of the motion, in any case, is itself determined by the ratio of the actual velocity, v in equation (120), or $Q/\pi a^2$ in equation (119), to this characteristic velocity. In particular, we assume that as actual velocities are increased, stream-line motion persists for values of v/v_0 (or $Q/\pi a^2 v_0$) less than a critical value, and turbulence sets in when this critical value is exceeded. This assumption is fully justified by experiment—and with it our prior assumption that the density of the liquid is the other property involved in these problems of flow. It should be recognised that v/v_0 (or $Q/\pi a^2 v_0$) is a dimensionless quantity, a pure number: its critical value, characterising the onset of turbulence in a particular type of experimental arrangement—moving sphere, or flow-tube, or any other general situation—is referred to as the critical Reynolds's number for that arrangement. For flow in long cylindrical tubes, this critical number is 1000, or thereabouts.

To consider the general characteristics of turbulent motion further is beyond the scope of this book, but one special case may be dealt with briefly by an extension of the argument from dimensions which we have just concluded. Stokes's equation (120) may be generalised

$$R = \eta r v . f\left(\frac{v}{v_0}\right),$$

where $f\left(\dfrac{v}{v_0}\right)$, a pure number, is some as yet unspecified function of the ratio of the velocity of the sphere to the characteristic velocity. Concerning the nature of this function, we already have, for values of v/v_0 less than the critical Reynolds's number for this case,

$$f\left(\frac{v}{v_0}\right) = 6\pi.$$

For larger values of v/v_0, we may write formally

$$f\left(\frac{v}{v_0}\right) = A + B\left(\frac{v}{v_0}\right) + \cdots$$

If there is a range of high velocities for which the second term in this expansion is predominant, then, over this range, we have approximately

$$R = B\eta r \frac{v^2}{v_0} = B\rho r^2 v^2,$$

indicating that in such circumstances the resistive force is proportional to the density of the liquid and independent of its viscosity, and that it varies as the square of the velocity. We may recall that it was to this law of velocity-dependence that Newton devoted most attention in book 2 of *Principia* (see p. 255).

At the beginning of this section we remarked that with liquid lubricants used in cylindrical bearings at low speeds the frictional torque decreases rapidly as the temperature rises. This is a general result: for all liquids the coefficient of viscosity decreases rapidly with increase of temperature: water, for example, is only half as viscous at 25° C as it is at 0° C, and at 65° C the coefficient of viscosity has decreased by a further factor of 2.

13.4. VISCOSITY OF GASES

In general, most of the statements concerning resisted motion made in the last section are true, with minor modifications, when the resisting medium is a gas rather than a liquid. In respect of Newtonian viscosity we are primarily concerned with the fact that the medium shall offer no permanent resistance to change of shape —that it shall be 'mobile'. That is a property common to liquids and gases, and in this connection the term 'fluid' is commonly used for matter in either state, indiscriminately. Apart from the fact that liquids may to a good approximation be regarded as incompressible, whereas gases are certainly markedly compressible fluids, the formal results of § 13.3 remain valid, only the magnitude of the coefficient of viscosity is usually very much smaller than we have hitherto considered, when gases are in question.

In particular, equation (120) gives the resistive force correctly, and, when combined with equation (112), the terminal velocity for a sphere of radius r falling through a gas. In such a case we can reasonably neglect ρ_0, the density of the gas, in comparison with ρ, the density of the material of the sphere, and we have explicitly

$$ v_f = \frac{2}{9} \frac{r^2 \rho g}{\eta}, $$

under conditions of stream-line flow. The ratio of the terminal velocity to the characteristic velocity v_0 (p. 260), in these circumstances, is

$$ \frac{v_f}{v_0} = \frac{2}{9} \frac{r^3 \rho \rho_0 g}{\eta^2} = \frac{1}{6\pi} \frac{\rho_0}{\eta^2} W, $$

W being the weight of the falling sphere. Suppose, now, that the critical Reynolds's number for the arrangement is Σ, then for spheres of mass greater than m_c, given by

$$ m_c = 6\pi \eta^2 \Sigma / \rho_0 g, $$

the steady-state terminal motion is turbulent in character.

For small drops of water falling through air, as to order of magnitude, $\eta = 1 \cdot 8 \times 10^{-4}$ poise, $\Sigma = 1000$, $\rho_0 = 1 \cdot 2 \times 10^{-3}$ g. cm.$^{-3}$, $g = 1000$ cm. sec.$^{-2}$, thus the critical mass, m_c, is 5×10^{-4} g. and the critical radius $0 \cdot 5$ mm. Such a drop would have a terminal velocity of about 3×10^3 cm. sec.$^{-1}$.

The formal results are the same as before, but there is one feature of the situation which acquires an importance which it did not previously possess. We have just calculated the critical value of the terminal velocity, $_c v_f$, for water drops falling in air, such that for larger drops the steady-state motion is turbulent. If we make a comparison, in this connection, of values of $_c v_f$, for fall in different fluids, of spherical bodies for which $(\rho - \rho_0)$—the effective density making allowance for buoyancy—is constant, it is easy to show that $_c v_f^3 \rho_0^2 / \eta$ is the same in all cases. Now the distance through which the body must fall in the fluid, in order to acquire the velocity $_c v_f$, is proportional to $_c v_f^2 / 2g$, the distance through which it would have to fall freely to achieve the same velocity (see below). Let us call this distance h_c. Then $h_c \rho_0{}^{4/3}/\eta^{2/3}$ is constant in the conditions we have specified. For water drops in air h_c is approximately $4 \cdot 5 \times 10^3$ cm. For spheres of the same effective density in olive oil, for which $\rho_0{}^2/\eta$ is about 100 times greater than the corresponding value for air, h_c is some 20 times less, that is about 200 cm. We have here been dealing with the extreme situation in which stream-line flow breaks down into turbulence, but this feature is equally characteristic of the general situation at lower speeds, the distance through which a spherical body must fall in air in order to acquire its terminal velocity through the interplay of the forces of gravity and viscosity is, when the comparison is appropriately made, in general much greater than the distance through which its counterpart must fall in a fairly viscous liquid in order that its velocity shall become constant.

We stated above that in all cases of fall through a viscous fluid the characteristic distances involved are proportional to h, the distance, in free fall, which would be required for the body to achieve its actual terminal velocity v_f. In fact, when the matter is studied in detail, it is found that the notion of a terminal velocity is strictly an ideal notion: a body falling under the conditions which we have been discussing never fully attains the velocity v_f, as given by the formula. Its velocity reaches the value $0 \cdot 5 v_f$ after it has fallen through a distance $0 \cdot 193h$, $0 \cdot 9 v_f$ after it has fallen through $1 \cdot 40h$, $0 \cdot 99 v_f$ after $3 \cdot 61h$, $0 \cdot 999 v_f$ after $5 \cdot 91h$, and so on. For most practical purposes the body may be considered to move uniformly with its true terminal velocity after it has fallen through five times the height through which it would have to fall to achieve that velocity under gravity alone.

In respect of Poiseuille's equation (119), there are minor modifications to take count of the compressibility of gases, the situation in question being one in which the pressure varies throughout the motion. For an ideal gas, at constant temperature, the product of pressure and volume is constant for a given mass (see Chapter 15). Under conditions of steady flow, obviously the rate of entry of gas at the high-pressure end of the flow-tube is the same as the rate of discharge from the low-pressure end. If, therefore, a volume V_2 measured at the higher pressure p_2 enters in time t, and a volume V_1 measured at the lower pressure p_1 is discharged in the same time, we have $p_2 V_2 = p_1 V_1$, the temperature being constant throughout. Then detailed calculation shows that Poiseuille's equation is modified as follows: namely

$$\frac{p_2 V_2}{t} = \frac{p_1 V_1}{t} = \frac{\pi a^4 (p_2{}^2 - p_1{}^2)}{16 \eta l} \qquad (121)$$

the other symbols having the same meaning as before. We may note that V/t in equation (121) has the same dimensions as Q in equation (119); it is clear, therefore, that there must be an additional power of p on the right-hand side of the modified equation to balance the introduction of the new pressure-term on the left-hand side. In fact, in equation (121) we have $(p_2{}^2 - p_1{}^2)$ where we had $(p_2 - p_1)$ in equation (119), which satisfies these requirements.

We now turn to less formal considerations, and in particular to the question of the variation of viscosity with temperature and pressure. In the case of liquids we were able to neglect the effect of pressure altogether: as we have already stated, it is a sufficiently good approximation, in this connection, to consider liquids as incompressible. We were also able to neglect as trivial any effect of temperature on the density: in relation to turbulence we could regard the density and the coefficient of viscosity of the liquid as unconnected parameters. With gases, however, the problem requires further consideration. As would appear reasonable, physically, we shall consider possible variations with density and temperature separately, and in that order.

In 1860, James Clerk Maxwell (1831-1879), developing the consequences of the kinetic theory (see Chapter 15) in relation to gaseous viscosity, predicted that the viscosity should be independent of the density, within wide limits. In 1866 he verified this surprising prediction by mounting a rigid system of three circular plates, carried on a rod passing through their centres, on a long torsion wire, assembling four fixed plates around them, as shown in fig. 64, enclosing the whole in a large glass vessel, and observing the torsional oscillations of the suspended system when the air in the vessel was at different pressures. In such an arrangement the oscillations die down chiefly as a result of the frictional drag of the air in the narrow spaces between the fixed and moving plates, and Maxwell found that the rate of decrease of angular amplitude, at a given amplitude, was the same at all pressures from atmospheric pressure downwards, until the vessel was almost completely exhausted of air. This is the behaviour to which his theoretical

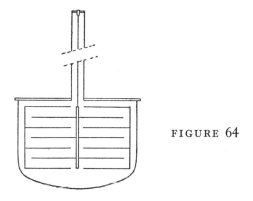

FIGURE 64

investigations had pointed; here we must leave its further discussion until we come to consider the kinetic theory in its own right (§ 15.5).

We can now deal with the matter of temperature-dependence of viscosity very briefly. At constant density the coefficient of viscosity of a gas increases with increasing temperature. In this respect liquids and gases behave differently, but, again, the behaviour of gases is very much as would be predicted on the basis of the theory which Maxwell elaborated.

CHAPTER 14

HEAT AND ENERGY

14.1. CONCEPTS OF HEAT AND TEMPERATURE

In Chapter 1 we classed together, loosely, the subjects heat and the bulk properties of matter as those which have been developed by analysis of primary sensations received through our sense of touch. In respect of heat, certainly, the initial experience is of bodies which can be arranged in a sequence of 'hotter' or 'colder' in accordance with our intuitive judgment of how they 'feel' when we place our hands in contact with them (and, if the bodies are neither too hot nor too cold, if we keep our hands perfectly still and relaxed). We do not analyse the basis of this judgment, though we have considerable confidence in its validity. Following its deliverances we already recognise a fair degree of order in phenomena. Two bodies, one hotter than the other, retain this difference in physical condition for a relatively long time if they are suspended in still air, but they quickly lose any such difference if they are brought into intimate contact. Our tactile sensation itself may have some such basis. As the subject becomes systematised, we introduce the notion of 'temperature' to specify the degree of hotness of a body, and the notion of an entity 'heat', which naturally tends to transfer itself from a body at a higher to one at a lower temperature, until the temperatures are equalised. Introducing these notions, we obviously aspire to make them quantitative: to set up a numerical scale for the specification of temperature, to define a unit in terms of which to measure quantities of heat.

In logic, as in the history of the subject, the establishment of a scale of temperature precedes the definition of a unit quantity of heat. For this purpose, in the initial stages at least, it is necessary to make use of a measureable property of some common substance, the measure of which varies with the degree of hotness of a sample of the substance in such a way as to make unambiguous specification possible over a considerable range of conditions. The property of volume has been regularly utilised in this way from the time when Galileo first devised a crude thermometer in the year 1597, or thereabouts, to the present day.

Galileo's thermometer consisted on a glass bulb blown on the end of a long tube standing with its open end in a vessel containing a coloured liquid, the height of the liquid in the tube indicating the temperature of the air in the bulb. As we now recognise, this arrangement is sensitive to changes in atmospheric pressure as well as to changes in temperature. To obviate this difficulty, thermometers depending upon the expansion of liquids such as alcohol, and constructed with sealed-off stems, were introduced by Rinieri in Florence in 1646, and about 1670 mercury began to be employed in such instruments in spite of its smaller relative expansion. Its opacity, and the fact that in contact with glass it does not 'wet' the glass, are greatly in its favour. But difficulties remained, owing to imperfect purification, and these were not finally overcome until 1724, when Gabriel Daniel Fahrenheit (1686-1736) discovered the method of filtration through leather. For the purposes of this chapter we may regard the mercury-in-glass thermometer of Fahrenheit as our standard instrument.

In the foregoing we have briefly described our thermometer, but we have not defined its scale. It was not, in fact, until about the middle of the eighteenth century that uniformity of usage in this respect was achieved—and it is well known that even today at least two different scales are still widely used. But what is now agreed, and what was not agreed originally, is the definition of the 'fixed points' on these scales. The lower fixed point is defined by the position of the end of the thread of mercury in the thermometer stem when the thermometer is in thermal equilibrium with melting ice, the upper fixed point by the position of the end of the thread when the thermometer is in thermal equilibrium in steam arising from water boiling under standard conditions of pressure. It is customary to ascribe the definition of the lower fixed point to Newton (1701), and the first suggestion that the upper fixed point should thus be defined to Halley. The ice- and steam-points having been determined, the stem of the thermometer is subdivided uniformly. The difference between the Fahrenheit and centigrade scales relates only to the details of this subdivision. On the former scale the ice-point is marked as 32° and the steam-point as 212°; on the latter scale, suggested by the Swedish astronomer Anders Celsius (1701-1744), the ice-point is marked as 0° and the steam-point as 100°. The centigrade scale is the one now generally employed in the physical laboratories of the world.

Having established our scale of temperature, we are at last in a position to explore the quantitative aspects of the notion 'amount of heat', remarking that we have as yet no clear idea what may be the nature of this new entity 'heat' which we have introduced into our conceptual scheme. It is a truism to state that, unless 'heat' can be defined so that in an ideal isolated system its total quantity is conserved under a wide variety of conditions, the introduction of this new concept is wholly unjustified.

It is relatively simple to frame our definition so as to achieve a conservation law for simple exchanges of heat between bodies when no change of state is involved. We find it logical to suppose that, when the temperature of a body of mass m changes from T_1 to T_2, the quantity of heat associated with the body increases by an amount proportional to the product $m(T_2 - T_1)$, and it is only necessary to define a quantity s, characteristic of the material of which the body is made, in order to say that the amount of heat involved is $ms(T_2 - T_1)$, in terms of a suitable unit. In this way we obtain a consistent description of phenomena. If an 'isolated' system consists of two bodies of masses m_1, m_2 at temperatures T_1, T_2, and if the bodies in thermal contact reach a final common temperature T, the general conservation equation

$$m_1 s_1 (T - T_1) + m_2 s_2 (T - T_2) = 0 \qquad (122)$$

allows the ratio s_1/s_2 to be deduced from experiment, and this ratio in fact turns out to be characteristic of the materials concerned— with slight variations which can be correlated with the temperatures at which the different determinations are made. The ratio s_1/s_2 of equation (122) is referred to as the ratio of the 'mean specific heats' of the two materials, over the temperature range T to T_1 in the one case and T_2 to T in the other. In order to choose a suitable unit we effectively decide that the measure of the mean specific heat of some particular substance over some particular range of temperature is unity. For most scientific purposes the substance chosen is water, and the standard range of temperature is from 14·5° C to 15·5° C. In this way we have the following broadly equivalent definitions:

1. Unit quantity of heat, '1 calorie', is the amount by which

the heat associated with 1 gramme of water increases when the temperature of the water increases from 14·5° C to 15·5° C.

2. The mean specific heat of water over the temperature range 14·5° C to 15·5° C is 1 calorie per gramme per degree centigrade.

The significance of the quantity now defined as specific heat was first clearly appreciated by Joseph Black (1728-1799) in 1760.

To Black we owe also the notion of 'latent heat', whereby the first difficulty in the way of a more general law of conservation of heat was overcome. We have already stated, by implication at least, that the notion of specific heat is irrelevant when changes of state are involved. Black was the first to recognise (1761) that a consistent description of experiment can be achieved only if we admit that, in the processes of melting and boiling, relatively large quantities of heat are communicated to substances without any consequent increase in temperature. In the reverse processes of freezing and condensation this heat reappears in 'sensible' form, being communicated from the substances to 'the surroundings'. He referred to heat 'stored' in this way as latent heat, and he showed that its amount is proportional to the mass of the substance melted or vaporised. Nowadays, we define L, the latent heat (of fusion or vaporisation) of a substance, by the equation

$$H = mL,$$

where an amount of heat H is involved in the change of state of a mass m of the substance concerned. The unit of measurement is, in consequence, 1 calorie per gramme.

It will be seen that the introduction of the notion of latent heat in our present discussion is in many ways analogous to the introduction of the notion of potential energy in dynamics (§ 11.1). In each case it is a device—albeit a perfectly legitimate one—by which the scope of a conservation law is extended. In each case, however, this extension of scope falls short of universality—in relation to heat, far short. It is common experience that heat appears in many systems undergoing chemical change, particularly in combustion, and that heat may be generated by friction. Indeed we are led to believe that it was in that way that man first achieved controlled combustion. It is also a fact of experience that heat appears in wires carrying currents of electricity, though the position is more complicated in that case, for the current-carrying wire cannot be regarded as an isolated system. In its essentials, however, the situation is clear-cut: there are many circumstances in which heat appears in a way which cannot be reversed, to which the idea of latent heat is inapplicable. In all these circumstances the law of conservation of heat alone is invalid.

In our present account of the subject we cannot follow the implications of all these apparent failures of the conservation law in detail, but one of them relates to the phenomena of friction, and it was in the same connection that we had to admit the failure of the law of conservation of energy in dynamics. In dynamics the notion of potential energy is inapplicable when the force depends on velocities (in respect of magnitude or direction) as it does in all cases of friction. We may well find it fruitful to enquire whether there is any underlying connection between these two conclusions —that in respect of friction neither the law of conservation of quantity of heat, nor the law of conservation of dynamical energy, is valid.

14.2. EXPERIMENTS OF JOULE AND OTHERS

In 1798 Benjamin Thompson, Count Rumford (1753-1814), presented to the Royal Society an *Enquiry concerning the Source of Heat which is excited by Friction*. A man of many parts, born in America, Fellow of the Royal Society at the age of twenty-six, at one time under-secretary of state for the British colonies, in 1798 he had just recently returned to London after eleven years service with the elector of Bavaria—as minister of war and commander-in-chief of the Bavarian army. His 'enquiry' had been an experimental one, and it had been carried out in the arsenal at Munich. Being at one time responsible for the boring of cannon, Rumford had been well placed to make a large-scale experiment on the heating produced by friction. He arranged for a blunt boring tool to be used on a mass of some 60 kg. of gun-metal, covered with flannel to minimise loss of heat. When only 54 g. of metal had been ground off, the temperature of the mass had risen from 15° C to 54° C. He determined the specific heat of the abraded metal, and found it to be the same as that of gun-metal in bulk.

Rumford regarded these results as showing that the pulverisation of the metal was in no direct way responsible for the appearance of heat, in the sense that the heat which appeared in the large block had not previously been associated with the fragments (it was the fashionable belief at the time that heat was a subtle material fluid permeating the pores of bodies), but that it had been produced in the boring—and that it would have been produced, in roughly the same amount, even if no metal had been abraded.

Rumford's main reasons for this conclusion were, first, that the thermal properties of the abraded fragments were the same as those of the metal in bulk, as attested by specific heat determinations, and, secondly, that such a large quantity of heat had been produced and such a small mass of fragments. He added the luminous comment, 'and it appears to me to be extremely difficult, if not quite impossible, to form any distinct idea of anything capable of being excited and communicated in these experiments except it be motion'. There is an echo here of a wise judgment of Francis Bacon, Baron Verulam (1561-1626), Lord Chancellor of England, delivered two centuries earlier, 'the very essence of heat, or the substantial self of heat, is motion and nothing else'. But that was only a philosopher's dictum.

The year after he presented his *Enquiry* to the Royal Society, Rumford was instrumental in promoting the foundation of the Royal Institution. For four years from its incorporation in 1800 he resided in the Institution's premises in Albemarle Street, and, in his capacity as patron and manager, on 16 February 1801, he appointed Humphry Davy (1778-1829) as assistant lecturer in chemistry and director of the laboratory. Davy was self-taught; less than four years previously he had begun his study of experimental science, but during that time he had carried out an experiment (1799) which is our only reason for referring to him here— and which possibly was the determining reason for his appointment by Rumford. Davy had shown that ice may be melted simply by friction between one piece of ice and another. Here certainly heat had been produced which was not previously associated with the bodies concerned: the specific heat of water is roughly twice as great as the specific heat of ice.

The experiments of Rumford and Davy, at least as we have described them, were largely qualitative experiments; those of Joule, which we are now to describe, were rigorously quantitative. James Prescott Joule (1818-1889) began his scientific career as a self-taught electrical engineer in Manchester. Before he was twenty-two he had established the quantitative relationship, now known as Joule's law, between the rate of production of heat in a wire carrying an electric current and the measures of the current and the difference of potential between the ends of the wire. He began to see that this relationship connected an amount of heat measured in calories with the measures of two electrical quantities ultimately defined in dynamical terms—in terms of force and work. After further electrical experiments, Joule became convinced that what he had been investigating was a special example of a much more general phenomenon, and in 1843 he introduced the term 'mechanical value of heat' (or, as he later wrote, 'mechanical equivalent of heat') to express the view that it is possible to produce heat merely by doing mechanical work, and that when this occurs the amount of work which is not otherwise accounted for can be accounted for by supposing that it has been 'converted' into heat. Within the restricted field of dynamics we have hitherto recognised only the conversion of work into energy—kinetic energy or potential energy, according to the circumstances of the case. According to Joule's view, mechanical work can be converted either into energy or into heat. For long periods during the next thirty-five years, he devoted himself to many series of careful experiments which in their overall result left no doubt of the essential validity of this assertion.

Here, according to plan, we must confine attention to Joule's experiments on the heat produced by friction. In an early series of experiments carried out before 1850, Joule measured the heat produced when water or mercury was forced through capillary tubes; when water or mercury was stirred by means of a paddle-wheel arrangement; when two cast-iron rings were in relative rotation 'lubricated' by mercury. Making allowance for the small amounts of work done otherwise than in friction in these various arrangements, he found that, for a given amount of work performed, the same quantity of heat was produced in each case.

After carrying out many investigations by other methods, Joule repeated his paddle-wheel experiments in 1875 and 1878. The later of these repetitions was the more convincing and the more thoroughly planned. The essential feature of the apparatus was a shallow cylindrical calorimeter in which an arrangement of vanes fixed to an axle could be rotated so as to agitate the water in the calorimeter without causing it to rotate in bulk. To achieve this result the calorimeter was designed as shown in vertical (a) and horizontal (b) section in fig. 65. Four fixed vanes of E-shape were

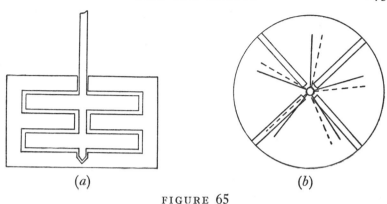

FIGURE 65

arranged symmetrically in the calorimeter, and the axle carried
two sets of five equally spaced rectangular vanes (paddles), one set
moving through the upper and the other through the lower gaps of
the E. The angular positions of the vanes of the lower set differed
by 9° from those of the upper set. In this way, there being 10
moving vanes and 4 that were fixed, the resistance to rotation
varied smoothly during each rotation, passing through a maximum
40 times at 9° intervals. The calorimeter was supported on three
pointed uprights carried on a hollow vessel floating in a larger
vessel containing water. The axle, passing through fixed bearings
above the calorimeter, could be rotated by belt drive from driving
wheels operated by hand. Had there been no constraint, the whole
calorimeter would have tended to take up the rotation of the
paddles when the latter were maintained in steady motion. Restraint was provided by equal weights, W, hanging by silk threads
over pulleys, the threads being fixed to the outer surface of the
calorimeter and wrapped round it, so that the effect of each weight
was applied to the calorimeter tangentially and in a horizontal
plane. Then the method of experimenting was to rotate the paddles
with a constant angular velocity ω, so that the weights neither rose
nor fell, and to determine the rate of increase of temperature of the
calorimeter and its contents. The mass of water in the calorimeter
being known, and the mass of the calorimeter itself and the specific
heat of its material, the rate of production of heat was calculable.
As regards the rate of performance of work, since the arrangement
was in every way equivalent to one in which the paddles are
stationary and the calorimeter is rotated with angular velocity ω by

S

falling weights, the appropriate rate is given by $2Wr\omega$, r being the radius of the calorimeter. Here $r\omega$ is the distance through which each weight would descend in unit time in the equivalent arrangement. Varying the conditions as much as possible, and making appropriate corrections for small effects which we cannot here describe in detail, Joule again confirmed his original assertion that the measure of the work done against the forces of friction bears a constant ratio to the measure of the heat produced.

The paddle-wheel experiment was repeated in the following year by H. A. Rowland (1848-1901) in Baltimore, U.S.A., with even greater refinement. The general conclusion was essentially the same as before, but Joule's accuracy was improved upon, and Rowland was able to demonstrate the variation of the specific heat of water with temperature, in terms of the variation with initial temperature of the amount of work necessary to raise the temperature of a mass of water by one degree by the process of stirring. From that date until the present time, other experiments, by many different methods, have merely added to the volume of evidence for the belief, now held to be incontrovertible, that whenever heat appears which cannot be accounted for in terms of the simple conservation law, then mechanical work has been done, either at the macroscopic or at the molecular level, and that for every calorie of heat so appearing $4 \cdot 1855 \times 10^7$ ergs of work have been performed. This conversion factor, $4 \cdot 1855 \times 10^7$ ergs per calorie (or $4 \cdot 1855$ joules per calorie), is the mechanical equivalent of heat, according to the best modern determinations.

14.3. THE CONSERVATION OF ENERGY

Joule's experiments, as we have seen, spanned a period of some forty years, from 1840 to 1880. By the end of that period their full significance had come to be appreciated by scientists in general, but it is fitting to record that for a young Prussian army surgeon, Hermann Ludwig Ferdinand von Helmholtz (1821-1894), the evidence which was available as early as 1847 was sufficient to engender in his mind notions which, far ahead of their time, were found as the years passed to bear the hall-mark of genius. On 23 July 1847 Helmholtz presented his ideas to the Physical Society of Berlin in a paper entitled *On the Conservation of Force* (Thomas Young's 'energy' had at that time no counterpart in the German language—see p. 228). Helmholtz had previously made an im-

portant discovery in physiology, but this was his first real contribution to physics. Indeed, he was to hold, in succession, three
university chairs of physiology before he became officially recognised as a professional physicist, on his appointment to the chair
of physics at Berlin in 1871. However, Helmholtz's genius was
many sided, and in his later life he returned to reinforce the grand
sweep of his early conception—of a law of conservation of energy
which was universal in its scope—with modern instances. Ever
since his death that process of proof by justification has continued.

Work done by a force when its point of application moves in its
own direction, may appear as kinetic energy, as potential energy
or as heat, depending upon whether there is resistance to motion
and, if so, upon the nature of the resistance—that is the conclusion
which we have drawn from the experiments described in the last
section. Clearly, it makes sense only if the various forms under
which work may appear are of the same kind, only, that is, if the
concepts energy and heat refer essentially to the same attribute of
matter. Historically, the origins of the concepts are separate and
distinct; logically, one of them, however convenient, is superfluous.
Logically, there is no reason for the retention of the calorie as a
separate unit in the c.g.s. system, once a distinctive name of convenience has been given to a unit of comparable size (1 joule $= 10^7$
ergs, 1 calorie $= 4.1855$ joules), but logic alone has a poor power of
persuasion even with scientists. Bacon affirmed that heat 'is motion
and nothing else': we have not yet come as far as this as a result of
the quantitative study of phenomena, but we have at least shown
that heat and kinetic energy are physical quantities of the same
kind, which takes us a long way towards that conclusion. We defer
the last step in the argument to the next chapter.

In this chapter we have intentionally left on one side any detailed
consideration of the production of heat in chemical change or in
electric circuits. In Helmholtz's formulation of the law of conservation of energy in general, these effects find their natural place:
heat so produced results from work done at the molecular level.
That is the justification of our statement (p. 274) 'whenever heat
appears which cannot be accounted for in terms of the simple
conservation law [of heat alone], then mechanical work has been
done, either at the macroscopic or at the molecular level'. We
cannot pursue the matter further here; we merely note the result.

There is one further comment, only. It is due to Tait (1883).

Being a comment of a somewhat philosophical nature, of the late nineteenth century, not surprisingly, perhaps, it has to do with the question of ultimate reality. Tait pointed out that, of the various conservation laws of physics—the conservation laws of dynamics which we have discussed, and the law of conservation of electric charge which we have not considered—only two relate to scalar quantities which are represented by positive magnitudes exclusively. Negative mass and negative energy are meaningless in relation to the physical universe as we have described it. It is possible, therefore, Tait concluded, that the concepts of mass and energy stand apart from all other physical concepts as corresponding to features of the universe having objective existence as real entities. It is tempting for the historian of science to find in this conjecture the first intimations of the conclusion, which now is securely based on the experiments of nuclear physicists, that in certain circumstances mass itself may be transformed into energy. When this happens, the conversion factor is the square of the measure of the velocity of light, as predicted by the theory of relativity of Einstein: $E = mc^2$. Obviously, we cannot follow this topic further, either in this chapter or the next; we merely refer back to our previous mention of it, in our original discussion of the setting up of the material standard defining the unit of mass (p. 146).

CHAPTER 15

THE KINETIC THEORY OF GASES

15.1. THE CONCEPT OF THE IDEAL GAS

The word 'gas' was introduced into the vocabulary of science by Jean Baptiste van Helmont (1577-1644), Belgian nobleman and alchemist, who was the first to recognise that there are substances other than atmospheric air which share its general physical properties but which differ from it in their chemical and biological effects. During the next 150 years, however, progress in chemistry was slow and uncertain, and the whole century and a half had to pass before anything approaching the modern view of the matter emerged. In 1674 John Mayow (1643-1679), Fellow of All Souls and physician of Bath, gave reasons for the view that air is not uniform in its substance; in 1727 Stephen Hales (1677-1761), perpetual curate of Teddington, came near to the discovery of oxygen; in 1754 Joseph Black (see p. 269) set a pattern for the future by his work on carbon dioxide; in 1766 Henry Cavendish (see p. 217) gave the first systematic account of the preparation and properties of hydrogen; during the next ten years Karl Wilhelm Scheele (1742-1786), Swedish pharmacist, and Joseph Priestley (1733-1804), English nonconformist minister, independently isolated oxygen and described its behaviour; then, in 1789, Antoine Laurent Lavoisier (1743-1794) published his *Traité élémentaire de chimie (présenté dans un ordre nouveau et d'après les découvertes modernes)*, and almost at once the subject was systematised, as it had not been before. Over the previous seventeen years, during the intervals in his duties as administrator and civil servant, supplementing by his own sometimes hasty observations those of his predecessors which he appropriated, Lavoisier had gradually and by design come to a comprehensive view of his subject which was not matched in his age. He died by the guillotine, in Paris on 8 May 1794. 'It took them no more than a moment, but a hundred years may not suffice to fashion another head the like of his'—so said Lagrange (p. 228).

It will be clear, from this brief survey of events, that such knowledge of the physical properties of gases as was available at the end of the eighteenth century had been obtained in the main in experiments with ordinary air. On that basis Boyle's law had been formulated; and Charles's law was a precarious generalisation: it remained for later investigators to establish the limits of validity of these empirical laws for gases in general.

Robert Boyle (1627-1691) was the fourteenth child of Richard, Earl of Cork. Having spent three years at Eton and five years in travel abroad with a French tutor, he returned to England at the age of seventeen to inherit estates left to him by his father. Thereafter he devoted his life to experimental research. In 1660 he published an account of experiments which he had made with an air-pump, constructed with the help of Hooke (p. 203), whom at that time he employed as his assistant. In correspondence afterwards with one of his critics, a Jesuit, Franciscus Linus, he enunciated the 'law' that the product of the measures of pressure and volume is constant, for a given mass of air at a fixed temperature. Boyle's experiments did not extend to pressures greater than 4 atmospheres, and it is doubtful whether he himself regarded the law as of great generality. The same law was, however, enunciated by Edme Mariotte (*c.* 1620-1684), prior of St. Martin, Dijon, in an essay entitled *De la nature de l'air* published in 1676, though it is even more doubtful whether he deserves the credit which he has sometimes been given for its independent discovery.

Charles's law refers to the variation of volume with temperature, at constant pressure. As we have already mentioned, Galileo made use of gaseous expansion in the crude air thermometer which he constructed in the last years of the sixteenth century, but nearly two hundred years were to pass before accurate measurements of the volume expansion of air and other gases, in terms of temperatures measured on the mercury thermometer, led to the enunciation of an empirical law by Jacques Alexandre César Charles (1746-1823) in 1787. In fact, Charles's law had in some ways been anticipated by Guillaume Amontons (1663-1705), a celebrated designer of scientific apparatus, whose air thermometer (1702) was greatly in advance of earlier instruments of a similar type, but his views received scant notice at the time. Indeed, Charles, who cannot have had more than a very few different gases on which to experiment, possibly for that reason did not publish his results.

His fellow-countryman Joseph Louis Gay-Lussac (1778-1850) rescued them from oblivion, when in 1802, in his first scientific paper, he mentioned in a footnote that the results which he himself had obtained 'had been noted 15 years previously' by Charles. Quite independently of Gay-Lussac, John Dalton (1766-1844) had obtained very similar results in the previous year (1801). The empirical law describing these results, which for brevity we shall continue to refer to as Charles's law, may be expressed as follows: At constant pressure the volume of a given mass of gas increases by equal increments for equal increases of temperature, and for a given initial temperature the fractional increase of volume is the same for all gases for the same temperature increment.

It must be clear at the outset that, expressed in this way, Charles's law claims much more than the experimental results of Dalton and Gay-Lussac could possibly justify. On the other hand, there was a simplicity in the behaviour of gases which liquids and solids did not in any way exhibit, and this difference appeared significant in 1802—as indeed it is fundamentally significant today. By the beginning of the nineteenth century, also, it had become clear that Boyle's law was similarly valid, over a considerable range of conditions, for all gases investigated. But the laws are empirical laws, and, until we can understand them in terms of some theory, we should be wary of assuming them accurate beyond the range over which they have been verified by observation. Accepting the *prima facie* case for their significance, however, let us introduce forthwith the concept of the 'ideal gas', as one for which the laws of Boyle and Charles are precisely accurate in all circumstances. It is hardly necessary to say that we do not expect to find any real gas entirely matching up to this specification.

15.2. THE EQUATION OF STATE

If V represents the volume of a mass m of a gas, measured at a pressure p, and at temperature T' on the centigrade scale of the mercury-in-glass thermometer, and V_0 the volume of the same sample of gas at the same pressure and at the ice-point temperature, Charles's law states that $V = V_0(1 + aT')$, where a, the temperature coefficient of volume expansion, is the same for all gases. Amontons had estimated the numerical value of a for air to be 1/240, Gay-Lussac amended this figure to 1/267, Henri Victor Regnault (1810-1878) to 1/273, the number, of course, representing in each case the fractional dilation per degree centigrade rise in temperature. If we write $\alpha = 1/T_0$, we have

$$\frac{V}{T_0 + T'} = \frac{V_0}{T_0},$$

or

$$\frac{V}{T} = \frac{V_0}{T_0},$$

where $T = T_0 + T'$. What we have done here is effectively to transfer the zero of temperature measurement from the ice-point, which depends on the properties of one particular substance, water, to an 'absolute zero' which does not depend upon the properties of any one substance, but represents in an idealised way the properties of all substances in the gaseous state. According to the best modern determinations, this temperature is $-273 \cdot 15°$ C, or $-459 \cdot 67°$ F. On this basis the ice- and steam-point temperatures are $273 \cdot 15°$ C ($491 \cdot 67°$ F) and $373 \cdot 15°$ C ($671 \cdot 67°$ F). In these last statements the symbols C and F merely represent the size of the degree: in general scientific usage, however, the centigrade scale is employed exclusively when absolute temperatures are involved. Then, conventionally, the symbol K is used, thus the absolute (centigrade) temperatures of the fixed points are quoted as $273 \cdot 15°$ K and $373 \cdot 15°$ K respectively.

When absolute temperatures are specified, Charles's law becomes $V/T =$ constant, for a given mass of gas at constant pressure. For the same mass, m, at constant temperature, Boyle's law may be written $pV =$ constant. Now, for a given mass, the volume determines the density, and for a particular gas we must consider the density as the significant independent variable, the measure of which depends on the pressure to which the gas is subjected by the walls of the containing vessel and on the temperature at which it is maintained. We cannot well imagine any other factors on which it should depend. The equation which represents this dependence of density (represented by m/V) on pressure and temperature is referred to as the equation of state of the gas. The laws of Boyle and Charles are to be regarded as partial forms of this equation, when restrictions are placed upon the values of temperature or pressure, as the case may be. We shall now derive the complete equation.

Clearly, the constant in the Boyle's law equation is proportional to the mass of gas taken, for, other factors being unchanged, the volume must be proportional to the mass. Also, the constant will be different at different temperatures for the same sample of gas, and, for the same mass and the same temperature, will be different for different gases. Thus we may write

$$pV = mf_1(T) \tag{123}$$

where f_1 is an unknown function of the temperature the value of which at a given temperature is different for different gases. On the basis of an exactly similar argument, Charles's law may be written

$$\frac{V}{T} = mf_2(p) \tag{124}$$

f_2 being an unknown function of the pressure the value of which depends upon the gas as well as on the pressure. Equations (123) and (124) are alternative forms of the equation of state: essentially they must be identical. As an expression for the density, the former gives $p/f_1(T)$, the latter $1/Tf_2(p)$. These expressions can only be the same if $f_1(T) = rT$, $f_2(p) = r/p$, when

$$\frac{p}{f_1(T)} = \frac{1}{Tf_2(p)} = \frac{p}{rT}.$$

Then the equation of state becomes

$$pV = mrT \tag{125}$$

in which the numerical constant r is the only quantity which depends upon the gas concerned. We must now consider the nature of this dependence.

On 3 August 1804, the German naturalist and explorer, Friedrich Heinrich Alexander von Humboldt (1769-1859), landed at Bordeaux after five years spent in travel in South and Central America, during which time he had traversed the course of the Orinoco and climbed Chimborazo. On 1 October of the same year, in collaboration with Gay-Lussac (p. 279), he read a paper in Paris in which they reported their discovery that when oxygen and hydrogen combine it is in the proportion of one volume of oxygen to two volumes of hydrogen, the measurements being made at the same temperature and pressure. It subsequently became known that Henry Cavendish had recorded the same observation in 1783, but he had not had the opportunity to extend his observations to other cases of gaseous combination, as Gay-Lussac was able to do at a later date. In 1809, as a result of these further researches, Gay-Lussac enunciated the law of volumes which is generally associated with his name. This empirical law states that, in every case of chemical combination of gases, the volumes of the reactants and the volume of their product, if gaseous, are in the ratios of small integral numbers when measured under common conditions of temperature and pressure. In 1809 Gay-Lussac was appointed professor of chemistry at the École Polytechnique, and André Marie Ampère (1775-1836) was appointed professor of mathematics at the same institution. In the previous year John Dalton (p. 279) had published the first part of his *New System of Chemical Philosophy*; the second part was to appear in 1810. The notions of chemical element and compound, and the classical notion of atoms, had suddenly become endowed with a new cogency. Only the simple results of Gay-Lussac provided a challenge that could not immediately be met. For a brief spell it seemed almost that they demanded fractions of atoms for their elucidation. Then, in 1814, Gay-Lussac's mathematical colleague, Ampère, suggested the way out of the difficulty. To the notion of atoms was added that of molecules. Molecules were closely bound structures containing one (in the extreme case), two, three, . . . atoms, of the same kind or of different kinds, the smallest units of matter having individual existence in a gas. Then Gay-Lussac's observations implied that equal volumes of all gases, measured at the same temperature and pressure, contain the same number of molecules. This generalisation is usually referred to as Avogadro's hypothesis. Thereby historical justice is done, for Amedeo Avogadro (1776-1856), professor of physics at Turin, enunciated it first in 1811.

When the chemists finally came to appreciate the significance of Avogadro's distinction between the concepts atom and molecule, which in general they did not do for nearly fifty years—until they were swayed by the powerful advocacy of Stanislao Cannizzaro (1826-1910) in 1858—they defined the molecular weight of a compound substance by a number giving the mass of the molecule in terms of the mass of the atom of hydrogen (later, in terms of 1/16 of the mass of the atom of oxygen). On this basis, a mass equal to 'the molecular weight in grammes', which we define as 1 mole of a substance, contains the same number of molecules (Avogadro's constant), whatever the substance, and, as a gas, occupies the same volume (the molar volume) under standard conditions of temperature and pressure. On the basis of equation (125), whatever the temperature and pressure, the quantity represented by pV/T will therefore be the same when 1 mole of any substance is in question. We represent this constant magnitude by R, and we refer to it as the universal gas constant. If M is the molecular weight of any gas, therefore, $Mr = R$, and equation (125) becomes explicitly

$$pV = \frac{m}{M}RT \qquad (126)$$

Equation (126) is now the equation of state for a mass m of an ideal gas of molecular weight, or, strictly, of molar mass, M.

We have only to emphasise, in conclusion, that equation (126) is not rigorously valid for any real gas over any considerable range of conditions: our ideal gas is a figment of the theorist's imagination.

15.3. THE KINETIC THEORY OF THE IDEAL GAS

The mathematical foundations of the kinetic theory of gases had been firmly laid a year before Cannizzaro finally succeeded in persuading the chemists to accept the notion of molecules in its original simplicity. In 1857 Rudolf Julius Emmanuel Clausius (1822-1888), at that time professor of physics at Zürich, published a paper entitled *Concerning the Nature of the Motion which we call Heat*. In it he calculated the relation between the temperature, pressure and density of a gas, on the basis of simple assumptions which indeed had been in the minds of physicists for more than two hundred years. Pierre Gassendi (1592-1655) had used the classical notion of atoms for a discussion of the three states of matter, and had indicated clearly his belief that it is unnecessary to assume more than small size, rigidity and ceaseless motion for such atoms in order to explain many properties of gases without further particular hypotheses. Robert Hooke (p. 203) envisaged the pressure of a gas in a containing vessel as due to the impact of its atoms on the walls of the vessel. In 1738 Daniel Bernoulli (p. 228) explained Boyle's law on a similar basis. Then there was a lull in progress for nearly a century, until, drawing inspiration from the revival of atomism as a scientifically based belief, many physicists considered the problem in one aspect or another. We shall not do serious injustice, however, if we look back no further than the paper of Clausius, just quoted, for the origin of the modern theory which we are now to describe.

We assume, then, that our ideal gas is made up of molecules, all alike, each of mass μ, of negligibly small size, and which exert no forces on one another, except in collisions which are perfectly elastic (p. 238). We note, at the outset, that these assumptions involve an inconsistency: if the molecules are indefinitely small and do not attract one another, they will never collide. The collisions, as we shall see, are a necessary feature of the situation; on the other hand, the inconsistency is logical rather than essential —it results from stretching our simplifying approximations to the limit, we can relax these sufficiently to meet the logical objection, without inconvenience, as the need arises.

Imagine now a volume of gas enclosed in a vessel at a fixed temperature. The velocity of each molecule is continually changing, in magnitude and direction, as it collides with other molecules or with the walls of the vessel (we assume that the latter collisions, also, are perfectly elastic). But the total number of molecules is so great that, if we could make an instantaneous determination of all their velocities, we should get the same overall picture whenever we made such a survey. The instantaneous directions of motion of the molecules would be uniformly distributed in space—the number lying within any particular cone of directions in space being proportional to the solid angle of the cone (see § 2.17)—and the same distribution curve would always be obtained in respect of the magnitudes of the individual velocities. This aspect of the matter was first stressed by James Clerk Maxwell (p. 264) in 1859. He showed that in fact the distribution curve would have the general form given in fig. 66. The convention adopted in drawing the curve is that, on the scale on which the total area under the curve is taken as unity, an area such as PQNM represents the fraction of all the molecules the velocities of which at any instant have magnitudes between OM and ON on the scale of the figure.

Having described the basic situation assumed in the theory, we shall proceed to idealise the picture still further so that we may make a simple calculation. Instead of a continuous distribution of magnitudes of velocities such as is represented by fig. 66, we shall

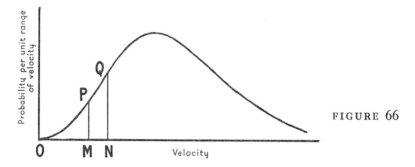

FIGURE 66

suppose that there are instantaneously n_1 molecules per unit volume with velocity c_1, n_2 molecules per unit volume with velocity c_2, and so on. Instead of a uniform distribution of directions of motion, we shall suppose that only the six directions associated with an arbitrary set of rectangular axes, OX, OY, OZ, are allowed, so that there are at any instant $\frac{n_1}{6}$ molecules per unit volume moving

(with velocity c_1) along OX, $\frac{n_1}{6}$ molecules per unit volume moving

(with the same velocity) along XO, . . ., $\frac{n_2}{6}$ molecules per unit

volume moving (with velocity c_2) along OY (or any one of the other five allowed directions), and so on.

Now imagine a mass of gas enclosed in a cubical vessel, the faces of the cube being at right angles to the rectangular axes above mentioned. Consider unit area of any face of the cube. Of the molecules moving with velocity c_1, the number which reach this area in any small interval of time t will be equal to the number which were within a distance $c_1 t$ of the area at the beginning of the interval, and which were moving in the appropriate direction, that

is $\frac{n_1}{6} c_1 t$ molecules. Each such molecule, rebounding elastically on

impact, will transfer momentum in amount $2\mu c_1$. Thus, considering all possible velocities, the rate of transfer of momentum per unit area of the wall of the vessel per unit time, is seen to be

$$\tfrac{1}{3}\mu(n_1 c_1{}^2 + n_2 c_2{}^2 + \ldots + n_s c_s{}^2).$$

Transfer of momentum per unit time (normal to the wall) is the measure of the force acting, and the normal force per unit area is the measure of the pressure on the wall. Thus

$$p = \tfrac{1}{3}\mu(n_1c_1{}^2 + n_2c_2{}^2 + \ldots + n_sc_s{}^2).$$

The total number of molecules per unit volume is

$$n = n_1 + n_2 + \ldots + n_s,$$

and if we define a velocity c (the 'root mean square' velocity) by the equation

$$nc^2 = n_1c_1{}^2 + n_2c_2{}^2 + \ldots + n_sc_s{}^2,$$

we have

$$p = \tfrac{1}{3}\mu nc^2,$$

or

$$p = \tfrac{1}{3}\rho c^2 \qquad (127)$$

where ρ is the density of the gas.

We started from a gross approximation, at least in relation to the directions of the molecular velocities, and, although we did not thereby obscure the essential physics of the problem in any way, we obviously cannot be confident, on the basis of our simple calculation, that the numerical factor $1/3$ in equation (127) is the correct factor. Here we must accept it on trust, for detailed calculation does indeed show that it is correct. We should be in no doubt however, that the quantities ρ and c^2 in the equation are correct— at least that they follow inevitably once a kinetic theory description of phenomena has been accepted as valid.

Let us now compare equation (126) and (127). The former equation may be written

$$p = \frac{R}{M}\rho T \qquad (128)$$

In this form the empirical equation of state is identical with the equation deduced from theory if

$$\tfrac{1}{3}Mc^2 = RT.$$

Now, because of the way in which c^2 is defined (see above), $\tfrac{1}{2}Mc^2$ is precisely the kinetic energy of translation of all the molecules in 1 mole. Thus the empirical gas laws, interpreted on the basis of kinetic theory, imply that the total kinetic energy of translation of the molecules in 1 mole is the same for all gases at the same temperature, being given by $\tfrac{3}{2}RT$. By definition, 1 mole contains the same number (Avogadro's constant, N) of molecules, whatever the gas (p. 283). We see, therefore, that to say that two gases are at the same temperature T, is essentially to say that the mean kinetic energy of translation of the individual molecules of each gas is the same, namely, $\frac{3}{2}\frac{R}{N}T$. The constant $\frac{R}{N}$, frequently denoted by k, is referred to as Boltzmann's constant. Currently accepted values are:

$R = 8 \cdot 314 \times 10^7$ ergs per degree centigrade per mole,

$N = 6 \cdot 023 \times 10^{23}$ molecules per mole,

$k = 1 \cdot 380 \times 10^{-16}$ ergs per degree centigrade per molecule.

15.4. SPECIFIC HEATS

In the last chapter (p. 268) we made the assertion that, once a suitable unit has been chosen, the measure of the mean specific heat of a substance, over a particular range of temperature, is 'characteristic of the material concerned'. This is equivalent to the assertion that the quantity of heat which must be communicated to a given mass of a particular substance, in order that its temperature shall increase through a specified range, is a perfectly definite quantity, the same whatever the conditions of the experiment. This assertion is broadly justified by the facts, provided the substance in question is solid or liquid over the whole range os temperature involved. In that case the 'state' of the substance if sufficiently well specified by its temperature alone.

When the substance is gaseous, however, the situation is quite otherwise. The 'state' of a gas is completely specified only when the pressure, or the density of the gas, is known in addition to the temperature (§ 15.2). It remains an open question, therefore, whether the specific heat of a given gas is a uniquely known quantity when only the temperature at which it has been determined has been stated. In particular—to take the two simplest cases—it is an open question whether the specific heat is the same, at a given temperature, under conditions in which (a) the density, (b) the pressure, of the experimental sample of gas remains constant. In the last resort only experiment can decide this question, but we may profitably discuss it in terms of our idea of the equivalence of heat and energy, and on the general basis of the kinetic theory, before we make our final appeal to the facts. Our aim will be to enumerate—and if possible to calculate the values of—the various contributions to the total amount of work which must be done if the temperature of a given mass of gas is to be increased, and the volume which it occupies possibly increased also.

If we make no assumption concerning the nature of the gas, except that it is constituted of similar molecules which behave as minute rigid bodies, we shall conclude that work may be done under three heads: first, to increase the total kinetic energy of the molecules, secondly, against the forces of mutual attraction when the average separation of the molecules is increased, and, finally, on the surroundings when the expanding gas pushes back whatever is containing it against its natural tendency to expand. Clearly, if the change takes place at constant volume (constant density), only the first of these contributions is effective: thus, for a given increase in temperature, less work must be done when the volume of a given mass of gas remains constant than is necessary if the volume is allowed to increase. If we assume heat and work are completely equivalent, we shall conclude that the 'specific heat at constant volume' must be less than the 'specific heat at constant pressure', at any specified temperature.

This is a general qualitative conclusion. To render it fully quantitative we must make certain assumptions concerning the nature of the gas. Let us assume that it is an ideal gas, in the sense that the laws of Boyle and Charles apply, and equation (126) (or its equivalent, equation (128)) is the appropriate equation of state. Each is an empirical equation, and we know that the behaviour of actual gases conforms to it, as a sufficient approximation over a wide range of conditions in each case. Let us also adopt the postulates of the simple kinetic theory as set out in § 15.3. These are theoretical postulates, the plausibility of which we have already demonstrated in that they provide a basis for an 'explanation' of equation (128), but they remain unproved assumptions which have to be tested against experiment at every opportunity. It may be necessary to make further assumptions, also, as the argument proceeds, but with these two we may evaluate the second and third of the contributions, listed above, to the work done when the temperature of a given mass of gas is increased at constant pressure.

The second contribution—the work done against the forces of molecular attraction—is by assumption zero: we have adopted the postulate that the forces of attraction are themselves zero at all dis-

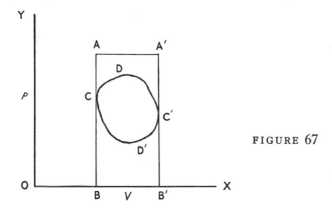

FIGURE 67

tances of separation of the molecules. Only the third contribution
—the work done on the surroundings—remains to be calculated:
it becomes responsible for the whole of the difference between
the two 'principal specific heats' of our ideal gas, the specific
heat at constant pressure and the specific heat at constant volume.
But we must first digress at some length in order to establish a
more general result, before we can proceed to calculate this difference directly, on the basis of our assumptions.

In fig. 67 we take co-ordinate axes of pressure and volume. On
such a diagram we can represent the instantaneous 'state' of a
given mass of gas by a point such as A. For the position of A
specifies directly the pressure and volume of the mass of gas taken:
its temperature is given, in terms of the equation of state, when
these quantities are known. Suppose now that our sample of gas
expands from a volume V_1, represented by the length OB, to a
volume V_2, represented by OB′ on the diagram, at constant pressure p, represented by BA. Then the point A′ will represent the
final state of the sample of gas, if B′A′ is parallel to BA and OY,
and AA′ is parallel to OX. We wish to calculate the work done on
the surroundings during the expansion (represented on the diagram by the straight line AA′).

In order to simplify the problem we idealise the situation, imagining the gas to be enclosed in a vertical cylinder—and all the
attributes of the actual surroundings to be symbolised by a suitably
loaded piston, which fits the cylinder perfectly and without frictional constraint. Then, if the cross-sectional area of the cylinder

T

is S, and the total weight of the piston and its load is F, since a pressure p is maintained, $F = Sp$. Again, if the gas enclosed in the cylinder expands from a volume V_1 to V_2, the effective length of the cylinder changes from V_1/S to V_2/S, and the height of the piston (and its load), reckoned from any suitable reference point, increases by $(V_2 - V_1)/S$. Work equal in amount to $F(V_2 - V_1)/S$, that is equal in amount to $p(V_2 - V_1)$, has been done—and has been stored, in this case, as additional potential energy in the idealised 'surroundings'. We note that this amount of work is represented, on the scale of the diagram (fig. 67), by the area of the rectangle AA′B′B, and we adopt two generalisations of this result as obviously valid without further examination.

In the first place we accept the result as valid whatever the nature of the surroundings on which the work is done (though the work done need not be stored as gravitational potential energy in any actual case), and in the second place we assert that the work done on the surroundings in any continuous increase in volume (not necessarily a change at constant pressure) is represented on the scale of the appropriate p-V diagram by the area enclosed by the curve representing the change, the ordinates through its extreme points and the axis of abscissae. Justification of this second generalisation follows from considerations which have already been fully explored in other connections (see §§ 4.4, 11.3). We make one general proviso, only, which reference to our idealised experimental arrangement is sufficient to clarify. In calculating the work done on the loaded piston, we took account of the increase in the potential energy of the system, but not of its kinetic energy. Our result would be invalid if in the expansion a significant amount of kinetic energy had been given to the piston and its load. In general, therefore, our simple result is applicable only to changes in volume which take place slowly—to changes in which there is never more than an infinitesimal difference of pressure across the boundary separating the 'sample' from the 'surroundings'. Such changes are referred to as 'reversible' changes, since, if the sign of the infinitesimal pressure difference were at any stage reversed, the subsequent 'sequence of events' in time would in every respect be the reverse of the sequence which had previously occurred.

Consider, now, a closed curve such as CDC′D′C on a p-V diagram (see fig. 67). Such a curve represents a cycle of changes by which a sample of gas may be restored from a given initial state

—say the state represented by the point D on the curve—to the same state again, the sequence of intermediate states being entirely arbitrary. Without loss of generality we may consider the simplest case in which such a closed curve has two vertical tangents only. Let CB, C'B' be these tangents in a case of this kind. In addition, let us suppose that the cycle of changes is such that the representative point describes the curve in a clockwise direction. Then the work done on the surroundings, during that part of the cycle represented by CDC' on the diagram, is given, on the appropriate scale, by the area CDC'B'BC, if the change is reversible throughout. Under the same conditions, the work done by the surroundings on the sample during the remainder of the cycle is similarly given by the area CD'C'B'BC. On balance, therefore, the work done on the surroundings during the whole cycle is given by the area CDC'D'C enclosed by the curve. Alternatively, if the same cycle were followed in the reverse sense in time, so that the representative point described the curve in an anti-clockwise direction, the area enclosed by the curve would give the net amount of work done by the surroundings on the sample considered. In either case the initial state of the sample is restored at the end of the cycle— and it is axiomatic that the energy content of the sample is the same when its 'state' is the same. In either case, then, work has been done—by the sample on the surroundings, or by the surroundings on the sample—and the energy content of the sample has remained the same in the end. We remind ourselves, moreover, that the temperature of the sample has changed cyclically in the process. If we accept the generalised conservation law of Helmholtz (p. 274), we must seek to balance the energy account in terms of heat supplied or abstracted—heat supplied to the sample in amount equivalent to the net amount of work performed on the surroundings, or abstracted from the sample in amount equivalent to the net amount of work performed by the surroundings on the sample itself.

Throughout our digression we have made no assumption concerning the nature of the sample of gas with which we have been concerned; indeed our arguments would apply equally if the sample were liquid or solid. In what follows we re-introduce our assumptions; we return to our particular problem, that of an ideal gas, and we calculate the difference between the principal specific heats of such a gas by submitting, in imagination, a sample of the gas to a cycle of changes for which the heat transfer can be evaluated in detail in terms of the assumptions which we make. The work done in the cycle being given by the area of the representative curve on the p-V diagram as before, our final result depends only on the generalised conservation law, which in this context we express by the equation

$$W + \mathcal{J}H = 0 \qquad (129)$$

Here, by convention, W is the measure, in dynamical units, of the work performed on the sample by the surroundings, and H is the measure, in thermal units, of the heat added to the sample during the cycle. $\mathcal{J}$ is a pure number, being the mechanical equivalent of heat in terms of the units employed.

Let us assume, then, that our sample consists of a mass m of an ideal gas of molecular weight M, and that its initial state is represented by the point A on a p-V diagram (fig. 68). In that state let the pressure be p_1, the volume of the sample be V_1, and the temperature T_1. Let heat be supplied at constant volume so that the temperature of the sample rises to T_2 (and the pressure to p_2). The line AB on the diagram represents this change. Now let the gas expand at constant temperature T_2 (according to Boyle's law) until the pressure has fallen to its original value p_1. This change is represented by BC on the diagram. Finally, let heat be abstracted from the gas at constant pressure so that the temperature of the sample is reduced to T_1 again (and its volume to V_1). This change is in accordance with Charles's law, and is represented on the diagram by the line CA. We have to calculate the quantities W and H of equation (129) in relation to this cycle of changes.

If f is the factor relating the measure of area on the diagram to the measure of work done, we have directly

$$W = -f . \text{area ABCA},$$

for, in the case considered, on balance, work has been done by the sample on the surroundings, not by the surroundings on the sample. We shall more easily calculate the net amount of heat added to the sample during the cycle if we consider each stage of the cycle separately, writing

$$H = H_1 + H_2 + H_3.$$

Then, if c_V is the mean specific heat at constant volume, and c_p the

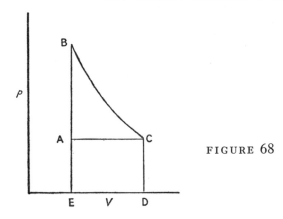

FIGURE 68

mean specific heat at constant pressure, over the temperature range concerned, we have by definition,

$$H_1 = mc_V(T_2 - T_1)$$
$$H_3 = -mc_p(T_2 - T_1),$$

leaving only H_2, the heat added during the constant temperature ('isothermal') change for further consideration. It is at this stage that our assumption that the gas is an ideal gas becomes important. In the isothermal expansion, represented by BC in the diagram, the sample does work on the surroundings in amount f. area BCDEB. If the gas is an ideal gas in the 'theoretical' sense (p. 284) that the force of attraction between the molecules is zero for all finite distances of separation, and if the total kinetic energy of the molecules of the sample depends only on the temperature, which remains constant in this change, then no work is done 'internally' on the sample of gas during the change. Heat must have been supplied to the sample during the expansion, but only in amount sufficient to account for the 'external' work done. We have, therefore,

$$\mathcal{J}H_3 = f.\text{area BCDEB}.$$

For the complete cycle equation (129) takes the form

$$W + \mathcal{J}(H_1 + H_2 + H_3) = 0.$$

By substitution, therefore, we obtain

$$-f.\text{area ABCA} + \mathcal{J}m(T_2 - T_1)(c_V - c_p) + f.\text{area BCDEB} = 0.$$

Rearranging, we have

$$\mathcal{J}m(T_2 - T_1)(c_p - c_V) = f.\text{area ACDEA},$$

or $\qquad \mathcal{J}m(T_2 - T_1)(c_p - c_V) = p_1(V_2 - V_1).$

If the gas is an ideal gas in the empirical sense that equation (126) is the appropriate equation of state, then

$$p_1(V_2 - V_1) = \frac{m}{M} R(T_2 - T_1)$$

and $\qquad\qquad\qquad c_p - c_V = \dfrac{R}{M\mathcal{J}} \qquad\qquad\qquad (130)$

Equation (130) indicates that the difference between the principal specific heats of an ideal gas is independent of the temperature, and that the quantity $M(c_p - c_V)$, sometimes referred to as the difference between the principal molar heats of the gas and denoted by $C_p - C_V$, is the same for all such gases and all temperatures, being given by $R/\mathcal{J}$. The numerical value of $R/\mathcal{J}$ (pp. 274, 287) is almost exactly 2·0 calories per degree centigrade per mole. If this prediction from equation (130) is verified by experiment in respect of gases which behave as ideal gases in that for them the laws of Boyle and Charles are empirically valid laws, then it must go far towards establishing the theoretical postulate of Clausius that for such gases the intermolecular forces are zero at all finite distances. Here, however, we defer this comparison of theory and experiment, for we have still to calculate the value of the specific heat at constant volume on the basis of our assumptions (p. 288).

According to these assumptions, the total kinetic energy of translation of the molecules comprising our sample is given (p. 286) by

$$\tfrac{1}{2}mc^2 = \frac{3}{2}\frac{m}{M}RT$$

at temperature T. The work which must be done to increase this kinetic energy, when the temperature of the sample rises from T_1 to T_2, is, therefore,

$$\frac{3}{2}\frac{m}{M}R(T_2 - T_1).$$

If this is the only increment of internal energy in a constant volume change, in our former notation,

$$\mathcal{J}H_1 = \frac{3}{2}\frac{m}{M}R(T_2 - T_1)$$

and
$$C_V = Mc_V = \frac{3}{2}\frac{R}{\mathcal{J}} \qquad (131)$$

Equation (131) predicts that the molar heat at constant volume is the same for all ideal gases and all temperatures, and that its numerical value is very closely 3 calories per degree centigrade per mole. Taken together with equation (130), it further predicts a unique value of 5 calories per degree centigrade per mole for the molar heat at constant pressure when the ideal gas laws are valid. We are at last in a position to compare theory with experiment.

The classical experiments are those of Regnault (p. 279) and Joly (1857-1933), the former concerned with c_p, the latter with c_V. Practically, the difficulties in the way of an accurate determination of specific heats at constant volume are considerable, for the mass of gas employed must generally be small compared with the mass of the vessel used to contain it. Determinations at constant pressure are easier, for a continuous-flow method may be used and a larger quantity of gas employed. Fortunately the ratio of the principal specific heats, c_p/c_V, may be deduced indirectly from a variety of experiments which we cannot here describe (see p. 328). Nowadays, therefore, our knowledge of the situation is derived chiefly from direct determinations of c_p and indirect determinations of c_p/c_V. It may be summarised as follows. There are a few gases, but only a few, for which the predictions of the simple theory are entirely fulfilled. The first such case was that of mercury vapour, for which a value of c_p/c_V (generally denoted by γ) very close to 5/3 was obtained in 1876. Thereafter, until the discovery of argon and helium at the end of the century, no similar case was reported. Then it was found that all the gases of the helium group gave the same value of γ, and that when the molar heat at constant pressure could be determined it was in fact very nearly 5 calories per degree centigrade per mole, as predicted. For almost all other gases the value of γ was found to be smaller, and the value of C_p greater, than equations (130) and (131) would predict. On the other hand, for all gases for which the laws of Boyle and Charles are a sufficient approximation to the truth, it was found that the difference $C_p - C_V$ is correctly given by the 'theoretical' result. The conclusion is obvious: our assumption that intermolecular forces are negligibly small under conditions in which the ideal gas laws are valid receives strong support from experiment, but the assumption that the kinetic energy of translation of the molecules is the only form of internal energy in an ideal gas is contradicted—except possibly in respect of the inert gases and certain metallic vapours. In order to clarify the position we must enquire more closely, therefore, into the values of C_V deduced from experiment for other gases.

Over a considerable range of conditions, the value of C_V for oxygen, nitrogen and hydrogen is very closely 5 calories per degree centigrade per mole, and the same value has been obtained with certain other simple gases, such as nitric oxide, over a narrower range. For water vapour at 100° C, for ammonia and nitrous oxide, a value approximating to 6 calories per degree centigrade per mole appears appropriate, when the ideal gas laws apply. For the hydrocarbons, and for organic vapours generally, larger values are found. But in no case, at ordinary temperatures, has a value of C_V been deduced from experiment which lies between 3 and 5 calories per degree centigrade per mole. This is perhaps the most significant result of all: it is particularly significant when the closely integral ratios, 3:5:6, of the three lowest recorded values are taken into account. For the groups of gases to which these values apply are seen to be natural groups. The inert gases and the metallic vapours are monatomic gases, that is the molecule is composed of a single atom in each case, oxygen, nitrogen, hydrogen and nitric oxide are diatomic gases, water vapour, ammonia and nitrous oxide are polyatomic, with three or more atoms in the molecule. Outside these three groups, the hydrocarbons, and the organic vapours generally, have even larger molecules of complicated structure.

Now, we have seen how it is possible to explain the common value of C_V for the monatomic gases: we have merely to suppose that the internal (molecular) energy of such a gas is kinetic energy of translation of the molecules and nothing else. In such a gas, at temperature T, the mean kinetic energy per molecule is $\frac{3}{2}kT$ (p. 287), where k is Boltzmann's constant. It was Ludwig Boltzmann (1844-1906), for twenty years professor at Graz, in Austria, who, with Maxwell, first thought of this energy as equally distributed among three 'degrees of translational freedom' of the molecule. In any volume of gas, confined in a vessel at rest, the mean value of the components, in any specified direction, of the instantaneous velocities of the molecules is obviously zero, for there is no mass motion of the gas. Similarly, the mean value of the squares of the components of instantaneous velocity is the same in whatever direction the velocities are resolved, for there can be no favoured direction amid the molecular chaos of a gas at rest. But, for any individual molecule, the instantaneous velocity c_r is related to its components with respect to arbitrary rectangular axes by the quadratic expression $c_r^2 = c_{xr}^2 + c_{yr}^2 + c_{zr}^2$. If, therefore, c^2 is the mean value of c_r^2 for all the molecules, c_x^2 the mean value of c_{xr}^2, and so on, obviously $c_x^2 = c_y^2 = c_z^2 = \frac{1}{3}c^2$. Then $\frac{1}{2}\mu c_x^2 = \frac{1}{2}\mu c_y^2 = \frac{1}{2}\mu c_z^2 = \frac{1}{6}\mu c^2 = \frac{1}{2}kT$. This is the simplest example of Boltzmann's principle of equipartition: the mean kinetic energy associated with each of the degrees of translational freedom of the molecule is the same; at temperature T it is $\frac{1}{2}kT$ per molecule (or, in thermal units, roughly T calories per mole).

Maxwell and Boltzmann realised that, if the molecules of a gas behave as small rigid bodies, then the principle of equipartition would imply that they should take on rotational energy, also. As a result of multitudinous collisions, the internal energy of the gas should quickly become shared between translational and rotational motions according to the degrees of freedom available. Now, in general, a rigid body has three degrees of rotational freedom: it has three principal axes of inertia among which its instantaneous kinetic energy of rotation can be regarded as distributed.

Apparently none of these degrees of rotational freedom is 'available' in the case of the monatomic gases. In the case of the simple polyatomic gases we may assume that all are effective (with the heavier polyatomic gases we require all these degrees of freedom, and more): in that way values of C_V of 6 calories per degree centigrade per mole may be explained. But, with the diatomic gases, only two of the three degrees of rotational freedom can be operative. Maxwell, in 1879, regarded this last conclusion as posing one of the most serious difficulties with which the kinetic theory had had to contend. Somewhat later, Boltzmann suggested that in this case, with the diatomic molecule, it is the degree of freedom associated with the principal axis of inertia through the centres of the two atoms of the molecule which is inoperative. No better suggestion was forthcoming, but neither was a convincing argument justifying the suggestion made. It could be pointed out, as a measure of rationalisation, that each of the three principal axes of inertia of a monatomic molecule (the degrees of freedom corresponding to which are equally inoperative) is an axis 'through the centre of an atom', so that a plausible rule could be evolved 'all degrees of rotational freedom are effective except those associated with principal axes of inertia which pass through the centres of all the atoms in a molecule'—but no significance could be attached to such a rule. Not until after 1911 was it recognised that the 'centre' of an atom has any properties of importance. Then, with the acceptance of the nuclear atom of Rutherford (§ 12.2), it became clear that there is a very real distinction to be made between the principal axis of inertia which passes through the two atom nuclei of a diatomic molecule and the other two principal axes of inertia at right angles to it. Because of the minute size of the nucleus, and the concentration of almost the whole mass of the atom in it, the magnitude of the first principal moment of inertia in this case is smaller than that of either of the other two by a factor of the order of 10^8. A few years afterwards, the newly developed quantum theory of the atom provided a good reason why rotational motion should not occur, at ordinary temperatures, about a principal axis around which the moment of inertia of the molecule is as small as this. Thus Boltzmann's suggestion found justification after some forty years, and a unifying 'explanation' could be given why one degree of rotational freedom is ineffective in a diatomic molecule—and all three degrees of rotational freedom similarly ineffective in a molecule which is monatomic.

Here, then, we leave the problem of the specific heats of gases, merely adding that it is not difficult, at this stage, to find the additional degrees of freedom necessary to explain the larger molar heats of the heavier polyatomic gases. In the complex molecules involved there are many possible modes of mutual vibration of the constituent atoms. With the advent of the quantum theory it is now no longer a complete mystery why, at any given temperature, some of these modes are effective and others not. In general, as the temperature increases, so the number of effective modes, the number of degrees of vibrational freedom available, and the molar heat, increase also.

15.5. REAL GASES

In § 15.3 we pointed out the logical inconsistency of the assumptions which we adopted as a basis of the simple kinetic theory of the ideal gas. Taken literally, these assumptions exclude the possibility of collisions between molecules, and the collisions are indispensable for our whole programme of theoretical description of the phenomena concerned. The successes of the simple theory, as we have so far developed it, justify, however, the assertion that we made at the outset: the inconsistency is logical rather than essential. In this section we remove the inconsistency, as a first step towards the consideration of real gases, untrammelled by assumptions which we know to be approximations at the best, at the worst distortions of the truth. We begin, then, by accepting the fact that the molecules of a gas are of finite size.

This acceptance allows us to introduce at once a new concept, that of the 'mean free path'. The mean free path of the molecules of a gas may be thought of as the average distance between the successive collisions which any molecule of the gas makes with its 'neighbours'. We do not attempt to specify more closely the precise basis of the process of averaging which in a formal definition would require to be specified—there are alternative procedures which we do not need to discuss—but we note that the magnitude of the mean free path, however defined, must depend upon the total number of molecules per unit volume of the gas, and upon the size of the molecules. If we denote the mean free path by λ, and the molecular concentration by n as in § 15.3, it is reasonable to suppose that λ varies inversely as n—the larger the number of molecules per unit volume, the smaller in inverse ratio is the average distance which a molecule must move before it makes a collision. But the dimensions of λ are L^1, and those of n are L^{-3}. We require, therefore, another factor having dimensions L^2, multiplying n in the equation for λ, in order to achieve dimensional homogeneity. This factor must be of the nature of a molecular target area, or a molecular 'collision cross-section'. We denote it by σ, then we obtain

$$\lambda = \frac{d}{n\sigma} \qquad (132)$$

where d is a pure number.

Equation (132) allows us to comment further upon Maxwell's experiment on the variation of gaseous viscosity with density already described (§ 13.4). The coefficient of viscosity is a measure of the tangential force per unit area, in a fluid in which there is a gradient of drift velocity at right angles to the area concerned, and under conditions in which the force is proportional to this velocity gradient (p. 255). We introduce the qualifying epithet 'drift' in this statement in order to emphasise that, in the case of a gas, the macroscopic velocities with which we have to deal—the velocities of mass motion—are small compared with the velocities of molecular motion (see below). Now the measure of a force is the measure of a rate of increase of momentum. In the situation which we are considering, and which fig. 69 represents (see also fig. 62), the strata of gas above the plane AB exert a tangential force on the gas below AB by communicating momentum parallel to AB to this gas. Similarly, the strata of gas below AB tend to retard the drift motion of the gas above AB by communicating momentum parallel to BA to the upper layers of gas. The mechanism of momentum transfer is the collisions of the molecules; no other process can be effective. If there were no variation of drift velocity across AB, clearly there would be no net transfer of momentum parallel to the plane. When there is a finite gradient of drift velocity, as represented in fig. 69, the rate of transfer of momentum will be proportional to the velocity gradient. It will also be proportional to the molecular concentration n, and to the average velocity of molecular motion (the greater this velocity, the greater the number of molecules which cross unit area of AB in unit time). It is necessary to mention this last point, though for Maxwell's experiment it is inessential: at constant temperature the average velocity of molecular motion is constant. Finally, the net rate of transfer of momentum across AB will obviously be proportional to the average distance from AB at which a molecule crossing AB makes its last collision, for this distance of last collision determines the stratum of gas of which the molecule in question can reasonably be regarded as a 'sample', as it crosses the plane. The more distant the stratum, the larger the excess momentum.

Our analysis, therefore, leads to the result that, at constant temperature, the coefficient of viscosity of a gas should be proportional to the product $n\lambda$. Equation (132) shows that $n\lambda$ is constant for a given gas: d is a pure number, and σ is an area repre-

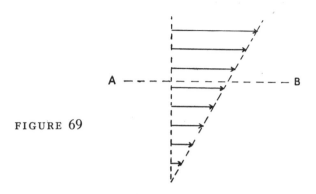

FIGURE 69

sentative of the size of the molecule concerned. We conclude then, as Maxwell did, that the coefficient of viscosity should have the same value whatever the density of the gas, the temperature being constant. As we have reported (p. 264), Maxwell not only derived this theoretical result on the basis of the then newly developing kinetic theory, but he verified it experimentally. It is fair to say that this single experiment did much to secure acceptance of the kinetic theory by those who had been doubtful of its significance.

There is one point we must not overlook at this stage in the argument. We claim to have proved that, for a given gas, the coefficient of viscosity is the same whatever the density, provided the temperature is constant. Now it would appear contrary to reason if in Maxwell's experiment the frictional drag on the circular plates of his suspended system (see fig. 64) had remained absolutely constant until the pressure in his apparatus was finally reduced to zero. In fact this did not occur. From atmospheric pressure, downwards, the frictional drag was essentially the same, until, when the pressure reached a certain critical value, it began to decrease rather rapidly. Later experiments by Crookes (1832-1919) confirmed that the experimentally observed drag tended to zero at zero pressure. We have to resolve the apparent discrepancy between experiment and theory in this connection. The way of resolution is simple—and significant. According to equation (132), the mean free path varies inversely as the molecular concentration, that is inversely as the pressure of the gas, at constant temperature. As the pressure of the gas in Maxwell's apparatus was reduced, therefore, a stage would be reached at which the mean free path of the gas molecules was of the same order as the mutual separation of the plates. In that case a molecule might well pass from a fixed plate to a moving one without any intermediate collision. The general basis of our theoretical discussion would then no longer obtain, and the conclusion that, at constant temperature, the co-efficient of viscosity is independent of density would become irrelevant to the experimental situation. Its ultimate validity is not in question—it remains true down to the lowest densities in an infinite expanse of gas—but, for any given apparatus and any specified gas, there is a value of the density below which it is no longer relevant.

Our general account of gaseous viscosity has been based on the assumption that drift velocities are small compared with the veloci-ties of molecular motion (p. 300). Equation (127) allows us to calculate the root mean square velocity, in terms of the pressure and the density, for an ideal gas. At standard temperature (0° C) the density of hydrogen is very nearly $9 \cdot 0 \times 10^{-5}$ g. cm.$^{-3}$, when the pressure is 1 atmosphere (very nearly 10^6 dyne cm.$^{-2}$). For the hydrogen molecule, at 0° C, therefore

$$c^2 = 3 \times 10^6 / 9 \times 10^{-5} \text{ cm.}^2 \text{ sec.}^{-2},$$

or
$$c = 1 \cdot 8 \times 10^5 \text{ cm. sec.}^{-1}.$$

This velocity is a little greater than 1 mile per second. Equations (127) and (128) together show that, for gases generally, the corre-sponding velocity is inversely proportional to the square root of the molecular weight (so that, for a molecular weight of 200, the root mean square velocity at 0° C is $1 \cdot 8 \times 10^4$ cm. sec.$^{-1}$), and, for a given gas, that the root mean square velocity is directly propor-tional to the square root of the absolute temperature. These results which we have quoted derive directly from the simple kinetic theory of the ideal gas, but it should be emphasised that they do not depend upon that theory for their validity. The general prin-ciple of the equipartition of energy applies equally to real gases, as it does to that very convenient abstraction the ideal gas.

Let us now relax the second of the assumptions upon which we based the simple kinetic theory—the assumption that intermole-cular forces are zero for all finite distances of separation—for we know it to be strictly untenable. When a gas condenses to a liquid, or solidifies, the distances of separation of the molecules are still

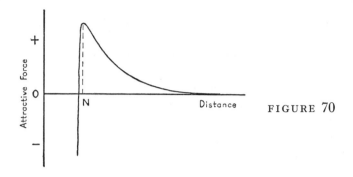

FIGURE 70

finite (at least they are still capable of further slight change, with decreasing temperature or increasing pressure), and certainly, then, very strong forces of attraction are effective. It is clear that these forces must decrease rapidly as the distance increases, but it is an over-simplification to regard them as zero. For any real gas the situation must be somewhat like the one indicated in fig. 70. Here the force of attraction between two molecules, supposedly spherically symmetrical, is plotted in relation to the distance separating their centres. For distances smaller than some distance r_0, corresponding to ON in the figure, the attractive force is very rapidly replaced by a repulsive force of great magnitude. It is almost as if the molecules were rigid bodies having perfectly definite boundaries, though we know they are not: whether or not, the collision cross-section σ of equation (132) is clearly a quantity of the order πr_0^2. We realise that it should be the object of detailed research to deduce the precise form of the curve of fig. 70 for each type of molecule.

The programme of research which we have just indicated is obviously too ambitious for our further consideration. We may, however, consider the matter from the opposite point of view. If we accept fig. 70 as providing a generally correct account of the way in which the force between two molecules varies with their separation, we may enquire how we should expect the equation of state to be modified. Our aim would be, if possible, to derive an equation of state which would be valid not only at relatively high temperatures and low pressures, when the behaviour of the gas would approximate very closely to ideal gas behaviour, but also at low temperatures and high pressures; to derive an equation which would, in fact, describe with reasonable accuracy the transition from gas to liquid in the process of condensation.

The first to approach the matter from this point of view was J. D. van der Waals (1837-1923), professor of physics in Amsterdam from 1877 to 1907. In 1873 he published a paper *On the continuity of the gaseous and liquid states*. Although many later attempts have been made towards its improvement, the equation of state which van der Waals proposed is still more widely used than any of the 'improved' versions. For a sample consisting of 1 mole of any gas, this equation is conventionally written

$$\left(p + \frac{a}{V^2}\right)(V - b) = RT \tag{133}$$

For a sample comprising a mass m of a gas of molecular weight M the corresponding equation is

$$\left(p + \frac{m^2}{M^2}\frac{a}{V^2}\right)\left(V - \frac{m}{M}b\right) = \frac{m}{M}RT.$$

In equation (133) R is, as before, the universal gas constant—the same for all gases—only the quantities a and b vary from one gas to another. For any one gas, a and b are constant. Obviously two constants are not sufficient to represent completely a curve such as that of fig. 70, but the fact, which we have already noticed, that the actual situation is very similar to that which would obtain if the molecules were indeed rigid bodies attracting one another with a short-range force, justifies van der Waals's simplification. The constant b, representing the so-called molar co-volume, takes account of the approximate impenetrability of the molecules (to be precise, $b = \frac{2}{3}\pi N r_0^3$ in our previous notation, N being Avogadro's constant), the constant a determines the additional 'internal' pressure which results from the molecular attraction (the term a/V^2 is a measure of this pressure).

In order to compare the predictions of van der Waals's equation with the results of experiment, it is most convenient to consider the 'isothermal' curves (p. 293) by which the equation is represented on a p-V diagram.

Equation (133) may be written in the form

$$pV^3 - (pb + RT)V^2 + aV - ab = 0 \tag{134}$$

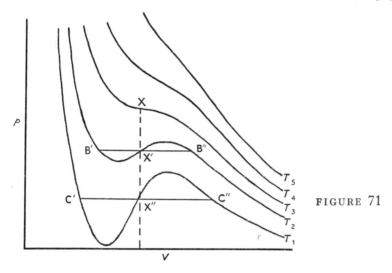

FIGURE 71

To obtain the isothermal curves, we assign to T in equation (134) a series of definite values; and for each such value we take a series of values of p, solving the resulting equation for V for each of them. Each solution for V is the solution of a cubic equation: such an equation may have one real root and two imaginary roots, or three roots all of which are real. In the latter case two of the roots may be equal, or, in special circumstances, all three may be equal. Fig. 71 shows the general form of the isothermal curves which are obtained in this way, when, as in equation (134), the signs of the coefficients of the terms succeeding the first term in the cubic equation, in order, are minus, plus, minus, respectively. Five curves are shown, for temperatures $T_1 < T_2 < T_3 < T_4 < T_5$. The isothermal curve for temperature T_5 approximates fairly closely in form to that for an ideal gas, $pV =$ constant. The curve for T_4 is already less 'regular', but only one value of V is indicated for each value of p. The two additional real roots of the cubic equation for V are represented first in the curve for T_3—uniquely at X, where there is a point of inflection with a 'horizontal' tangent. The remaining curves, for the lower temperatures T_2 and T_1, are characterised by progressively wider ranges of p over which they represent three real values of V for each value of p (these ranges limited, of necessity, by pressures for which two of the three calculated values of V are equal).

U

Now suppose we take the calculated isothermal curves for T_2 and T_1 and draw constant-pressure lines B′B″, C′C″ across them, dividing the 'anomalous' pressure range of three real roots symmetrically in each case. Let us replace the calculated curves, between the points in question, B′ and B″ in the one case, C′ and C″ in the other, by these straight-line sections. Then the assertion may be made—and justified by comparison with the results of experiment—that the isothermal curves so modified represent with very fair accuracy the behaviour of real gases, and particularly the phenomenon of condensation. For, if we arrange for a sample of gas to be compressed at constant temperature, then, provided the temperature is low enough, we find that, when a certain pressure is reached, the gas begins to liquefy, and this process continues with progressive decrease in volume of the sample until the whole is liquid. This transition from gas to liquid takes place at constant pressure (the so-called saturation vapour pressure corresponding to the temperature concerned), and the sample will not sustain a pressure greater than this until the transition is complete. Thereafter, the pressure on the sample may be increased through a wide range and there will be little further decrease in volume. This is precisely the type of behaviour predicted by a modified isothermal curve such as that for T_2 or T_1 in the diagram. Moreover, our modification of the calculated curve is not as arbitrary as it might seem. The theoretical basis for van der Waals's equation includes the assumption that the sample to which it refers remains an homogeneous fluid in all circumstances. The equation cannot, therefore, be expected to describe in detail the situation when the sample is inhomogeneous, part liquid and part vapour, as it is whilst the process of condensation is taking place.

We have just stated that a real gas may be liquefied by pressure alone, provided the temperature is low enough. This is a well-established fact of experience. For each gas there is a 'critical temperature' above which there is no abrupt change of volume when the pressure to which a sample of the gas is subjected is gradually increased. At temperatures higher than the critical temperature the sample remains homogeneous, even though the pressure be increased indefinitely. Equation (133) describes this situation with complete fidelity. The isothermal curve for temperature T_3 in fig. 71 is the critical isothermal, and the point X represents the critical state. When the material under investigation is in this state, the pressure and density have unique values and it is matter of indifference whether we regard it as liquid or gaseous.

Our last statement may be demonstrated in a very direct manner under laboratory conditions if a suitably volatile liquid is chosen. Di-ethyl ether is such a substance. Its critical pressure is 35·5 atmospheres and its critical temperature 193·8° C. If a thick-walled glass capillary tube is about one-third filled with ether at room temperature (the critical density is about one-third of the normal density of the liquid), and sealed after gentle pumping to remove the remaining air, the state of the enclosed material will be represented by a point such as X″ in fig. 71. If the sealed tube is heated, the representative point will move upwards on the figure, through X′ to X (the quantity of liquid having been accurately adjusted). At each stage the state will be part liquid part vapour, until suddenly, when the temperature reaches the critical temperature, the whole contents of the tube will become homogeneous An experiment of this kind was first performed in 1822 by Charles Cagniard de la Tour (1777-1859). If the tube, having been heated above the critical temperature, is allowed to cool, a meniscus will suddenly re-appear in the tube, as the critical temperature is passed, in the place where it previously disappeared. Thereafter, the position of the meniscus will change very little, though its outline will become sharper and more curved as the temperature falls to that of the laboratory.

CHAPTER 16

ELASTICITY

16.1. DEFINITIONS

We have made frequent reference in earlier chapters of this book to situations in which the size or shape of a body has been altered as a result of forces applied to it. We have alluded to the sagging of the material standard of length under its own weight when supported on transverse rollers, we have discussed the deformation of bodies in collisions, the elongation and twisting of wires, and, in the last chapter, the compression of gases. The branch of our subject to which the name 'elasticity' is given treats systematically of this type of effect; it deals with the changes in size and shape of bodies brought about by the action of systems of forces in equilibrium. We cannot in this short chapter consider all aspects of such phenomena: we shall in fact confine our attention almost wholly to those situations in which the deformation is proportional to the intensity of the forces producing it. For most bodies there is a range of small forces for which this condition obtains, but, for all bodies, when the applied forces are large enough more complicated results ensue, the deformation may not disappear completely when the forces are removed, or it may increase with time as long as the forces are maintained—and fracture may ultimately occur.

We have spoken hitherto of forces, but in what follows we shall be concerned exclusively with the effects of forces acting uniformly over surfaces, and the appropriate measure in that case is that of a pressure—a force per unit area—rather than a force. In the mathematical theory of elasticity the term 'stress' is conventionally applied to denote this quantity. It is convenient that a special term should be used in this connection, since the forces with which we have to deal are sometimes normal, sometimes tangential, to the surfaces over which they act. The term 'pressure' is properly reserved for the force per unit area normal to a surface. In the mathematical theory the term 'strain' is generally employed to denote a deformation of any type. The measure of a strain is a non-dimensional quantity, a fractional increase of length or of volume, or an angle specifying the change of shape of a solid body. The restriction that we have imposed on our considerations in this chapter is that we shall confine attention in the main to those situations in which the strain is proportional to the stress producing it.

We shall also impose a restriction on the type of body the deformations of which we shall consider. We shall deal only with bodies of which the material substance is homogeneous and isotropic. An homogeneous material is one of which the chemical constitution and the density are uniform throughout. Under ordinary laboratory conditions a sample of gas is necessarily homogeneous, a sample of liquid or solid need not be.

An isotropic material is one of which the physical properties do not depend on direction. Homogeneous samples of gas or liquid may generally be regarded as isotropic also, but a single crystal of a solid substance which is homogeneous is not necessarily isotropic: more often than not its elastic properties depend upon the direction of application of stress in relation to the natural axes of the crystal. With one reservation, we shall not consider crystalline solids in this chapter. Our reservation is as follows: if a sample of solid substance is homogeneous, and if it is constituted of a very large number of single crystals arranged at random, we may regard it as isotropic from our point of view. In this way we admit consideration of the elastic properties of the common metals which are generally of this constitution.

As we have already hinted, there are two types of stress which are fundamental for our considerations. A body may be in equilibrium under the action of two equal and oppositely directed forces, or of two equal couples oppositely applied about a common axis. In the former case the stress is referred to as 'tensile' or 'contractile', depending upon whether the length of the body along the common line of action of the forces is increased or decreased by their application. In the latter case the stress is spoken of as a 'shearing' stress. In the former case the strain is an elongation (positive or negative), in the latter it is most directly measured by the 'angle of shear'. When the strains are small, as we shall assume them to be throughout our discussion, effects are additive. If any length in a body is increased by a factor $1 + e_1$ through the operation of one applied stress system, and by a factor $1 + e_2$ when another system of stresses is operative, then the length in question is increased by a factor $(1+e_1)(1+e_2)$ when the two systems are in operation together. If $e_1 \ll 1$, $e_2 \ll 1$, as we assume, this factor may be taken to be $1+e_1+e_2$, to a sufficient approximation.

From this last point of view we may consider the relation between a simple contractile stress and a uniform 'hydrostatic' pressure, which is the third type of stress system with which we shall be dealing. A body subject to a uniform hydrostatic pressure is acted on by forces normal to its surface such that the force per unit area of surface is the same over whatever region of the surface it is reckoned. Consider, therefore, a cubical body, AC′, as represented in fig. 72.

If this body is subject to a uniform hydrostatic pressure p, the normal inwards force over each of the six faces of the cube is pL^2, where L is the length of the cube edge, and these forces taken in three pairs constitute three systems of contractile stress, each of magnitude p, parallel to the cubic axes. We conclude that a uniform hydrostatic pressure can be represented by equal contractile stress systems, of magnitude equal to the magnitude of the pressure, acting along any three directions mutually at right angles.

When the measures of stress and strain are proportional, we may define a quantity, of the nature of a pressure, to which the general name 'modulus of elasticity' is given, using the defining relation

$$\text{Stress} = \text{Modulus} \times \text{Strain}.$$

It is a fact of experience that, for a given type of stress, the modulus of elasticity is a property of the material of which a body is made. The measure of it is independent of the size and shape of the experimental body, once the material is specified. For each type of stress system there is the appropriate modulus. For a simple tensile or contractile stress system we define 'Young's modulus' (named after Thomas Young, see p. 224) by the equation

$$p = Y\frac{l}{L} \qquad (135)$$

Here Y is the measure of the modulus, and l is the change of length of a line in the body of original length L in the direction of the applied stress of which the measure is p. When the stress

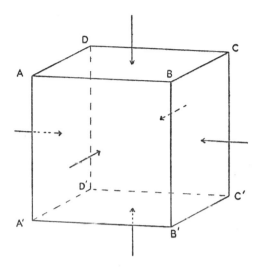

FIGURE 72

system is a uniform hydrostatic pressure of magnitude p, the 'bulk modulus', k, is similarly defined by the equation

$$p = k \frac{v}{V} \qquad (136)$$

In this equation v is the measure of the decrease in volume of a volume of the body of which V is the original measure.

Referring again to fig. 72, if Y represents Young's modulus and k the bulk modulus of the material of which the cubical specimen is made, the fractional decrease in volume of the specimen, resulting from the application of the uniform hydrostatic pressure p, is p/k (equation (136)). Similarly, the fractional decrease in length of any edge of the cube, resulting from the application of a contractile stress system of magnitude p parallel to that edge, is p/Y (equation (135)). If only one such system of contractile stress is operative (so that four of the cube faces are unconstrained by any force), our expectation would be that contraction along the direction of stress would be accompanied by extension of the specimen at right angles to that direction. We might be wrong in this expectation—only controlled experiment can decide: equation (135) tells us nothing in the matter—meanwhile, however, we shall suppose that the fractional extension at right angles to the applied stress is σ times the fractional contraction along the direction of the stress. In the end we shall discover whether σ is finite or zero.

Suppose now that three systems of contractile stress, p, are operative on the specimen of fig. 72, one along each of the axes of the cube. The net fractional decrease in length of any edge of the cube is $(p/Y)(1-2\sigma)$, representing the superposition of one contraction and two extensions according to the result which we have already obtained (p. 310). But this system of contractile stresses is equivalent to the uniform hydrostatic pressure, as we have previously shown, and the fractional decrease in volume which it produces is three times the fractional decrease in linear dimensions of the cube, by a further application of the principle of superposition. Thus

$$p/k = 3(p/Y)(1-2\sigma),$$

or
$$Y = 3k(1-2\sigma) \qquad (137)$$

Equation (137) provides the basis for appeal to experiment which we require. If experiment were to show that the value of Young's modulus is always three times the value of the bulk modulus of a material, clearly σ would be zero. This however is not the case. Since the pioneer experiments of E. H. N. Amagat (1841-1915) on the compressibilities of solids, towards the end of the last century, accurate values of the bulk modulus have been available for many solid materials, and these values are generally of the same order as—and in some cases greater than—the corresponding values of Young's modulus. The quantity σ is certainly finite (it cannot be greater than 0·5, according to equation (137)) and characteristic of the material concerned. It is referred to as Poisson's ratio for the material (after S. D. Poisson, see p. 256).

Let us return now to a consideration of the effects produced by a shearing stress. Suppose that equal forces F are applied tangentially over four faces of a cubical specimen as shown in fig. 73. The specimen is in equilibrium under the action of equal and oppositely directed couples, and we may refer its resulting deformation to the plane of the face A'B'C'D' as reference plane. In that case it should be clear that the deformed specimen has the shape represented by A"B"C"D"A'B'C'D' in the figure. The originally square face ABB'A' is deformed into the rhombus

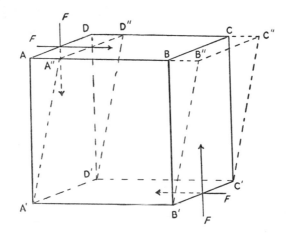

FIGURE 73

A″B″B′A′, and the face ABCD remains square in its new position A″B″C″D″. The strain is measured by ∠AA′A″, the angle of shear, which we shall denote by θ. If L is the measure of the length of the cube edge as before, and p the measure of the shearing stress, we define the 'modulus of rigidity', n, by the equation

$$p = \frac{F}{L^2} = n\theta \qquad (138)$$

It will be obvious at once that there is a second method of specifying the strain produced by a shearing stress. Such a stress deforms a square prism into a rhombic prism, the prism axis being the common axis of the couples by which the stress is applied. For our first specification we have used the angle θ, the difference between the acute angle of the rhombus and one right angle, as a measure of the strain, and we have emphasised this aspect of the matter, in fig. 73, by referring the deformation to the cube face A′B′C′D′ as reference plane. But the diagonals of a rhombus are mutually perpendicular, as are the diagonals of a square. Thus we might equally well relate the deformed and undeformed prism sections, as in fig. 74, by supposing that the initial and final directions of the diagonals are the same. Then if ABCD represents the undeformed section, the deformed section is represented by A′B′C′D′ in the figure. It will be seen that, for small deformations, the fractional increase in length of one diagonal, represented by

AA′/OA, is equal to the fractional decrease in length of the other, represented by B′B/OB.

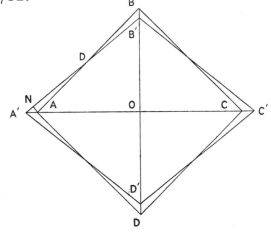

FIGURE 74

We may equally well describe a shear strain, therefore, as one in which the lengths of two lines, originally at right angles in a plane perpendicular to the axis of shear, are the one increased the other decreased by the same fractional amount e, the two lines remaining at right angles after the shear. It is our immediate object to relate the fraction e, representative of this method of specification, to the (radian) measure of the angle θ, representative of the other. If, in fig. 74, AB and A′B′ intersect in D, and if AN is drawn perpendicular to A′B′ from A, when the deformation is small,

$$AA' = \sqrt{2}.AN$$

$$= \sqrt{2}.DA.\angle ADA'$$

$$= \sqrt{2}.\frac{AB}{2}.\frac{\theta}{2},$$

also
$$OA = \frac{AC}{2}$$

$$= \frac{\sqrt{2}.AB}{2}.$$

Thus
$$\frac{AA'}{OA} = e = \frac{\theta}{2} \tag{139}$$

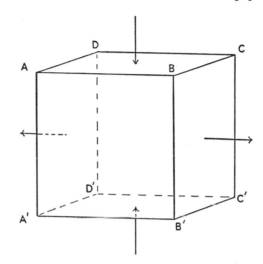

FIGURE 75

If the strain produced by a shearing stress—or, strictly, by a system of shearing stresses in equilibrium—may be described as we have just described it, obviously the stress system itself may be given an alternative specification. Suppose that systems of tensile and contractile stress, of equal magnitude p', be applied to four faces of a cubical specimen as shown in fig. 75. Then the lengths of the cube edges parallel to the direction of application of the tensile stress will be increased by a fractional amount $(p'/Y)(1+\sigma)$, and the lengths of the cube edges parallel to the direction of application of the contractile stress will be decreased by the same amount. The lengths of the other four edges of the cube will be unaltered: the effect of the tensile stress will be to decrease, and that of the contractile stress will be to increase, these lengths by a fractional amount $\sigma p'/Y$ in each case. The overall effect will be precisely that of a shear strain: it will be essentially the same as that illustrated in fig. 73.

It remains only to relate the magnitude of p', representing our new specification of the stress system, to the magnitude of p representing the other. For this purpose consider a right-angled isosceles triangular prism of material, of section ABC as represented in fig. 76. Suppose that forces be applied uniformly over the prism faces as shown, namely equal tangential forces F acting over the faces which are mutually perpendicular, and a normal force F' over the opposite

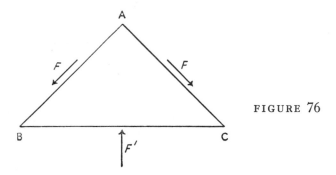

FIGURE 76

face. Then, since the resultant of the two forces F is a force of magnitude $\sqrt{2}.F$ acting uniformly along the edge through A and bisecting the right angle BAC, the triangular prism will be in equilibrium if $F' = \sqrt{2}.F$. But the area of the prism face through BC is also $\sqrt{2}$ times the area of either of the other two prism faces, that through AB or that through AC. Thus, when the prism is in equilibrium, the common measure of the tangential stress over the faces which are mutually at right angles is equal to the measure of the normal stress over the opposite face. Under the conditions represented in fig. 73, therefore, the equal tangential stresses p over the faces ADD'A', ADCB of the square prism AC' are transmitted in a direction normal to the diagonal plane BCD'A' as a normal stress of the same magnitude p. This is one of the normal stresses required in our alternative specification of the system of shearing stresses under consideration. In our previous notation, therefore, $p' = p$.

Now, combining equations (138) and (139), we have

$$p = 2ne.$$

Also, we have shown that

$$e = (p'/Y)(1 + \sigma).$$

Thus, if $p' = p$, as we have just proved,

$$Y = 2n(1 + \sigma) \qquad (140)$$

In this section we have defined three moduli of elasticity, which we have denoted by Y, k and n, and one non-dimensional quantity

σ, as representing the elastic properties of an homogeneous iso-tropic solid material. Equations (137) and (140) show that these quantities are necessarily interrelated. It may be convenient to retain all of them, as appropriate each to a clear-cut experimental situation; it is obviously unnecessary to do so if our sole aim is to catalogue elastic properties in the most economical manner pos-sible. Any two of the four quantities are sufficient for that purpose.

16.2. ELASTICITY OF SOLIDS

In the last section we attempted, wherever possible, to avoid pointing the distinction between solid, liquid and gaseous materials. In the final paragraph, however, for sake of accuracy, we were compelled to restrict our reference to solid materials only: the elastic properties of an homogeneous isotropic solid material re-quire two constants of their complete specification. It is appro-priate that we should now make the necessary distinction clearly. From our present viewpoint, the difference between a solid and a fluid (see p. 261) is that the elastic properties of the latter, once the state of the fluid and the thermal character of the change have been specified, are fully described by a single modulus. Our definitions of Young's modulus and the rigidity modulus—and of Poisson's ratio, which may be related to them by equation (140)—are strictly meaningless in respect of liquids and gases. For fluids generally, only the bulk modulus is a significant physical constant. In this section, however, our immediate concern is with solid materials: all four elastic constants, therefore, remain significant.

The simplest situation in which Young's modulus may be deter-mined for a solid material occurs when a uniform wire, rigidly supported at its upper end, is allowed to hang vertically under the action of a load attached to the free end of the wire. The tensile stress is given by the load per unit cross-sectional area of the wire, and the strain by the measured extension expressed as a fraction of the original length.

A more complicated situation occurs when a load is applied to the free end of a uniform beam, the other end of which is firmly clamped so that the beam protrudes horizontally from the face of a rigid vertical support. A beam supported in this manner is referred to as a cantilever, and we may simplify our initial con-sideration of its behaviour by assuming that the weight of the beam is very small compared with the applied load. We shall also assume that the cross-section of the beam is rectangular, of (horizontal) breadth b and (vertical) depth d. To begin with we shall not make any assumption as to what modulus of elasticity is significant for our problem. We shall assume that some modulus is significant, and we shall denote the measure of it by E. We wish to calculate z, the depression of the free end of the cantilever when the load is W.

Clearly, if the cantilever were of breadth $2b$ a load $2W$ would give the same depression, for we could regard the load as equally divided, and the cantilever of double breadth as constituted of two independent cantilevers equally deflected by equal loads. Also, because the depression is necessarily proportional to the load (the basic assumption underlying all our considerations in this chapter), it is also inversely proportional to the modulus E (only in that way will the dimensions of force cancel in the equation for z). If l is the length of the cantilever, therefore, we may write

$$z = c.\frac{W}{Eb}.l^x d^y \qquad (141)$$

c being a numerical constant, and x and y unspecified exponents yet to be determined. Obviously, the method of dimensional analysis does not allow us to determine x and y independently: we cannot in this way distinguish one length, the length of the cantilever, from another, its depth. But we have the following relations, namely,

$$[z] = L^1,$$

$$\left[\frac{W}{Eb}\right] = \frac{M^1 L^1 T^{-2}}{ML^{-1}T^{-2}.L^1} = L^1.$$

We conclude, therefore, that $x+y=0$: if we can determine one of these exponents, the other is given without further enquiry. It happens that in practice it is very much easier to determine x than it is to determine y. We have only to clamp the cantilever at a series of decreasing distances from its free end, and to measure the equilibrium depression of that end under the same load W. A careful experiment of this nature will show that $x=3$. We conclude, then, that $y=-3$.

We are left, now, with the identity of the modulus E, and with the magnitude of the numerical constant c in equation (141), as

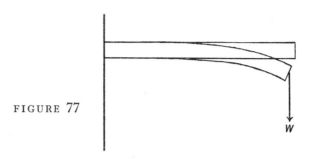

FIGURE 77

matters for further consideration. Fig. 77 represents, in vertical section, the cantilever in its undeflected and deflected configurations. We assume, intuitively, that the free end of the cantilever is no longer vertical when the load is applied, indeed that in the deflected configuration sections of the cantilever, previously perpendicular to its longitudinal axis, remain perpendicular to that axis. If this assumption is accepted—and it cannot be seriously in error—then those filaments of the cantilever parallel to the axis and near the upper surface of the cantilever have been extended, and the corresponding filaments near the lower surface equally compressed, in the course of the deformation. The length of the central axis itself must have remained practically unchanged in the process. We see, now, that the problem is essentially one of longitudinal extension and compression, the sideways stresses having negligible effect, and we conclude that Young's modulus is the appropriate modulus for our calculation: $E = Y$. As regards the numerical constant c, we cannot here elaborate the theory by which it may be evaluated. If we are prepared to accept its value on trust, we may write

$$z = \frac{4W}{Y} \frac{l^3}{bd^3} \tag{142}$$

When a uniform 'light' beam, supported only at its two ends, sags under a central load, the problem of its deformation is in all essential particulars identical with that which we have just considered. Fig. 78 illustrates the new situation. The load, which we denote by W, acts through the lowest point on the longitudinal axis of the beam in its deformed state. The reactions at the supports are equal vertical forces each of magnitude $W/2$. The situation is as if two

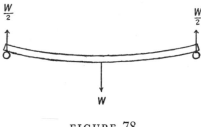

cantilevers, each of length $l/2$ (l being the length of the beam), were inverted and joined together at their clamped ends. Obviously the depression of the centre of the loaded beam, in this case, is given by the expression

$$z = \frac{W}{4Y} \frac{l^3}{bd^3} \tag{143}$$

Here b and d denote the breadth and depth of the rectangular cross-section of the beam as before.

When a uniform light beam is supported symmetrically at two points which are not at its ends, and equal loads are applied at the ends, the situation is as illustrated in fig. 79.

The reactions of the supports are equal to one another and to the loads W, and the centre point of the beam is raised, through a distance which we shall denote by z, as before. This is the simplest situation which can be devised in relation to the bending of beams. If the two supports A and B (fig. 79) are separated by a distance l, and if the loads are applied each at a distance l' from the nearer support, the external forces acting on either portion of the beam

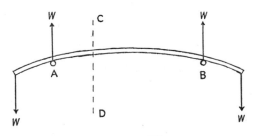

FIGURE 79

into which any plane such as CD, lying between A and B, divides it, constitute a couple, of constant magnitude Wl', of which the axis is horizontal and normal to the beam. We say that the 'bending moment' of the external forces is constant in magnitude for all sections of the beam between the points of support.

Consider, now, the equilibrium of that portion of the beam which lies to one side, say to the left, of the plane CD (fig. 79). The external forces constitute an anti-clockwise couple acting on this portion of the beam. The counterbalancing clockwise couple must be provided by the internal forces brought into play by the

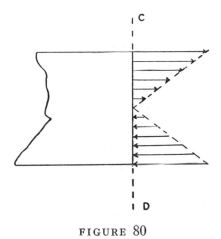

FIGURE 80

bending of the beam. The upper filaments of the beam are extended, and the lower filaments compressed. The internal forces, acting from that portion of the beam to the right of CD on the portion to the left, are therefore as indicated vectorially in fig. 80. It is evident that they are of the character to produce the clockwise couple required. The important point is that, in the arrangement which we are discussing, the magnitude of this clockwise couple is constant for all sections of the beam between A and B. The detailed distribution of stress across the section must therefore be constant, and the bending, which is responsible for the internal stresses, uniform, over the whole length of the beam between the supports. We conclude, in fact, that the radius of curvature of the longitudinal axis of the beam is the same at all points between A

X

and B (fig. 79), or that the shape of this axis, between the points of support, is that of the arc of a circle. It is in this sense that this situation is the simplest which it is possible to devise in relation to the bending of beams. If ρ is the radius of curvature of the longitudinal axis of a rectangular beam of breadth b and depth d which is bent in this way, it can be shown that

$$\rho = \frac{Y}{12W}\frac{bd^3}{l'}.$$

This result being accepted, then (see p. 136)

$$z = \frac{l^2}{8\rho} = \frac{3W}{2Y}\frac{l^2l'}{bd^3} \qquad (144)$$

When a heavy beam sags under its own weight the situation is more complicated. We shall quote the theoretical result for one case only. If a uniform beam of total weight W is supported at its ends, as illustrated in fig. 78, and is otherwise unloaded, the depression of its mid-point is given by the expression

$$z = \frac{5W}{32Y}\frac{l^3}{bd^3} \qquad (145)$$

in which the other symbols have their usual meanings. It is no coincidence that equations (142) to (145) are almost identical, except for the value of the numerical constant. This indeed follows from the dimensional argument: it is the main concern of the detailed theory to calculate the value of constant appropriate to each case in turn.

We have already stated (p. 317) that our definition of Young's modulus and the rigidity modulus are irrelevant to the consideration of the elastic properties of fluids. The situation in which the rigidity of solid materials is most commonly in evidence is that in which a wire is twisted by axial couples applied to its ends. It is clear that the strain involved in this situation is of the nature of a shear: if we regard one end of the wire as fixed, the rotation of any section of the wire is proportional to its distance from the fixed end, thus, throughout the length of the wire, adjacent sections are rotated relatively by an amount which is proportional to their separation. If we consider the unstrained wire as made up of filaments parallel to its length, we shall see that the angle of shear varies directly as the distance of a filament from the axis of the wire. In the limit, the axial filament is undeformed; a filament on the surface of the wire is characterised by an angle of shear of magnitude $r\phi/l$, r being the radius and l the length of the wire, and ϕ being the total twist. Our aim is to relate the total twist to the common measure of the applied couples, which we shall denote by G, and to n, the modulus of rigidity of the material of which the wire is made.

We assume, in conformity with our general assumption in respect of small strains, that ϕ is proportional to G and inversely proportional to n. We have seen that, for a wire of given radius, the shear on any filament is inversely proportional to the length of the wire, so that the internal couple is inversely proportional to the length for a given total twist. We have, therefore, only to determine the exponent x and the numerical constant c in the equation

$$\phi = c.\frac{G}{n}\, lr^x$$

in order to obtain the result which we seek. The angle ϕ is non-dimensional, and we have

$$\left[\frac{G}{n}\right] = \frac{M^1 L^2 T^{-2}}{M^1 L^{-1} T^{-2}} = L^3.$$

Thus $x = -4$. Detailed calculation shows that $c = 2/\pi$, therefore

$$\phi = \frac{2G}{\pi n}\frac{l}{r^4} \tag{146}$$

Because the strain is a shear strain, the volume of a wire which suffers a simple twist is unaltered by the twist; on the other hand, when a wire is strained by the application of a longitudinal tensile stress p, as described on p. 317, the volume of the wire is increased by a fraction $(p/Y)(1-2\sigma)$, or $p/3k$ (see equation (137)), of its original volume.

Our last result deserves brief further consideration. If, instead of a solid wire under tension, we had a long hollow cylinder, of internal and external cylindrical radii r_1, r_2, and length l $(r_2 \ll l)$, loaded with a weight W uniformly applied over the annular end-section of the cylinder, the fractional increase in the internal volume of the cylinder would similarly be $W/3\pi(r_2{}^2 - r_1{}^2)k$. If the cylinder were closed at the two ends by thin end-plates, through the upper of which a narrow glass capillary tube projected, open to the atmosphere, and if the whole were filled with a suitable liquid the meniscus of which provided an index mark in the capillary tube, changes of internal volume would be measurable in terms of the movement of the meniscus in the tube. Such an arrangement would then afford a means of determining k, the bulk modulus of the material of which the hollow cylinder was made. It was, in fact, precisely this arrangement which Amagat (p. 312) used with success during the years 1888 to 1891.

16.3. ELASTICITY OF LIQUIDS AND GASES

When the elasticity of fluids is in question, only the bulk modulus is significant. For the common liquids, and at moderate pressures, experimental values are some 10 to 50 times less than for the common metals. In this connection, mercury in the liquid state exhibits the higher elasticity characteristic of the metals: the bulk modulus of mercury over a range of pressures up to 100 atmospheres is about 13 times that of water over the same range. In surveying this information there is nothing of fundamental importance to note, at our level of interest, only a large body of detail concerning experimental methods which it would be beyond the scope of the present treatment to include.

In respect of the elasticity of gases the position is very different. It was with gases in mind that we made the reservation (p. 317) 'once the thermal character of the change has been specified', when we claimed that the elastic properties of a fluid could be represented by a single modulus—and the earlier reservation (p. 309) that we should be confining attention 'in the main' to those situations of small strain in which the strain is proportional to the stress producing it. In practical situations, with gases, strains are not always 'small', in the technical sense, and in general there is no finite range of stress over which strict proportionality between stress and strain obtains. Also, as we observed when considering specific heats, so now with elasticities, we recognise that the bulk modulus of a gas, at a given temperature and pressure, is a many-valued quantity the magnitude of which in any situation depends upon the precise specification of the heat transfer which accompanies the strain. In this section we shall confine attention to two such specifications only, one which requires the change to be isothermal (see p. 293), the other which requires that it shall be 'adiabatic'. An adiabatic change is a change (of pressure and volume) in which no heat enters or leaves the specimen concerned. It is our object, then, to calculate the bulk modulus of an ideal gas under conditions of constant temperature and zero-heat exchange, respectively. Following convention, we shall refer to these two values of the bulk modulus as values of the 'isothermal elasticity,' k_i, and the 'adiabatic elasticity, k_a, of the gas in question.

First, however, it is necessary to re-shape our definition of the modulus itself. In dealing with liquids and solids we have never found it necessary to remind ourselves that the experimental sample, under ordinary conditions, is subject to the hydrostatic pressure of the atmosphere in its 'unstrained' initial state. The stresses with which we have had to deal have generally been very large compared with 1 standard atmosphere (the elastic moduli of solids are of the order of 10^5 to 10^6 atmospheres, that is 10^{11} to 10^{12} dyne cm.$^{-2}$). It is entirely different when we are dealing with gases. In specifying the initial state of a sample of gas, we effectively specify the pressure, p, under which the sample is originally confined, and to make our definition of the modulus precise we have to consider the effect produced by an additional pressure which is small compared with p. Let us denote this small additional pressure by Δp. Let the original volume be V and the final volume be $V - \Delta V$. Then the numerical measure of the strain is given by $\Delta V / V$, and our defining equation (see equation (136)) becomes

$$\Delta p = k \frac{\Delta V}{V} \qquad (147)$$

We may now calculate the isothermal elasticity, k_i, directly as follows. For an ideal gas which undergoes an isothermal change, the variation of volume with pressure is given by Boyle's law (p. 278). We have, therefore,

$$(p + \Delta p)(V - \Delta V) = pV,$$

or $$\left(1 + \frac{\Delta p}{p}\right)\left(1 - \frac{\Delta V}{V}\right) = 1.$$

Neglecting small quantities of the second order in comparison with those of the first order, as we did in relation to the superposition of strains (p. 310), we obtain

$$\frac{\Delta p}{p} - \frac{\Delta V}{V} = 0,$$

or

$$k_i = V \frac{\Delta p}{\Delta V} = p \qquad (148)$$

Equation (148) states that the isothermal elasticity of an ideal gas is a quantity, of the character of a pressure, the magnitude of which is identical with that of the actual pressure of the gas in the experimental situation involved. This result gives precision to two statements which we have already made. It shows how very different, under ordinary circumstances, the magnitude of the bulk modulus of a gas is from that of the bulk modulus of a liquid or a solid material, and it confirms and extends the statement that there is in general no finite range of stress over which the modulus is constant and stress is proportional to strain. If we were to increase the pressure applied to a gas stepwise, over a finite range from p_1 to p_2, at each step, the pressure having increased further, so likewise would the value of the effective modulus have increased. Equation (148) also shows that, at a given temperature, the isothermal elasticity of an ideal gas is proportional to its density.

In order to calculate the adiabatic elasticity, k_a, let us make use of a p-V diagram similar to that of fig. 68. In fig. 81 let the coordinates of the points A and B, on the appropriate scale, be (p, V), $(p - \Delta p, V + \Delta V)$, respectively. Here p and V are the initial measures of the pressure and volume of a mass m of an ideal gas, and we suppose that the line AB in the diagram represents an elementary adiabatic change. Then the line BC represents a change at constant pressure, and the line CA a subsequent change at constant volume, by the successive operation of which the experimental sample of gas, having expanded adiabatically from volume V to volume $V + \Delta V$, might be brought back to its original state. Let its temperature in that state be T, and in the states represented by the points B and C in the diagram be $T - \Delta T_1$ and $T - \Delta T_2$, respectively. It will be noted that we do not assume that the temperature remains constant during the adiabatic change. Then the area ABCA in the diagram represents the net work done by the sample of gas in the cycle of changes

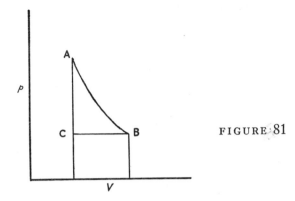

FIGURE 81

which we have described, and because the state of the sample is the same at the end as it was at the beginning of the cycle, this work is the equivalent of the net amount of heat taken in by the gas during the cycle.

Using our previous notation (p. 292), and remembering that by definition no heat is taken in during the adiabatic change, although the temperature changes from T to $T-\Delta T_1$, we express the equivalence of heat and work by the equation

$$-Jmc_p(\Delta T_2-\Delta T_1)+Jmc_V\Delta T_2 = J.\text{area ABCA} \qquad (149)$$

Now the ideal gas equation (126) is applicable to all changes which such a gas may undergo. Thus, in relation to the change represented by the line BC in fig. 81, we may write

$$\frac{V+\Delta V}{T-\Delta T_1} = \frac{V}{T-\Delta T_2},$$

and, in relation to that represented by CA,

$$\frac{p-\Delta p}{T-\Delta T_2} = \frac{p}{T}.$$

Neglecting small quantities of the second order, as before, after simplification of the former equation, we obtain

$$\Delta T_2-\Delta T_1 = T\frac{\Delta V}{V},$$

and, from the latter, we obtain directly

$$\Delta T_2 = T \frac{\Delta p}{p}.$$

Substituting these values in equation (149), and writing $mT = pVM/R$ (equation (126)), we have

$$\frac{\mathcal{J}M}{R}(c_V V \Delta p - c_p p \Delta V) = f.\text{area ABCA}.$$

But, as to order of magnitude, $f.\text{area ABCA} = \frac{1}{2}\Delta p \Delta V$. This quantity is of the second order, whereas the quantities $V\Delta p$ and $p\Delta V$, which occur on the other side of the equation, are of the first order of smallness. In the limit we neglect the second order quantity in comparison with the others, and we finally have

$$c_V V \Delta p - c_p p \Delta V = 0,$$

or
$$k_a = V\frac{\Delta p}{\Delta V} = \frac{c_p}{c_V}p = \gamma p \qquad (150)$$

Combining equations (148) and (150), we note that the ratio of the adiabatic elasticity of an ideal gas to the isothermal elasticity (when the state of the gas is the same) is equal to the ratio of the principal specific heats of the gas. This result forms the basis of some of the indirect methods of determining the ratio of the principal specific heats, to which we have already referred (p. 295), but on this occasion, as on the last, it would be beyond our scope to give practical details of these methods.

16.4. WORK IN ELASTIC DEFORMATION

In our discussion of potential energy (Chapter 11) we introduced the idea that energy may be temporarily stored, during a collision between elastic bodies, in the region of deformation of the bodies around the point of impact. Here we may consider the matter in more detail in relation to the various types of strain which we have recently discussed.

The simplest case is that of the stretched wire. The calculation of the work done against the 'elastic' forces developed during the deformation in this case is essentially the same as the calculation, of § 11.3, of the work done against the restoring force in linear simple harmonic motion. If the final extension is l and the final load W, the measure of the work done is $\frac{1}{2}Wl$. Again, if the wire is a cylindrical wire of cross-sectional area A and initial length L, since the strain is uniform throughout, we may regard this energy as being stored uniformly throughout the wire. In that case the potential energy density will be $Wl/2AL$ per unit volume. Now $W/A = Yl/L$, Y being the measure of Young's modulus for the material of the wire. Thus the potential energy density is $(Y/2)(l/L)^2$, or one-half the modulus multiplied by the square of the strain.

When the stress is a uniform hydrostatic pressure p, producing a decrease of volume v, similar reasoning shows that the measure of the work done (see p. 290) is $\frac{1}{2}pv$. If V is the original volume of the specimen, the potential energy density is then $pv/2V$. In this case $p = kv/V$, and the expression for the energy density becomes $(k/2)(v/V)^2$. The potential energy density is again given by the product of one-half the modulus multiplied by the square of the strain.

The result which we have now obtained in two simple cases is, in fact, perfectly general. It may be applied without inconsistency in more complicated cases, even though the strain is not uniform. We have already considered the case of the wire under torsion, and we have concluded (p. 323) that the local strain (angle of shear) is directly proportional to the distance from the axis of the wire. The density of potential energy is, therefore, proportional to the square of the radial distance in this case; the strain energy is located chiefly in the outer cylindrical layers of the wire. In a similar way the strain energy in a bent beam (pp. 317-322) is located chiefly near the upper and lower faces of the beam, when the plane of bending is vertical as we have previously assumed it to be.

CHAPTER 17

SURFACE TENSION

17.1. INTERFACIAL ENERGY

In the last section we were concerned with the energy stored in materials maintained in a state of strain by the action of stresses externally applied. In certain cases of the non-uniform strain of solid bodies we concluded that the energy of strain is located mainly in those portions of the body lying near an exposed surface. In this section we shall be dealing with the potential energy associated with a type of surface strain arising naturally from the action of internal forces. We shall find that this energy is located in a very thin stratum situated immediately below the geometrical surface of a body, the thickness of the stratum being only a few times greater than the average distance between the molecules. The notion of interfacial energy, to which we shall be led, will be found to be most immediately relevant to the phenomena exhibited by the free surfaces of liquids, but we should not lose sight of the fact that the bounding surface of any volume of liquid merely separates the liquid from some other material, be it its own vapour exclusively, or a gas, or another liquid, or a solid body. The precise details of the phenomena, in any particular case, depend to some extent on the nature of the material on the other side of the surface.

As starting-point of our discussion we may refer back to § 15.5. There we dealt with the properties of real gases, and with the transition from gas to liquid which experiment shows to be 'continuous' (or the notion to be without significance) at all temperatures above the critical temperature of the substance concerned. We concluded that, whatever the substance, the general form of the law of force between one molecule and another must be as represented schematically in fig. 70. There must be strong repulsion at the closest distances, and, as the separation increases, an attractive force which rapidly reaches a maximum value and then, almost as rapidly, falls effectively to zero. The range of distance over which this force is significantly different from zero cannot be more than a very few molecular diameters, whatever the substance.

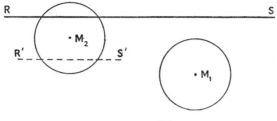

Now, consider an individual molecule within a volume of liquid. The molecules which at any instant are more distant than a few molecular diameters have no influence on the molecule under consideration. The force on it is determined entirely by a small number of nearer molecules—say a few hundred at the most—and most importantly by its nearest neighbours, not more than ten in number. Here we are considering only the 'steady' attractive forces. The repulsive forces which come into play during collisions are transient: they may be regarded as responsible for the random changes in the kinetic energy of our representative molecule. We are concerned now with changes in its potential energy. Clearly, if we imagine a molecule as remaining at a considerable distance from the free surface of the liquid, though the resultant 'steady' force on it will vary with time, both in magnitude and direction, the time-average of this force will be zero. With any distance from the free surface we can associate a value of the time-average of the steady resultant force acting on a molecule at that distance, and this time-average will be zero for all distances greater than a few molecular diameters.

The situation is different at smaller distances from the free surface. Although the resultant force acting on a molecule at such a distance will still vary with time, even more so than before, its time-average will be finite, and the direction of the mean steady force on the molecule will be away from the surface along the inwards normal. The situation is as represented in fig. 82. RS is the free surface, and M_1 and M_2 are two molecules in the liquid. The equal circles indicate the distance beyond which molecular attraction is ineffective. Obviously, the mean force on M_2 will be as stated: there are molecules of liquid, within the range of attraction, below the plane R'S' the attraction of which is not balanced by that of molecules above RS. We conclude, therefore, that the mean steady force on a molecule of the liquid varies with its distance from the geometrical free surface of the liquid as indicated in fig. 83. This force is everywhere directed along the inwards normal to the surface, and it becomes inappreciable at distances from that surface greater than a few molecular diameters.

Consider now a molecule brought to the free surface from the interior of the liquid. Over the range of distances represented by AO in fig. 83 it will be moving against a steadily increasing force. When it reaches a distance represented by OD, its potential energy will have increased by an amount represented by the area ADCA in the figure; when it reaches the surface, by an amount represented by the whole area between the curve AB and the co-ordinate axes. When the liquid is in a steady state, all the molecules in the 'anomalous' surface layer of thickness OA will have potential energy in excess of that which they would possess in the bulk of the liquid. We have every justification, therefore, for regarding the free surface of any liquid as the seat of potential energy, the amount of which, per unit area of surface, is characteristic of the liquid concerned, being ultimately related to the magnitude and range of the force of attraction which operates between one molecule of the liquid and another.

In the foregoing we have tacitly assumed that there is no material on the other side of the geometrical free surface of the liquid. This can never be precisely true in practice. If we are dealing with a system in a steady state, there must at least be vapour in equilibrium with the liquid at the temperature concerned. In that case there must also be attraction between the molecules above the free surface and those below, and our previous statements require slight modification in consequence. Only when the temperature approaches the critical temperature, however, is the situation very different from that which we have described. Then the densities of liquid and saturated vapour are of the same order (see fig. 71), and a little consideration in terms of fig. 82 will show that, if there is an abrupt discontinuity between liquid and vapour, the interfacial potential energy per molecule of liquid in the anomalous surface layer is proportional to the difference, $\rho_l - \rho_v$, between the densities

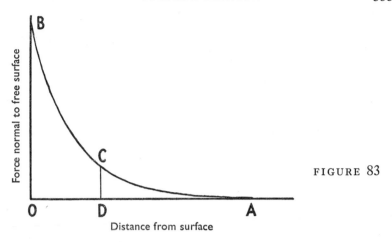

FIGURE 83

of liquid and vapour in the neighbourhood of the surface of separation. It will further show that molecules in the vapour, within an anomalous surface layer of the same thickness, experience a mean resultant force directed towards the liquid normally across the interface, which, for the same distance from the surface is of the same magnitude as that experienced by molecules in the liquid. The anomalous surface layer in the vapour is, therefore, a region of negative potential energy with respect to the bulk of the vapour. But the ratio of the numbers of molecules per unit area of interface in the anomalous surface layers of liquid and vapour is the ratio of the densities, ρ_l/ρ_v. Thus, on these assumptions, the net interfacial energy per unit area is proportional to $(\rho_l - \rho_v)^2$, the square of the density difference. It is consonant with this conclusion that, when liquid and vapour become otherwise physically indistinguishable in the critical state, the liquid-vapour interface should become a meaningless concept. Under these conditions there is no anomalous region of excess potential energy which this interface might determine.

Here we should interject a note of caution. Our last result has been derived on the basis of the assumption that there is a sharp boundary of discontinuity between a liquid and its saturated vapour, at all temperatures below the critical temperature. Moreover, it admits of comparison with experiment only if the densities ρ_l and ρ_v, of the liquid and vapour on the two sides of this boundary are identified with the densities of the liquid and vapour in bulk. In fact, the assumption is unlikely to correspond with reality, and, if this is so, the subsequent identification of densities is inadmissible. Qualitatively, our discussion is valid, and helpful to an understanding of the situation; quantitatively its conclusions are suspect. Experiment shows, indeed, that the interfacial energy per unit area, in the case we have considered, is for many substances closely proportional to the fourth power of the bulk density difference, not to its square, and for almost all substances proportional to a power greater than the third.

If we have failed to produce a quantitative theory of the interfacial energy of a liquid in contact with its saturated vapour on simple assumptions, obviously we shall not succeed when the interface under consideration is one separating two different liquids, or separating a liquid from a solid. In spite of this, the qualitative statement remains significant: in all such cases there is a unique interfacial energy, characteristic of the pair of materials concerned, and the general basis of explanation of this fact is to be found in terms of the idea of intermolecular forces, as we have already indicated.

In 1873 Joseph Antoine Ferdinand Plateau (1801-1883), who had been professor of physics at Ghent since 1835—and totally blind since 1843, published the results of a long series of experiments on surface phenomena. In one of these experiments he had introduced various quantities of olive oil into a mixture of water and alcohol the composition of which was such that the mixture had, as nearly as could be arranged, the same density as the oil. He found that in such circumstances even large quantities of oil, very many cubic centimetres in volume, collected into globules which were perfectly spherical in shape. The equalisation of densities ensured that gravitational effects were nullified, and the conclusion was drawn that, when external forces are reduced to zero, the interface between two immiscible liquids assumes the form of least area (a sphere is the figure of least surface for a given volume). This experimental observation, and Plateau's formal interpretation of it, are in full accord with the notion of interfacial energy, for it is true of all mechanical systems that they tend towards states of equilibrium in which the potential energy is as small as possible.

Plateau also devised many experiments with liquid films which admit of a similar interpretation (and he was the first to publish the recipe for a 'soap solution' of which really durable films could be made). Thus, if a closed loop of thread be laid lightly, in an arbitrary fashion, on a soap film formed on a framework of wire, and if the film inside the loop of thread be broken, then it will be observed that the film outside the thread will contract in such a way that the thread is drawn into a perfect circle. For a given perimeter a circle is the plane figure of greatest area, thus in this experiment the remaining film has contracted to the smallest possible area, as before.

17.2. SURFACE TENSION

The experiments of Plateau, which we have just described, if we had not interpreted them so satisfactorily in terms of interfacial potential energy, might well have suggested the notion of a surface tension, that is the idea that the situation in surface phenomena is determined by the action of forces in the interfaces, rather than by forces at right angles to them. The notion of energy in general, as we have already seen (p. 228), is a development of the mid-nineteenth century; on the other hand, many peculiarly surface phenomena had been observed and investigated in detail through-out the eighteenth century. It is not surprising, therefore, that the idea of a characteristic tension in a liquid surface should have arisen long before the idea of energy gained currency in any form. We cannot now admit that a coherent theory of these phenomena can be erected on this basis, but it was in fact the basis on which Gaspard Monge (1746-1818) attempted to explain them. 'By sup-posing the adherence of the particles of a fluid to have a sensible effect only at the surface itself, and in the direction of the surface, it would be easy to determine the curvature of the surfaces of fluids in the neighbourhood of the solid boundaries which contain them,' he wrote in 1787.

In spite of the facts here recited, the term 'surface tension', first introduced by Johann Andreas von Segner in 1751, is still com-monly employed in the treatment of the phenomena which we are now to discuss. Dimensionally considered, energy-per-unit-area and force-per-unit-length are quantities of the same kind, and it is certainly true that the bounding surfaces of liquids in contact with other liquids, with solids or with gases, behave as if, across any line in the surface, adjacent portions of the surface acted one on the other with a force proportional to the length of the dividing line considered. Moreover, if a film of liquid is formed on a rect-

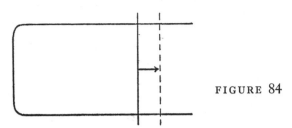

FIGURE 84

angular framework of which one side is movable, as shown in fig. 84, and if this side, of length l, is moved through a distance x, so that new surface of area $2lx$ is created in the process (the two sides of the film each contributing an additional area lx), the increase in interfacial potential energy is $2lxE$, where E is the measure of the potential energy per unit area of surface. Also, the mechanical work done is $2l\gamma x$, where γ is the measure of the surface tension, the notional force per unit length effective in the surface on each side of the film. If we were justified in equating these two quantities (see § 17.3, below), we should have $\gamma = E$. In that case a determination of 'surface tension', for example by measurement of the force required to maintain equilibrium in an arrangement such as that of fig. 84, would constitute a direct evaluation of the interfacial potential energy per unit area of surface.

Determinations of surface tension are frequently made by observations of the rise of liquids in capillary tubes. Such observations have been made systematically for the last two hundred and fifty years. In 1718 James Jurin (1684-1750), physician and physicist, master of the grammar school at Newcastle-on-Tyne from 1709 to 1715, and sometime secretary of the Royal Society of London, established the fact that, for a given liquid, the equilibrium height, when the tube is of varying circular section, depends only on the radius of the tube in the region of the upper surface of the liquid. As we have already indicated, an attempt was made by Monge to explain this phenomenon, in terms of purely surface forces, in 1787, but an explanation, acceptable today, in terms of forces acting throughout the volume of the liquid, was not given until some twenty years later. John Leslie (1766-1832), professor of mathematics and then of natural philosophy at Edinburgh, put forward a new view of the matter in 1802, and Thomas Young (see p. 224), in 1804, and P. S. Laplace (see p. 210), in 1806, gave detailed theories of the effect which, though very differently expounded, were essentially the same. Here we postpone further consideration of it until we have discussed the situation obtaining with small drops of liquid and bubbles of gas.

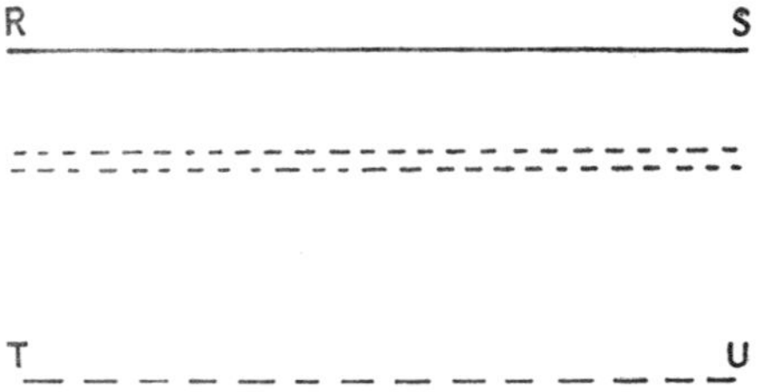

R   S
_____

- -

FIGURE 85

T   U
‾ _ _ _ _ _ _ _ _ _ _ _ _ _ _

To do this we must first reconsider the case of the liquid bounded by a plane surface, which we discussed in the last section with the help of figs. 82 and 83. Consider now a very thin stratum of the liquid, parallel to the surface and at a distance from it less than the distance a, represented by OA in fig. 83 as the range of molecular attraction. The situation is as represented in fig. 85, in which RS is the free surface, and the plane TU is at a distance a below the surface. Let the stratum be at a mean distance x from the surface, represented by OD in fig. 83. Then each molecule having its centre in the stratum is subject to a resultant downwards force represented by DC, and the total downwards force on the molecules in unit area of the stratum is, in suitable units, n times the area of a vertical strip in the figure, lying around CD and of width representative of the thickness of the stratum. Here n is the number of molecules per unit volume of the liquid. Now the stratum of liquid is in equilibrium, thus the pressure on its lower face must be greater than the pressure on its upper face. Since pressure is a measure of the normal force per unit area, we have the result that, quite independently of any gravitational effect, the pressure in the liquid immediately below the stratum considered is greater than the pressure immediately above the stratum by a quantity which, in suitable units, is n times the area of the aforementioned vertical strip in the figure.

A similar statement is true of every stratum of liquid within a distance a of the surface, thus we conclude that the pressure in the liquid builds up steadily with increasing distance from the surface, to reach a constant value in the interior (below the

Y

anomalous surface layer), and that this internal pressure is given by n times the whole area between the curve AB and the axes of co-ordinates in fig. 83.

But we have already shown (p. 332) that, in terms of the same units, the whole area in question is the excess potential energy of a single molecule in the bounding surface of the liquid. Now the number of molecules in unit area of the anomalous surface layer is an. Let the average value of the excess potential energy per molecule in this layer be a fraction f_1 of that of a molecule in the bounding surface itself. Then the interfacial potential energy per unit area of free surface is given by anf_1 times the whole area below the curve in fig. 83.

We have, therefore, two results, relating respectively to the internal pressure in the bulk of the liquid, the measure of which we shall denote by P, and to the interfacial potential energy per unit area of surface, which we have already denoted by E (p. 336). Combining these results, we have

$$E = af_1P \qquad (151)$$

Now let us consider the case in which the bounding surface of a volume of liquid is a sphere of radius r, not an 'infinite' plane. In fig. 86 the curvature of this spherical surface RS is grossly exaggerated in relation to the curvature of the sphere of molecular attraction, of radius a, shown drawn about M, the centre of a molecule situated within the anomalous surface layer. Let LMN be the common normal from M to the two spheres, and XY the plane tangential to RS at its point of intersection with LMN. Let R'S' and X'Y' be the 'reflections', in a plane through M parallel to XY, of RS and XY, respectively. Then the resultant inwards force on the molecule at M, in the situation considered, is that due to the molecules within the portion of the dotted sphere lying below R'S'. If, however, the surface of the liquid had been plane, the resultant inwards force would have been that due to the molecules in the portion of the dotted sphere lying below X'Y'. For the same distance from the surface, therefore, the inwards force is greater on a molecule close to a concave spherical surface than it is on a molecule close to a plane surface. The internal pressure within a spherical drop of liquid will consequently be greater than P as above calculated. Let us denote it by $P+p$.

Clearly the ratio p/P must depend on the ratio a/r; p/P is a

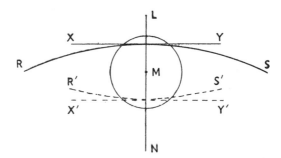

FIGURE 86

non-dimensional quantity, and the two lengths a and r are the only relevant quantities of the same dimensions which fulfil the condition that one of them (r) describes the difference between the case which we are now considering and that which we considered previously. The relation

$$p/P = f_2 a/r \qquad (152)$$

is the simplest relation which satisfies the requirement that $p = 0$ when $r \to \infty$. Here f_2 is a pure number. Detailed calculation shows that, in fact, equation (152) is of the correct form, thus we may combine it with equation (151) and so obtain the simple result

$$p = \frac{f_2}{f_1} \frac{E}{r} \qquad (153)$$

We have already cautiously identified E with γ, the surface tension which may be determined by experiments on thin films of liquid. On that basis we may justify the interpretation of equation (153) by the statement: a spherical drop of liquid in equilibrium has excess internal pressure in amount inversely proportional to the radius of the drop and directly proportional to the surface tension of the liquid.

If we had considered a bubble of gas in a liquid, rather than a liquid drop, the element of spherical surface in fig. 86 would have been convex towards the liquid rather than concave. In that case, our argument would have led through the same steps to the conclusion that the internal pressure just below the anomalous surface layer is $P - p$, not $P + p$, p being given by equation (153) as before.

We are now in a position to consider the situation in respect of a spherical bubble of gas contained within a thin film of liquid

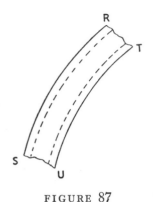

FIGURE 87

('soap bubble'). Let RS, TU (fig. 87) represent the outer and inner boundaries of a small portion of the spherical film. Let p_1, p_2 be the pressures, in the gas immediately outside RS, and in the gas inside TU, respectively. Then, if the thickness of the film is greater than $2a$ (see p. 337), there will be a median region of the film, as indicated, throughout which the pressure is constant. The value of this constant pressure is given, alternatively, by p_1+P+p or p_2+P-p, depending upon whether we use the pressure of the external or internal gas as reference pressure. Obviously, these two values must be identical, thus we have

$$p_2-p_1 = 2p = \frac{2f_2}{f_1}\frac{E}{r} \qquad (154)$$

Here we have taken the radii of curvature of the internal and external spherical surfaces of the film to be the same. If they were significantly different, we should have, instead of equation (154),

$$p_2-p_1 = \frac{f_2 E}{f_1}\left(\frac{1}{r_1}+\frac{1}{r_2}\right).$$

The case of the spherical soap bubble can be treated very simply using the alternative concept of surface tension, in a way which is not possible in other cases. From this treatment we can draw certain conclusions concerning the magnitude of the multiplying factor f_2/f_1 which we have hitherto left undetermined. Suppose S, fig. 88, represents a spherical bubble of radius r and centre O, Let AB be a plane passing through O. Each 'half' of the bubble (film and enclosed gas) as defined by this plane is in equilibrium under the forces acting. Round the circular section of the film, the lower half acts on the upper with a downwards force of resultant magnitude $2.2\pi r.\gamma$. The perimeter of the equatorial section is of length $2\pi r$, and the film has two surfaces in each of which the tangential force per unit length is of magnitude γ. The gas in the lower half of the bubble acts on the gas in the upper half with an upwards force of magnitude $\pi r^2 p_2$, p_2 being the pressure of the

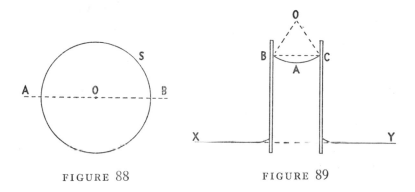

FIGURE 88   FIGURE 89

enclosed gas, as before. The gas surrounding the bubble at a pressure p_1 provides a resultant downwards force $\pi r^2 p_1$ (if the surface tension were zero, the film would be in equilibrium when the internal and external gas pressures were the same). We have, therefore,

$$\pi r^2 p_2 = \pi r^2 p_1 + 4\pi r\gamma,$$

or $$p_2 - p_1 = 4\gamma/r \qquad (155)$$

Continuing our identification of γ with E, and comparing equations (154) and (155), we have $f_2/f_1 = 2$, a result which we may use in equation (153), also. We then conclude that the excess pressure inside a spherical drop of liquid, of surface tension γ, is $2\gamma/r$, r being the radius of the drop.

We are at last able to take up again the question of capillary rise. Let the situation be as represented in fig. 89. A vertical capillary tube, of uniform circular section of internal radius r, dips into a liquid of density ρ, XY being the undisturbed plane surface of the liquid. We suppose the density of the surrounding gas or vapour to be σ. Let A, the lowest point of the free surface (meniscus) of the liquid in the tube, be at a height h above XY, when the system is in equilibrium. Then, if $r \ll h$, so that the whole depth of the meniscus is a very small fraction of the height of capillary ascent, we may neglect changes in gravity-produced pressure over the region which the meniscus occupies—and we may conclude that the difference of pressure across the meniscus, between the gas and the bulk of the liquid, is constant over the surface of the meniscus. In that case the form of the surface will be spherical: a single radius of curvature R will characterise it completely.

Let O, then, be the centre of curvature of the meniscus, and OB, OC, be drawn to its periphery, as shown. Let $\angle OBC = \angle OCB = \theta$. Then $r = R \cos \theta$. If p_2 is the pressure in the gas just above A, and p_1 the pressure in the liquid just below the anomalous surface layer at A, and if p_2', p_1' are the corresponding pressures on the two sides of the flat liquid surface XY, we have

$$p_2' = p_2 + g\sigma h,$$

$$p_1' = p_1 + g\rho h,$$

$$p_1 - p_2 = P - \frac{2\gamma}{R},$$

$$p_1' - p_2' = P,$$

g being the acceleration due to gravity, γ the surface tension of the liquid and P the internal liquid pressure defined by equation (151). From these relations we obtain the result

$$0 = -\frac{2\gamma}{R} + g(\rho - \sigma)h,$$

or
$$h = 2\gamma \cos \theta / g(\rho - \sigma)r \tag{156}$$

It will be recognised that in deducing equation (156) we have made the assumption that the meniscus meets the solid wall of the capillary tube at an arbitrary angle θ. Thomas Young was the first to draw attention to the fact that, when two immiscible fluids (one of which may be a gas) are brought into contact with the same solid surface, it may not be possible for equilibrium to be reached in such a way that three surfaces of separation, one between each fluid and the solid and the third between the two fluids, coexist, and that when this is possible it is possible only for a particular inclination of the fluid-fluid interface to the solid surface. In this latter case, when one of the fluids is a gas, it is general to refer to the equilibrium angle, as measured in the liquid, between the liquid-gas interface and the solid surface as the 'angle of contact' of the liquid and the solid in the presence of the gas in question. In our consideration of capillary rise, θ is the angle of contact according to this definition.

FIGURE 90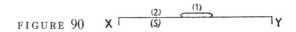

We may understand this general situation by reference to fig. 90. XY represents a solid surface, of finite area A_0, on which rests a large flat drop of liquid (fluid 1) of horizontal cross-sectional area A. The remainder of the space above XY is filled with the other fluid concerned (fluid 2). If the potential energy per unit area of the interface between the two fluids is denoted by $_1E_2$, and the corresponding quantities for the interfaces between the fluids and the solid are denoted by $_1E_s$ and $_2E_s$, respectively, the total interfacial surface energy is given, to a good approximation, by the expression

$$A(_1E_2 + {}_1E_s) + (A_0 - A)_2E_s.$$

This quantity will decrease as A increases if

$$_1E_2 + {}_1E_s - {}_2E_s < 0,$$

that is, if

$$_1E_2 < {}_2E_s - {}_1E_s \qquad (157)$$

If changes in gravitational potential energy are insignificant in relation to the other quantities involved, as we assume them to be, the inequality (157) will express the condition under which fluid 1 will spread completely over the solid surface, excluding fluid 2 from any contact with it. Obviously, the condition

$$_1E_2 < {}_1E_s - {}_2E_s \qquad (158)$$

mutually exclusive in relation to the other when two given fluids are concerned, determines the second possibility, that fluid 2 shall spread over the surface, excluding fluid 1. For two immiscible fluids $_1E_2$ must be a positive quantity, thus the third possibility, for two such fluids, is that

$$_1E_2 > |_2E_s - {}_1E_s|,$$

the symbol $|\ |$ denoting the difference, without reference to sign, between the two quantities in question. In this case, clearly, neither fluid can exclude the other completely from contact with the solid surface, and a situation of equilibrium must be possible in which the three surfaces of separation co-exist, intersecting in a line on

FIGURE 91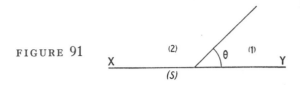

the solid surface. On an infinite solid surface, obviously the position of this line of intersection cannot determine the equilibrium: this must be determined by the angle of contact of the surfaces. If $_2E_s > {}_1E_s$, we can see, intuitively, that equilibrium will obtain, under the conditions represented in fig. 91, with

$$\cos\theta = \frac{{}_2E_s - {}_1E_s}{{}_1E_2},$$

for, identifying interfacial potential energies per unit area with surface tensions as before, this is the condition that the forces due to surface tension, acting across the line of intersection of the surfaces of separation, have no resultant parallel to the surface of the solid.

There is one further comment which we should make on the results obtained in this section. We have introduced the notions of internal pressure and interfacial potential energy per unit area of surface (or, alternatively, surface tension), and we have shown that the measures of these two quantities are related to one another through equation (151). The only other quantity involved in the relation is the range of molecular attraction, which we have denoted by a. We have also shown (p. 333) that, if certain simplifying assumptions are valid, the surface tension—and therefore the internal pressure of a fluid—is proportional to the square of the density when there are no molecules beyond the boundary of the fluid which exert forces on the molecules of fluid in the surface layer. It will be realised that in this result we have in fact reached the position to which van der Waals was led in 1873. The internal pressure which he envisaged, and that which we have been discussing in this chapter, are one and the same. In the equation of state of a mass m of an homogeneous fluid of molecular weight M, van der Waals's internal pressure is represented by the term m^2a/M^2V^2 (p. 304), that is by the expression ρ^2a/M^2, where ρ is the density of the fluid. It is satisfactory to note that this expression also involves the square of the density.

Suppose now that, by observations on the compressibility of a gas at different temperatures, the constant a in van der Waals's equation is deduced empirically. Suppose also that, for the same substance in the liquid state, the surface tension γ and the density ρ are determined. Then, equating surface tension with potential energy per unit area of surface, and using equation (151), we have

$$\gamma = af_1\rho^2a/M^2,$$

or
$$a = \gamma M^2/f_1\rho^2a \qquad (159)$$

In equation (159) all the quantities on the right-hand side are known except the numerical constant f_1. Detailed calculation of f_1 depends on assumptions regarding the law of force between molecules, which we have taken fig. 70 to represent schematically. Its value does not depend very critically on what assumptions are made, provided the form of the representative curve is not seriously different from that in the figure. We have, therefore, in equation (159) a reasonably precise method of estimating the range of molecular attraction, a, from measurements made on the properties of matter in bulk.

Thomas Young, much in advance of his time (1805), developed an argument, similar in essentials to that which we have here outlined, from which he made the first reliable estimate of a. His conclusions were lost sight of until they were rescued from oblivion by Lord Rayleigh, some fifteen years after van der Waals published his paper *On the continuity of the gaseous and liquid states* (p. 304).

17.3. THERMAL EFFECTS

In considering the expansion of gases, and the thermal exchanges associated with them, we found it convenient to employ a diagram in which the state of a given mass of gas is represented in terms of its pressure and its volume. In this section we wish to consider the thermal effects associated with the stretching of films, and it will be found similarly convenient to use a diagram in which the surface tension of the liquid and the area of the film are taken as variables. The two diagrams have this in common that an area on each represents an amount of work performed. The diagrams are different, however, in that, in the one case (in the p-V diagram), the positions of the representative curves are always different for different amounts of gas, when the same changes of pressure and

z

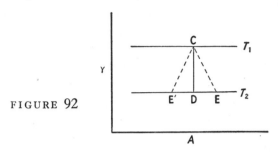

FIGURE 92

temperature are involved, whereas, in the other case (in the γ-A diagram), the position of an isothermal curve is independent of the mass of liquid contained in the film. Provided the thickness of the film is some few times greater than the range of molecular attraction, the surface tension is independent of its area—or, for the same area, independent of the mass of the film.

In fig. 92 isothermal curves are drawn, for a given liquid, showing the constancy of surface tension with area at two temperatures, T_1 and T_2 $(T_2 > T_1)$. For all liquids the surface tension decreases as the temperature rises, thus the relative positions of these isothermal curves is the reverse of that of the isothermals on the generalised p-V diagram of fig. 71. Consider now a change at constant area, whereby the temperature of the liquid film concerned increases from T_1 to T_2. Let this change be represented by the line CD in the figure. The amount of heat taken in by the film may be denoted by $mc_A(T_2 - T_1)$, where m is the mass of the film and c_A the specific heat at constant area under the conditions imposed. It is contrary to all experience that c_A should be zero. It must be a positive quantity.

Now suppose that the film is restored to its original state, represented by the point C on the figure, and that, instead of taking in heat at constant area, it is stretched, or allowed to contract, adiabatically (whichever produces the desired result) until its temperature has increased from T_1 to T_2. The change will be represented by the line CE (or CE', as the case may be). Next, let the change of area be reversed at constant temperature, the representative point on the figure moving from E (or E') to D. Finally, let the temperature of the film be reduced from T_2 to T_1 at constant area, heat in amount $mc_A(T_2 - T_1)$ being taken from the film, and its original state again restored.

For sake of argument, let us suppose that the cycle of changes which we have just described is in fact represented on the γ-A diagram by the sequence CEDC. Then work has been done on the film by the external forces, in amount represented by the area CEDC. Since the initial and final states of the film are the same, heat equivalent to this amount of work has been given up by the film to the surroundings. We have already specified the amount of heat which is given up to the surroundings in the change at constant area: it is proportional to the difference of temperature $T_2 - T_1$, and therefore, for small changes at least, proportional to the length CD on the diagram. We had an exactly similar situation (p. 326) when we were calculating the adiabatic elasticity of an ideal gas in terms of fig. 81. We saw then that, when the temperature difference is small enough, the amount of work represented by a triangular area on a p-V diagram is negligibly small compared with the work-equivalents of the amounts of heat involved in the individual changes which the sides of the triangular area represent. A similar result is equally valid in the case we are now considering. In the limit, when $T_2 - T_1$ is small enough to be represented in the conventional notation by ΔT,

$$\text{heat given out in change } ED + mc_A \Delta T = 0.$$

If we had started with the alternative supposition, that CE' is in fact the adiabatic curve through C, by the same reasoning we should have reached the essentially opposite conclusion

$$\text{heat given out in change } E'D + mc_A \Delta T = 0.$$

The two conclusions which we have just formulated are opposite conclusions, because the former implies that heat must be abstracted from a film of liquid, when it is stretched, if its temperature is to remain constant, whereas the latter requires that heat must be added to the film in the same circumstances. We cannot sharpen the argument, without appeal to a new principle, in order to decide which alternative is correct. But it is an important conclusion to have reached, that if surface tension varies with temperature, as it certainly does, a film of liquid cannot be stretched isothermally without additional heat being supplied to it from the surroundings (or excess heat abstracted from it), or stretched adiabatically without its temperature changing.

Without prejudice to the sign of the quantity, let ΔA represent the increase of area of the film which we have just been considering when its temperature increases adiabatically by ΔT. Let ΔH be the heat which has to be supplied to the film when its surface increases isothermally by an area ΔA. Then, recognising that this heat does not go to increase the temperature of the film as a whole, but that the creation of new surface is the essential physical situation in which it is involved, we must assume that $\Delta H = h \Delta A$. We may refer to the quantity h as the 'latent heat of extension' of the film. Still ignorant of the sign of $\Delta T / \Delta A$ and so of h, we have

$$h = -mc_A \Delta T / \Delta A.$$

Accepting the views which we have just expressed, we cannot allow that the magnitude of h should depend in any way on the total mass of the film. We conclude, therefore, that $m \Delta T / \Delta A$ is constant, or that, for a given liquid, the tangent of the angle of slope of the adiabatic line through any point on the γ-A diagram is inversely proportional to the mass of liquid in the film. As we have stated, the positions of the isothermal lines are independent of the mass of liquid considered; we have now shown that the positions of the adiabatic lines are not.

Let us return, very briefly, to our qualitative statement that heat must be supplied to (or abstracted from) a film of liquid, if its temperature is to remain constant, when its area is increased. Physically considered, this heat must be thought of as necessary to adjust the thermal state of that quantity of liquid which has been transferred from the interior to constitute a new volume of anomalous surface layer. If this quantity of heat were concerned solely in adjusting the kinetic energies of the molecules, which is certainly its main mode of distribution, it would represent a term in the expression for the total energy of the surface layer entirely distinct from the potential energy term which we have considered in the foregoing sections. But if, molecular vibrations are concerned —either internal vibrations within the molecule which might modify very slightly the law of force between molecules, or relative vibrations in semi-permanent groupings of molecules in the anomalous layer, then the independence of the interfacial potential energy of kinetic energy (and, therefore, of temperature), except in so far as it depends upon changes of density, would not be absolute, as we have supposed it to be. A full analysis of the whole position obviously presupposes much greater knowledge than we at present possess; meanwhile the assumption that surface tension and interfacial potential energy per unit area are one and the same quantity remains a sufficiently good approximation to the truth.

We have stated that we cannot determine the sign of h without appeal to a new principle. The sign is, in fact, positive, CE′, not CE, (fig. 92) is a representative adiabatic line—and the principle to which we have to appeal for this decision is the second law of thermodynamics. We shall not here make the appeal. This is not the place at which to embark lightheartedly on a totally new branch of physics: anyone who contemplates that adventure would be well advised to equip himself first with a knowledge of the calculus, and a facility in its use. He has not needed it for the reading of this book.

INDEX OF NAMES

Short **biographical details** are to be found on pages indicated in
heavy type.

INDEX OF SUBJECTS